CARPENTRY MATHEMATICS

CARPENTRY
MATHEMATICS

BY

J. DOUGLAS WILSON

*Supervisor, Trade and Industrial Education, Vocational and Practical
Arts Branch, Curriculum Division, Los Angeles City
Schools, Los Angeles, California*

AND

CLELL M. ROGERS

*Related Mathematics Instructor, Washington High School
Los Angeles City Schools, Los Angeles, California*

SECOND EDITION

McGRAW-HILL BOOK COMPANY, INC.

NEW YORK-TORONTO-LONDON

CARPENTRY MATHEMATICS

IX

PREFACE TO THE SECOND EDITION

The wide acceptance and use of this text have indicated that the general plan and arrangement of the book have been quite satisfactory. The text was used by the United States Armed Forces Institute during the war period and is now a basic requirement for numerous carpentry apprenticeship classes.

Trade practices as followed in the carpentry trade are still essentially the same, though methods in doing some specific jobs may have changed. The revision of the text has, therefore, been made chiefly in terms of clarity of expression and terminology. Some new illustrations have been included to show modern construction methods. All material prices have been left unchanged although it is recognized that, when compared with today's prices, many are too low. This permits instructors to use the answer book with which they are familiar. Using a price that may not conform with prevailing costs in no way lessens the value of the experience gained through solving the problems.

The main objective of the textbook is still that of providing opportunity for carpentry apprentices to acquire mathematical skill in the field of carpentry.

J. Douglas Wilson
Clell M. Rogers

PREFACE TO THE FIRST EDITION

The subject of carpentry, although new to the average high school, is becoming important. According to "Better Homes in America," 106 houses have been constructed by students in 19 different states in the past few years. The results of this kind of work have been so gratifying that many other schools are preparing to offer house-carpentry programs.

It is not within the scope of a carpentry program to give the training in mathematics that the student needs in order to be proficient in the building field as estimator. That field is separate from the one of actual construction. On the other hand, to be successful in carpentry a student should have a good background of mathematics, be familiar with the more common phases of carpentry mathematics, and, lastly, be able to make out intelligently a bill of material for an average house and do expeditiously and correctly such job mathematics as is involved in the daily work of the carpenter.

Little teaching material and less applied mathematics are available for house carpentry. The purpose of this book is to fulfill such a need. The main objective is to teach the students the practical application of mathematics to the carpentry trade. This is accomplished by:

a. Outlining a series of problems of a practical nature which will emphasize the fundamentals of mathematics as applied to carpentry.

b. Giving all trade facts necessary for solving these problems. For convenience this information is printed in small type.

c. Giving explanations of how the different parts of a building are "taken off" preparatory to ordering them.

Some constructional mathematical problems arise that can be solved only on the job; such cannot be covered in this book. Business mathematics as needed by the carpenter is treated briefly.

All problems are applied to actual trade situations. They are grouped to give a thorough review of the necessary fundamentals of mathematics.

Due to its scope and for convenience, the material has been divided into two books. This book treats of the fundamentals of mathematics as applied to carpentry situations.

The material in this book has been given a thorough tryout in a number of schools, such as the high school in Santa Cruz, Calif.; the Roosevelt High School and the Frank Wiggins Trade School in Los Angeles; and the Venice High School in Venice, Calif. It has been found to be fundamentally sound and of great interest and profit to the students.

The key charts at the beginning of each chapter were developed for the express purpose of organizing the material in that chapter in a logical way. They proved of such value, however, that we concluded that they would materially aid an instructor in getting a good bird's-eye view of each chapter. They also help the student to see a definite relation between mathematical operations and trade situations.

At the beginning of each chapter are check-up problems which are intended as a measuring device. By their use the instructor may, quickly and easily, find the mathematical abilities of the student. Should the check-up indicate a need for more review work, the student should then be required to solve some of the problems in Arithmetical Review, Chap. VIII. If, however, the check-up indicates a good working knowledge of the fundamentals covered in a particular chapter, the instructor can then assign work in that chapter with the assurance that the learner knows how to attack the problems.

Chapter IX is a compilation of the rules and tables used throughout the book and will serve as excellent reference material for the student.

We are indebted to the National Lumber Manufacturers Association, through their field engineer, Mr. Earl Bowe, for valuable help rendered in checking over the material in Chap. VII and in furnishing a number of illustrations. To Mr. Atwell Jobe and Mr. Ralph Allen, members of the printing staff of the Frank Wiggins Trade School of Los Angeles; to

Mr. Tom Holm, carpentry instructor of the same school; and to Miss Hazelle Moore, one of the vice-principals of this institution, we are indebted for much valuable assistance in the final preparation of the manuscript. To Mr. Tom Smethurst, drawing instructor of the San Bernardino High School, we owe our thanks for suggestions relative to many of the drawings. Mr. Harry Scott of Santa Barbara, Calif., and Mr. Charles V. Stewart, carpentry instructor in the high school at Santa Cruz, Calif., gave valuable aid in checking the problems.

If, as a result of this effort, carpentry mathematics is made of more direct value and interest to the many apprentices who enter the building industry and to the vast numbers of skilled artisans already employed at the carpentry trade, we shall feel more than repaid for our work.

J. Douglas Wilson
Clell M. Rogers

CONTENTS

SECTION I

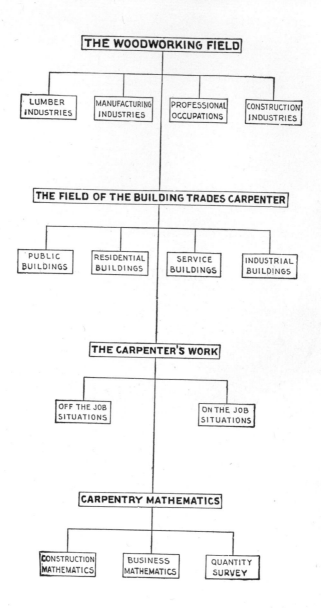

CARPENTRY MATHEMATICS

CHAPTER I

THE WOODWORKING FIELD

INTRODUCTION

Two centuries or more ago many present-day industries were undreamed of. The work that was done through the medium of wood was usually the result of one or two wood-

FIG. 1.—A logging train.   (*Courtesy, West Coast Lumbermen's Association, Portland, Oregon.*)

working crafts.   Today, there are literally hundreds of varying forms of woodworking jobs.   This will be evident after a study of Chart I, which pictures the woodworking field.   This field is very extensive and divides itself, naturally, into four major divisions, namely, the *lumber* industries, *manufacturing* industries, *professional* occupations, and *construction* industries.

3

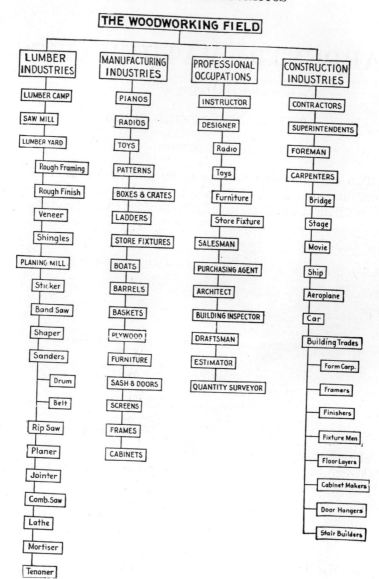

THE WOODWORKING FIELD

LUMBER INDUSTRIES
- LUMBER CAMP
- SAW MILL
- LUMBER YARD
- Rough Framing
- Rough Finish
- Veneer
- Shingles
- PLANING MILL
- Sticker
- Band Saw
- Shaper
- Sanders
  - Drum
  - Belt
- Rip Saw
- Planer
- Jointer
- Comb. Saw
- Lathe
- Mortiser
- Tenoner

MANUFACTURING INDUSTRIES
- PIANOS
- RADIOS
- TOYS
- PATTERNS
- BOXES & CRATES
- LADDERS
- STORE FIXTURES
- BOATS
- BARRELS
- BASKETS
- PLYWOOD
- FURNITURE
- SASH & DOORS
- SCREENS
- FRAMES
- CABINETS

PROFESSIONAL OCCUPATIONS
- INSTRUCTOR
- DESIGNER
  - Radio
  - Toys
  - Furniture
  - Store Fixture
- SALESMAN
- PURCHASING AGENT
- ARCHITECT
- BUILDING INSPECTOR
- DRAFTSMAN
- ESTIMATOR
- QUANTITY SURVEYOR

CONSTRUCTION INDUSTRIES
- CONTRACTORS
- SUPERINTENDENTS
- FOREMAN
- CARPENTERS
  - Bridge
  - Stage
  - Movie
  - Ship
  - Aeroplane
  - Car
- Building Trades
  - Form Carp.
  - Framers
  - Finishers
  - Fixture Men
  - Floor Layers
  - Cabinet Makers
  - Door Hangers
  - Stair Builders

CHART I

The *lumber industry* began when our forefathers cut the trees and built their log cabins. As time passed, better tools were invented, and gradually it was possible not only to cut the trees into logs, as shown in Figs. 1 and 2, but to split the logs into boards, then smooth them to an even thickness. Later on, as man became more resourceful, he invented handtools and shaped these boards into pieces of moulding.

Fig. 2.—Splash of building logs as they are unloaded at the log dump. (*Photo by John D. Cress, Seattle. Courtesy, West Coast Lumbermen's Association, Portland, Oregon.*)

With the invention of woodworking machinery the work of the woodworker changed very rapidly, so that today this industry is not one trade but many. Power machinery, at an astonishing rate, now cuts and shapes millions of feet of lumber each year. Figure 3 illustrates typical woodworking machinery.

The *manufacturing industries* use lumber in making many conveniences and necessities of life now found in almost every home. Although much of the work done in the factories is limited to operating high-speed machines, yet there are many jobs that require the services of a person who can use handtools skillfully. The person with this ability will find an opportunity for work in many of these plants.

The *professional occupations* offer many opportunities of working in some branch of the woodworking field, such as instructor of carpentry or cabinet-making, designer, architect, inspector, and estimator. Of necessity, the background of education for each will be different. All offer attractive employment to the person who is ambitious and who finds pleasure in working in wood or in designing something that is to be made of that material. To illustrate, the architect has much to do with the constructional layout of house building, inasmuch as he determines the type of architecture, the development of which

Fig. 3.—Woodworking machinery.

depends in no small degree on the methods used in fitting and fastening the many parts of a house together.

The *construction industries* offer another very fertile field of work. The invention of the moving picture, the airplane, and the radio has opened up new avenues of employment for the woodworker. Since thousands of carloads of agricultural products must be moved and millions of workers transported in street and passenger cars, new cars must be constructed and old ones repaired; some of this work is done by expert woodworkers.

By far the largest field of work in the constructional industries is the building trades. The carpentry trade furnishes work to more mechanics than any other building craft. Building permits are the barometer of the industrial life of a city, as they give evidence of progress. A large building program indicates new industries, an increase in the population, or prosperity, which requires that new houses be constructed

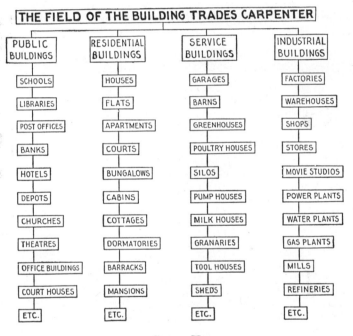

CHART II

or old ones remodeled—all of which furnish employment for thousands of carpenters.

From the job as a carpenter apprentice to superintendent or contractor is a long journey. Yet the goal is within the reach of anyone who has the will to study and prepare himself for each successive step. This process will pay large dividends to the person who is ambitious and not afraid to work, as the field of the building-trades carpenter is a large one.

THE FIELD OF THE BUILDING-TRADES CARPENTER
(SEE CHART II)

A building-trades carpenter works on interesting and varied buildings. Chart II suggests some of these, classifying

Fig. 4.—A public building. (Banning High School, Banning, Calif.) (*Courtesy, G. Stanley Wilson, architect, Riverside, Calif.*)

Fig. 5.—A typical frame and brick residence. (*Courtesy, G. Stanley Wilson, architect, Riverside, Calif.*)

them into four main groups: *public buildings*, Fig. 4; *residential buildings*, Fig. 5; *industrial buildings*, Fig. 6; and *service*

FIG. 6.—Mill construction, industrial building. (*Photo by John D. Cress, Seattle. Courtesy, National Lumber Manufacturers Association, Chicago, Ill.*)

FIG. 7.—Typical service buildings. (*Courtesy, N. & S. Pine Manufacturers Association.*)

buildings, Fig. 7.   There are on each of these buildings many jobs that require the services of expert carpenters.   The emphasis in the following pages will be on the carpenter work as related mainly to the construction of residence and service buildings.

Few other trades give such a variety of experience and require so great a knowledge of general building construction as does the house-carpentry trade.   Each house constructed will be different in many details, and the jobs completed from day to day will continually change.   One day the

FIG. 8.—A building layout.

work is inside finishing; the next day it may be a framing job.   Some of the time the carpenter is laying out complicated cuts of parts of a building, and then occasionally he has to expend his time and energy simply driving nails.   On one job the carpenter may be working in the heart of a city with its attendant noise and hustle.   On the next one he may be working in the quiet of the country.

The carpenter is usually the first man "on the job," staking out the foundation of a building, and he is generally the last man to leave, since putting on the finish hardware is usually the "wind-up" of the job.   Therefore, "from the foundation layout to front-door key" is an apt phrase that completely describes his part in the construction of a house.   A typical building layout is illustrated in Fig. 8.

THE CARPENTER'S WORK (SEE CHART III)

The carpenter's work divides itself into two classes; manipulative and technical. These are outlined on Chart III as *"on the job" situations* and *"off the job" situations.* His manipulative work on the job consists, of course, in using the many woodworking tools that are available, in occasionally drawing sketches when ordering materials, or in explaining to other workmen how a certain job is to be done. His

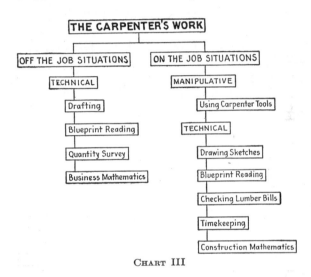

CHART III

drawing board in these cases is often a wide board or shingle.

The technical side of the carpentry trade, either on or off the job, is a fascinating one. A carpenter with technical ability has many problems of layout work to do, from the driving of the first stake to the laying out of the built-in cabinets and the stairways. Occasionally he draws house plans and does geometrical layout work. Not all carpenters possess this ability, but it is a worthwhile and valuable attainment. All of his work requires a knowledge of blueprint reading, constructional mathematics, and the steel square. The latter is a carpenter's tool which is very important in the framing process.

THE CARPENTER'S MATHEMATICS

The carpenter's mathematics is readily grouped into three parts, namely, *construction mathematics, business mathematics,* and *quantity survey* as outlined in Chart IV.

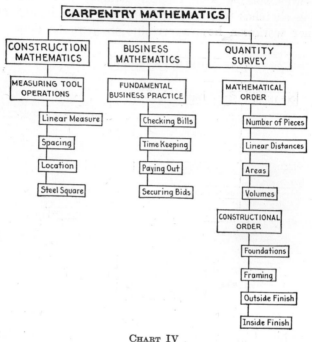

CHART IV

The *construction mathematics* that he uses on the job divides itself into four groups: linear measurements, spacing, location, and steel square.

The carpenter on the job has considerable figuring to do in laying out the many parts of a building, locating the exact positions of doors, windows, openings, etc. The steel square is used when framing the rafters for the roof[1] or laying out the

[1] For a detailed outline of roof framing see Wilson and Werner's "Simplified Roof Framing," McGraw-Hill Book Company, Inc.

stringers for the stairs. His rule, steel tape, and square are used constantly. Figure 9 illustrates these tools.

The *business mathematics* for the carpenter consists of checking bills, keeping time books, paying bills, and securing

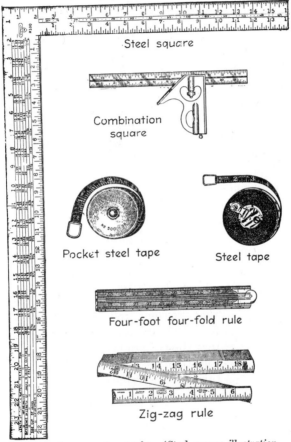

Steel square

Combination square

Pocket steel tape

Steel tape

Four-foot four-fold rule

Zig-zag rule

FIG. 9.—Carpenter's measuring tools. (*Steel square illustration. Courtesy Stanley Tools.*)

material bids. The one problem of securing bids for an average house requires considerable time and effort. This will be evident when one realizes that there are eight or ten types of work on a house, such as plumbing, painting, plastering, electricity, tilework, millwork, and sheet-metal work, besides the materials, such as lumber and hardware. If at least three bids were secured for each subcontract, that would mean 20 or 30 subcontractors and material dealers to see. Not all carpenters are qualified for this kind of work. The wise mechanic, however, prepares himself for all of these situations. To be able to read a house plan, take off the bill of materials, and estimate their cost is an attainment worthy of the best effort of the carpenter.

The last group in the mathematical field for the carpenter is *quantity survey*. This is the process of looking over, or "surveying," a set of plans and making a list of the quantity and kinds of materials necessary to construct the building. It is necessary to state the number of pieces, the kinds of material, the uses for which they are intended, the milling required, and other special information as to how the stock is to be made and how the material is to be put together after it is delivered on the job. The process is primarily mathematical, requiring a good background of blueprint reading and a knowledge of construction and of how these materials are ordered and purchased.

Quantity survey can be learned in two ways. The first method is termed the mathematical order and the second the constructional order. The mathematical order is based on grouping materials that are computed in the same way, such as by the piece, linear foot, square foot, or cubic foot. Constructional order means that the materials are "taken off" from the plans in the same order that the house is built, beginning with the foundation, on through the frame of the house, and ending with the interior finish.[1]

CONCLUSION

Ability to handle figures easily and correctly is of the utmost importance to a carpenter. If he agrees to do a piece of work

---

[1] See Wilson and Rogers, "Simplified Carpentry Estimating," 4th ed., Simmons-Boardman Publishing Corporation, N. Y., 1948, for detailed description and instructions on how to take off a bill of materials, using the *constructional* order.

for a stated amount, mistakes in his computations may prove costly to him. Once a contract is signed, he must do the work called for at the price agreed upon. Also, his measurements on the job must be carefully and accurately made in order to avoid costly constructional errors. His material lists must be absolutely correct as to quantities, sizes, and kinds; otherwise, delays will occur while waiting for the delivery of the proper materials.

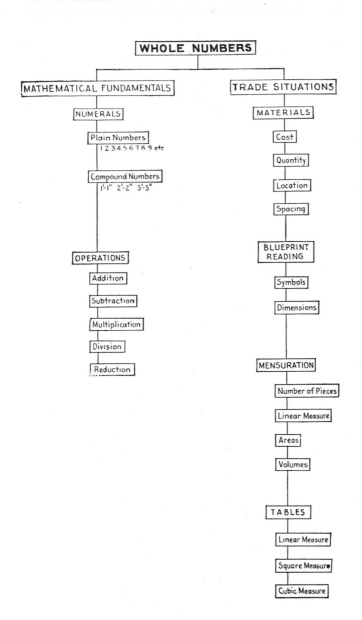

WHOLE NUMBERS

MATHEMATICAL FUNDAMENTALS

NUMERALS

Plain Numbers
1 2 3 4 5 6 7 8 9 etc

Compound Numbers
1'-1" 2'-2" 3'-3"

OPERATIONS

Addition

Subtraction

Multiplication

Division

Reduction

TRADE SITUATIONS

MATERIALS

Cost

Quantity

Location

Spacing

BLUEPRINT READING

Symbols

Dimensions

MENSURATION

Number of Pieces

Linear Measure

Areas

Volumes

TABLES

Linear Measure

Square Measure

Cubic Measure

MATHEMATICAL CHECK-UP

WHOLE NUMBERS[1]

Plain Numbers.

1. Add 9876, 127, 7829, 5, 67, and 54079.
2. Subtract 7693 from 8544.
3. Multiply 2929 by 989.
4. Divide 8272 by 752.
5. Change 372" to feet.
6. Change 9' to inches.
7. Change 495 sq. ft. to square yards.
8. Change 288 sq. in. to square feet.
9. Change 19 cu. yd. to cubic feet.
10. Change 29 doz. to pieces.

Compound Numbers.

11. Add 16' 4", 4' 2", 5' 3", 17' 5", 12' 6", and 11' 7".
12. Subtract 14' 5" from 18' 4".
13. Multiply 9' 5" by 8.
14. Divide 7' 8" by 2.
15. Change 16' 8" to inches.
16. Change 75" to feet and inches.
17. Change to inches and then divide 16' 8" by 3' 4".
18. Change to inches and then multiply 9' 11" by 2' 6".
19. Change 28 cu. yd. and 7 cu. ft. to cubic feet.
20. Change 159 cu. ft. to cubic yards and cubic feet.

[1] See p. 152.

18

CHAPTER II

WHOLE NUMBERS

The building-trades carpenter works on different types of buildings. One day it may be a four- or five-room house, such as that illustrated in Fig. 10, where the roof is being raised; the next job may be a garage (see Fig. 11) or it may be a commercial building or a school building.

The variable nature of the work makes it very interesting for the skilled craftsman.

Fig. 10.—Raising and framing the roof.

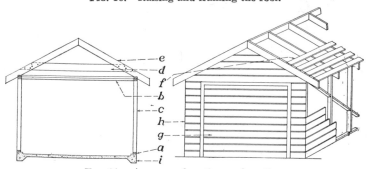

Fig. 11.—A garage elevation and section.

The work of figuring bills of materials and the quantities of each kind required is fascinating, particularly if one is informed as to the names of the different parts of the building. In fact, it is impossible to "take off" a bill of materials without a knowledge of these parts.

It is very important then that all drawings and charts be studied carefully. Figure 11 shows the framework of an ordinary frame garage, with a key to the names of the parts.

PLAIN NUMBERS

In problems 1 to 5 is found a list of the board feet of material used in constructing several different types of garages. Note that the names of the different parts of the building are lettered, these letters corresponding to the parts as shown in the drawing.

ADDITION

Problems

1 to 5. How many board feet of lumber were used in the following different types of garages?

Problems	1	2	3	4	5
	One car	Two car	Three car	Four car	Ten car
	Bd. ft.	Bd. ft.	Bd. ft.	Bd. ft.	Bd. ft.
a. Mudsill	56	72	80	120	192
b. Plate stock	56	86	110	168	118
c. Studding	354	516	572	9J2	2,116
d. Collar tie	32	40	36		
e. Rafters	152	232	278	363	418
f. Sheathing	240	468	416	1,128	1,516
g. Overhead door	72	144	162	346	834
h. Siding	…	…	…	928	1,362

6 to 10. In excavating for the basement of a large hotel, truck drivers were employed to haul away the dirt. How many loads were moved if each man hauled the number of loads as shown below?

Problems	6	7	8	9	10
Drivers:					
Jones	23	39	23	32	28
Berry	44	61	37	16	
Nevers	..	73	98	47	86
Newberg	92	34	..	62	43
Abbot	35	57	86	43	51
Johnson	45	..	98	..	81
Holmes	38	66	39	76	27
White	23	65			

11 to 15. A real-estate subdivider lays out a new addition to a city and takes bids on different kinds of buildings. What will the bids be if the materials and subcontracts for each type of building are figured to cost the following amounts?

Problems	11	12	13	14	15
	Single garage	20-car garage	5-room frame house	5-room Spanish	7-room English
Excavating...........	. . .	$ 21	$ 14	$ 57	$ 93
Lumber..............	$62	237	626	440	627
Carpentry labor.......	37	258	645	581	769
Fireplace.............	. . .	. . .	. . .	78	131
Plumbing.............	. . .	. . .	408	513	628
Sheet metal...........	17	63	31	51	92
Shingling.............	13	. . .	38	. . .	81
Wiring..............	9	. . .	53	82	109
Heating..............	. . .	. . .	. . .	124	188
Plastering............	. . .	. . .	402	687	735
Painting.............	27	126	325	392	697
Millwork.............	16	. . .	439	461	521
Hardware.............	13	24	78	93	121
Tilework.............	. . .	. . .	. . .	87	168
Hardwood floors.......	. . .	. . .	195	216	277
Electric fixtures........	. . .	. . .	78	97	113
Window shades........	. . .	. . .	22	226	34
Liability insurance.....	8	11	29	37	41
Miscellaneous........	6	14	19	31	29
Profit...............	21	85	341	380	452

Each of the items listed above appears on the list in about the same order that the material or work is required on the job. The term "miscellaneous" covers such items as drayage, telephone calls, water meters, permits, etc.

The distance around a building is known as its *perimeter*. This measurement is often required by the different mechanics, such as the plasterer who may be figuring the number of square yards of plaster in the outside walls; or the carpenter who may be estimating the number of linear feet of lumber. In the following problems find the perimeter of each building. In finding the perimeter there are two methods that can be used:

a. Add the widths together, then the lengths, then add these results.

b. Add the width and length together and then double this result.

16 to 20. Find the perimeter of the following types of buildings:

Problems	16	17	18
Barn.............	32' 0″ × 47' 0″	54' 0″ × 168' 0″	38' 0″ × 104' 0″
Two-story house...	24' 0″ × 30' 0″	28' 0″ × 38' 0″	68' 0″ × 76' 0″

Problems	19	20
Barn.............	51' 0″ × 118' 0″	64' 0″ × 210' 0″
Two-story house...	47' 0″ × 66' 0″	54' 0″ × 82' 0″

In laying cement sidewalks, garage floors, and driveways, it is always necessary to use a 2″ × 4″ piece of lumber (or some other suitable size) placed on edge to make a form to hold the wet concrete until it is set. The following problems will give practice in figuring the necessary form materials for several different situations:

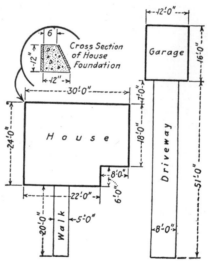

FIG. 12.—A concrete layout plan.

21. Figure the linear feet of 2″ × 4″'s needed to construct the forms for the walk, driveway, and garage as shown in Fig. 12. The walk and driveway each require a form at only one end.

22. How many linear feet of 2″ × 4″ rough stock will be required for the forms to make the garage floor, driveway, and walks for the house as shown in Fig. 13. Allow no material for ends of walk. Note that **where the driveway joins the garage floor only one form is needed.**

A house foundation form is often made by using 1″ × 6″ stock. A form for each side of the wall is always needed. The height of the form will vary, two 6″ boards making a form that will be 12″ high.

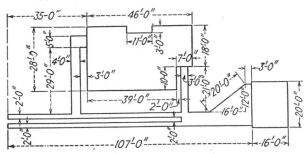

Fig. 13.—Concrete layout plan.

23. Estimate the number of linear feet of 1″ × 6″ stock required to make the forms for the house as shown in Fig. 12. The form is to be two boards high.

24. How many linear feet of 1″ × 6″ stock will be required to make the forms for the house foundation as shown in Fig. 13? The forms are to be three boards high.

25. Compute the linear feet for all the form materials needed for the job as shown in Fig. 14. The house forms are to be 1″ × 6″ stock and 24″ high; the walks, driveway, and garage floor require 2″ × 4″ stock. The rear walk requires no end forms; the front walk and driveway strips require but one end form each.

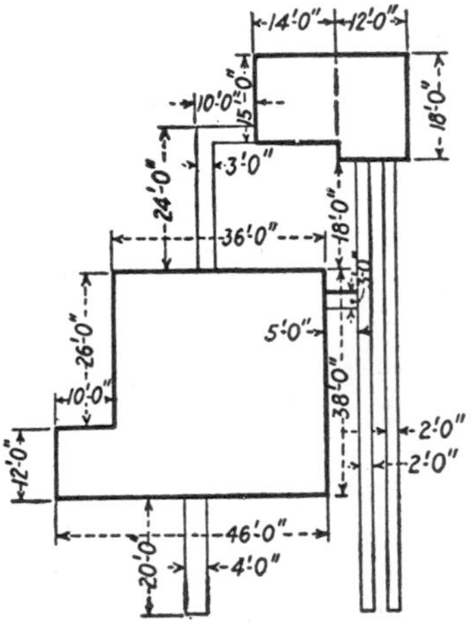

SUBTRACTION

Problems

26. A contractor buys 475 lin. ft. of picture moulding for the interior of a four-family apartment house. When the job is completed he checks and finds he has 58′ left. How much did he use?

Fig. 14.—A concrete layout plan.

27. The steel on a small building amounted to $983. If the total cost of the building is estimated at $7,298, how much will it be if the steel bid is omitted?

28. A house 46′ long with a 25′ setback is built on a lot 132′ deep. The single garage, 12′ 0″ × 20′ 0″, is placed 14′ back of the house. How far is it from the back of the garage to the alley?

29. Jones' total estimate on a garage is as follows: lumber, $66; concrete work, $47; hardware, $13; labor, $37; plastering, $52.   Martin,

FIG. 15.—A typical house foundation.

who is bidding on the same job, estimates his costs to be as follows: lumber, $72; concrete, $43; hardware, $16; labor, $42; plastering, $61. Which is the low bid, and how much lower is it?

FIG. 16.—Concrete ribbons to garage entrance.

30. A contractor figures the material for two buildings that are to be constructed on the same lot. The lumber yard delivered 2,142 bd. ft. of flooring. If he uses 978 bd. ft. on the first building, how much is left for the second?

31. A contractor secures the contract to put in foundations for three houses. A typical foundation is shown in Fig. 15. He buys 274 sacks of cement for the three jobs. On the first he used 68 sacks, on the second 81 sacks, and on the third 111 sacks. How much did he have left after the work was completed?

32. How far will a house with a width of 34' be from the side property line of a 60' lot, allowing 9' space on the driveway side?

33. In order to keep the cost of construction down for the interior woodwork on a church building, Douglas fir is substituted for oak. How much will the contractor's bid for the job be if he deducts

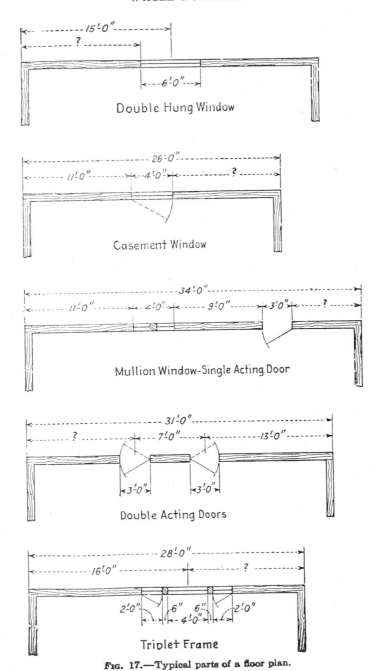

FIG. 17.—Typical parts of a floor plan.

$3,468 for the oak and adds $957 for the pine?   His original bid was $121,672.

34. How long will the concrete driveway ribbons be from the front of a garage to the front property line of the lot if the garage is set 27′ from the rear property line and is 12′ × 19′ in size?   The lot is 155′ deep.

The term "ribbons" means the two strips of concrete that are built from the street to the garage entrance to form a drive (See Fig. 16).

35. A contractor's bid on a school building totaled $74,568.   In order to cut the costs, one wing of the building was omitted.   The contractor cut his bid $11,469.   What was his new figure?

36 to 40. In the sections of the floor plan of a house shown in Fig. 17, find the missing dimensions.

MULTIPLICATION

Problems

41. Find the number of square feet of floor space in a house that is 32′ wide and 48′ long.

42. How many square feet of cement are there in a basement floor that is 68′ wide and 112′ long?

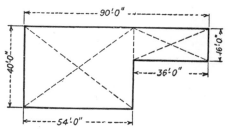

Fig. 18.—Illustrating method of figuring "L"-shaped basement.

43. How many square feet of floor space are there in the building as shown in Fig. 18?   Figure each rectangle separately as illustrated by the dotted line, then add results.

44. How many square feet of area has the building shown in Fig. 19?

45. How many square feet of floor area has a warehouse that is 68′ wide and 234′ long?

46. What is the area of the outside walls of a Spanish residence that is 32′ wide, 46′ long, and 12′ 0″ high?   Figure perimeter first.

47. How many square feet of wall area are there in a two-story building that is 33′ wide, 47′ long?   The walls are 19′ high.

48. What is the area of the outside walls of the building in Fig. 18 if the walls are 11′ high?

49. Find the number of square feet of exterior wall area in the building illustrated in Fig. 19.   The walls are 14′ high.

50. What is the total opening area in the 184 windows of a large factory? Each of the windows is 3' wide and 6' long.

51 to 55. In figuring the capacity of heating furnaces it is always necessary to find out how much air is to be heated for each room. What

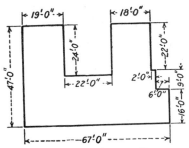

Fig. 19.—A building outline.

are the cubic contents of each of the following rooms? The first number given represents the width of the room, the second the length, and the last the height.

Problems	51	52	53
Bathroom.........	6' × 8' × 8'	5' × 8' × 9'	7' × 9' × 10'
Bedroom..........	11' × 13' × 8'	14' × 16' × 9'	15' × 18' × 11'
Dining room......	12' × 14' × 8'	13' × 17' × 9'	15' × 19' × 11'
Living room.......	15' × 19' × 9'	16' × 20' × 9'	14' × 22' × 11'

Problems	54	55
Bathroom.......................	5' × 9' × 9'	4' × 6' × 8'
Bedroom.......................	10' × 16' × 10'	12' × 12' × 8'
Dining room....................	17' × 18' × 11'	16' × 16' × 9'
Living room....................	19' × 24' × 12'	22' × 26' × 10'

56. How many board feet of lumber are there in 63 floor joists each containing 22 bd. ft. and in 14 girders each containing 34 bd. ft.?

57. Find the total number of board feet of lumber contained in the three following items: 64 pieces of 1″ × 6″ subfloor stock containing 16 bd. ft. each; 86 pieces of 1″ × 4″ sheathing stock containing 12 bd. ft. each; 72 pieces of 2″ × 4″ ceiling joist stock containing 18 bd. ft. each.

58. How many board feet are there in a load of lumber containing the following items? 16 pieces of mudsill stock, 14 bd. ft. to each piece;

8 posts 6″ × 6″, 56 bd. ft. to each piece; 17 planks 3″ × 12″, 66 bd. ft. to each piece; 34 pieces 2″ × 14″ floor joists containing 42 bd. ft. each.

59. How many board feet of lumber are there in the following bill of materials?

121 joists, 34 bd. ft. each
15 girders, 90 bd. ft. each
54 rafters, 24 bd. ft. each
16 posts, 40 bd. ft. each
285 boards, 14 bd. ft. each
146 studs, 12 bd. ft. each

60. The following bill of materials contains how many board feet of lumber?

54 studs, 7 bd. ft. each
14 girders, 22 bd. ft. each
121 boards, 16 bd. ft. each
16 beams, 46 bd. ft. each

DIVISION

Problems

61. Four sacks of cement are required to lay 60 sq. ft. of floor, using a standard concrete mix. How many sacks will be required to lay a garage floor 18′ × 30′ in size? Figure 20 illustrates a typical cement floor.

Fig. 20.—A cement floor for a garage.

The term "mix" has reference to the proportions of cement, sand, and rock. The quantities of each kind of material required will, of course, vary according to the work being done. Cement must be purchased in full sacks; therefore, if the result is not in "even sacks," count a portion of a sack as a full one.

62. Using the same general rule, how much cement will be used on a garage floor that is 35′ wide and 84′ long?

63. How many sacks of cement will be used for a sidewalk that is 5′ wide and 228′ long?

64. In laying out a new subdivision, the walks required totaled 5,760 lin. ft. Half of these walks were to be 4 ft. wide and the remainder 5 ft. wide. How many sacks of cement will be required if the estimator figures that four sacks will lay 64 sq. ft.?

65. How much cement will be required for a warehouse floor that is 60′ wide and 112′ long? Four sacks of cement will cover 64 sq. ft.

Fig. 21.—First floor joists.

66. How many floor joists, which are illustrated in Fig. 21, will be required on a building that is 46′ long if the joists are placed 12″ o.c.?

If we divide 46 by 1′ the result for this problem will not be joists but spaces. The answer will then be 46 one-foot spaces. Of necessity, there must be a joist at each end of the building; therefore, the general rule for this kind of a problem is that *there is always one more piece than there are spaces*. This is proved in Fig. 22. The letters "o.c." are an abbreviation for on center.

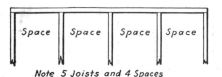

Note 5 Joists and 4 Spaces

Fig. 22.—A spacing problem.

67. For a building that is 34′ long how many joists will be required if they are spaced 12″ o.c.?

68. A building that is 58′ long will require how many joists, if they are placed 2′ 0″ o.c.?

69. The specifications for a building state that the joists are to be placed 24″ o.c. How many floor joists will be required if the building is 98′ long?

70. A warehouse building specification required that the joists be spaced 6″ o.c. due to the heavy load that was to be placed on the floor. How many joists were needed if the building was 118′ long?

71. A girder is the piece of stock that is used in the underpinning of a house to support the floor joists.   In an average house there will always

Fig. 23.—Underpinning girders.

be several of these girders, as illustrated in Fig. 23.   How many girders will a building require that is 35′ wide if they are placed 7′ o.c.?

One less piece of stock will be required on this type of problem as no girders will be used on the outside walls since the concrete foundation of the house will support the end of the joists.   Therefore, the rule is that *there will always be one less piece than there are spaces.*

Fig. 24.—Concrete piers in a house foundation.

72. How many girders will be required on a house that is 48′ wide, placing them at 6′ o.c.?

73. How many piers will be required for a building that is 55′ long, placing them 5′ o.c.?

The piers are concrete blocks which are placed at intervals inside a foundation for the purpose of supporting the girders, as shown in Fig. 24. Do not count any pier for the ends, as the foundation walls will serve as a support for the ends of the girders.

74. How many piers will be used in a building that is 36' wide and 60' long? Girder spacing is 6' o.c. and pier spacing is 5' o.c. Girders run the long way of the building.

75. How many 10" × 12" girders will be required on a storehouse that is 132' long? The girders are spaced 11' o.c.

REDUCTION OF UNITS

Many mathematical problems that the carpenter solves require the changing of the result into some unit that is recognized as the standard measurement in the trade. To illustrate, excavation problems are always thought of in terms of cubic yards or cubic feet. Plastering is estimated by the square yard and not the square foot, lumber is figured by the board foot and not the linear foot. Mouldings are bought by the linear foot and not the linear inch.

Problems

76. How many linear feet of moulding will be required to "cap" six square porch columns? Each piece of moulding will need to be 8" long in order to give sufficient material to make the miters.

Fig. 25.—A five-panel Colonial door.

77. It is desired to remove the two upper panels of eight 5-panel Colonial doors and replace them with glass. How many linear feet of moulding will be required to hold the glass in place if the glass size is 23" × 28"? Allow 6' for waste in cutting. Estimate moulding for both sides of the glass. Figure 25 illustrates a typical Colonial door, before and after panels are removed.

78. A French door is one composed of a number of lights of glass as shown in Fig. 26. How many linear feet of moulding will be required to "mould in" 24 lights of glass that are 8″ × 10″ in size? Add 4′ for waste.

79. A carpenter is given the job of cutting and nailing in a

FIG. 26.—French doors.

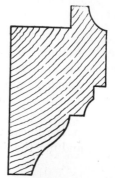

FIG. 27.—A raised moulding.

raised moulding on the back, end, and ceiling of a store window. How many feet of the moulding shown in Fig. 27 will have to be ordered if there are 32 panels 16″ × 20″ in size on the side walls and eight ceiling panels 26″ × 46″? Convert the moulding required for each panel into feet before finding the total number of feet required. Allow 12′ for waste.

80. How many linear feet of moulding will be required for the base of 36 columns? Each column is 7″ × 7″ in size. Allow 10′ for waste in cutting.

81 to 85. How many square yards of plastering are there in each of the following group of problems? Make no allowances for openings. Unless the openings are very large, the value of the material saved is expended in the extra labor involved in working around the openings; hence, no deductions are made.

Problems	81	82	83	84	85
Width of room, feet.........	12	18	21	81	14
Length of room, feet........	15	19	24	135	16
Ceiling height, feet.........	8	9	10	18	11

86. How many cubic yards of earth will be removed from a hotel basement that is 66′ wide, 91′ long, and 18′ deep?

87. How many cubic yards of earth will be moved in digging a ditch that is 3′ wide, 6′ deep, and 453′ long?

88. How many cubic yards of earth will have to be excavated in basement that is shaped as shown in Fig. 28? The depth is 15′.

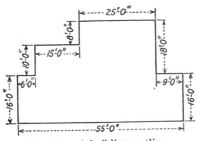

Fig. 28.—A building outline.

89. A dump truck contains 2 cu. yd. of earth. How many truck loads of earth will be hauled away from a tunnel that is dug for a steam pipe line? The tunnel is 4′ wide, 5′ high, and 540′ long.

90. How many cubic yards of earth must be removed to excavate a basement 7′ deep for a building 87′ wide and 148′ long?

COMPOUND NUMBERS

A compound number is one that is composed of two related measuring units, as feet and inches, yard and feet, pounds and ounces. In carpentry, the prevailing units are feet and inches.

ADDITION

Problems

91 to 95. What is the total mathematical length of the following building dimensions?

91	92	93	94	95
6′ 4″	7′ 9″	3′ 10″	3′ 2″	2′ 7″
4′ 4″	4′ 7″	8′ 7″	6′ 9″	1′ 8″
4′ 5″	5′ 11″	6′ 0″	1′ 2″	3′ 11″
		4′ 9″	11′ 5″	6′ 2″
			5′ 11″	4′ 9″
				2′ 4″

96 to 100. Find the mathematical perimeters of the following buildings:[1]

96	97	98	99	100
Italian	Colonial	Spanish	English	Moorish
21′ 8″ × 39′ 3″	26′ 7″ × 31′	26′ 8″ × 38′ 5″	54′ 2″ × 67′ 5″	42′ × 48′ 7″
56′ 2″ × 74′ 7″	32′ 4″ × 37′ 9″	28′ 0″ × 45′ 11″	35′ 3″ × 44′ 1″	58′ 7″ × 66′ 8″

101 to 105. Find the missing dimension in the parts of a floor plan shown in Fig. 29.

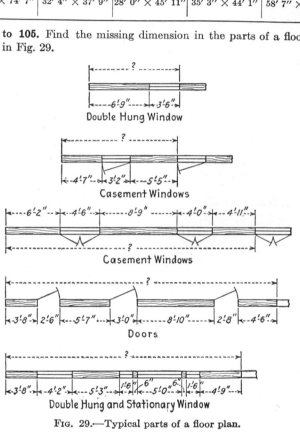

Double Hung Window

Casement Windows

Casement Windows

Doors

Double Hung and Stationary Window

Fig. 29.—Typical parts of a floor plan.

SUBTRACTION

Problems

106. How much will remain on a piece of lumber that is 18′ 7″ long if 4′ 4″ is sawed off?

[1] In trade practice, the estimator increases all fractional building measurements to the next half or whole foot when estimating perimeters.

107. A piece of pulley stile is 14′ long. How much will remain if two pieces are cut to make the sides of a window frame and one piece is cut for the head? The sides are 4′ 10″ and the head is 3′ 3″. See Fig. 30.[1]

108. A room requires five pieces of base-board of different lengths. How much will remain from a piece of interior finish stock of standard length after cutting 5 pieces that are the following lengths: 1′ 6″; 4′ 7″; 8′ 3″; 2′ 5″; and 9″?

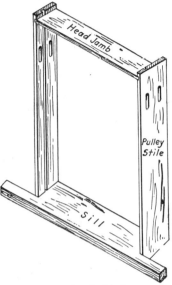

The standard length of stock required will be the next "even-foot" length above the actual quantity of material used. This is because lumber is sold on the basis of the even-foot length; that is, 8′, 10′, 12′, 14′, etc. Due to their scarceness, hardwoods are obtainable in the odd foot lengths.

109. The length of a rafter from the ridge to the plate line is 12′ 9″. The part of the rafter that "overhangs" the building is 2′ 9″ long. How long a piece of lumber will it take for this rafter? How much waste will there be?

FIG. 30.—A double-hung window frame with outside casings omitted.

110. A piece of dimension stock is 17′ 10″ long. Two cripple studs are required, one being 2′ 10″ long, the other 3′ 4″ long. How much remains of the original piece after these pieces are cut off?

111 to 115. In locating the position of a window in a wall during the construction process, the distance that this opening is placed from one end of the building is usually given on the plans. In the following problems find the distance from the window to the other end of the building:

Problems	111	112	113	114	115
Total wall length......	22′ 9″	15′ 10″	32′ 4″	34′ 10″	18′ 5″
Width of window	3′ 6″	3′ 6″	4′ 0″	5′ 4″	3′ 9″
Distance from one end of building to window.	6′ 5″	4′ 8″	11′ 7″	13′ 3″	4′7 ″

[1] See footnote, p. 70.

MULTIPLICATION

Problems

116. Five pieces 2′ 2″ long are cut from a piece of window-frame stock 14′ long. How much will remain?

117. A foreman gives a carpenter an order to cut 11 pieces of stock 1′ 1″ long, and 2 pieces 3′ 3″ long. How much will remain from a 20′ 0″ piece of stock?

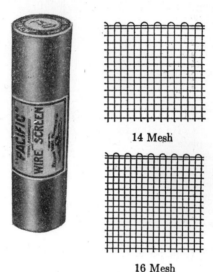

14 Mesh

16 Mesh

Fig. 31.—Screen-wire cloth.

118. What standard length of shelving stock will have to be ordered to cut five shelves 3′ 2″ long?

119. How many linear feet of 16 mesh black screen-wire cloth will be required to cover five window screens if each requires a piece 4′ 2″ long?

The term "16 mesh" means that there are 16 holes each way to every square inch of wire. The term "black" refers to the color. Copper and galvanized wire can also be bought. The mesh varies from 12 to 16 on ordinary screen wire. Figure 31 illustrates 14 and 16 mesh wire. One roll contains 100 linear feet but is made in many different widths.

120. How many linear feet of 14 mesh copper wire cloth are needed to cover 18 window screens, each of which is 3′ 6″ long?

121. What is the total length of six shelves, each of which is 2′ 7″ long?

122. How much waste will there be if seven cripples 1' 7" long are cut from a piece 2" × 4" × 12' long?

The term "cripple" refers to the piece of framing stock that is placed vertically over or under a framed opening as shown in Fig. 32.

Fɪɢ. 32.—A framed wall showing cripple studs.

123. A carpenter needs nine shelf cleats of 1" × 2" stock, each of which is 1' 5" long. How much stock will be left after cutting? He has a piece of stock 16' long.

124. What will be the outside length of a garage that is built to house ten cars on each side if 7' 11" is allowed for each space? Add 7½"

Fɪɢ. 33.—A twenty-car garage under construction.

to allow for the thickness of the two end walls and 4½" for each division post. Figure 33 represents a garage building of this type.

125. Eight cripple studs are required each 1' 4" long. How much will be left on a piece of framing stock that is 16' long after these cripples are cut?

DIVISION

In order to strengthen floor joists that have a wide span, it is customary to "cut-in" pieces of stock, usually 2″ × 3″ or 2″ × 4″. This material is known as "herringbone bridging" when cut and framed in as shown in Fig. 34.

Fig. 34.—Herringbone bridging.

Problems

126 to 130. In the following problems find the location of the bridging stock.   Measurements indicate the span of the joists.

Problems	126	127	128	129	130
Span of joists........	8′ 4″ 10′ 0″ 9′ 10″ 11′ 0″	10′ 8″ 8′ 10″ 11′ 6″ 9′ 8″	11′ 8″ 9′ 2″ 13′ 4″ 12′ 9″	18′ 6″ 15′ 9″ 16′ 0″ 17′ 3″	21′ 9″ 12′ 6″ 22′ 9″ 19′ 0″
Rows of bridging......	1	2	2	3	4

One row of bridging means two spaces; two rows of bridging means three spaces; etc. No cross bridging is required at the ends of the joists that rest on the wall.

In buildings such as sheds and barns, that require the exterior to be finished with vertical boards, usually 1″ × 12″, it is necessary to frame nailing pieces in the outside walls.   These are placed horizontally to give the proper nailing for the boards. The piece is called a "girt," illustrated in Fig. 35. The pieces of lumber at the

Fig. 35.—Girt in outside walls.

top and bottom of the wall are called "plates." One girt will divide the space between these two plates into two spaces. Hence, there is always one more space than girt.

131 to 135. Figure the spacing for these girts:

Problems	131	132	133	134	135
Wall heights........	10' 4"	12' 3"	12' 4"	20' 10"	16' 8"
	8' 6"	9' 6"	16' 8"	15' 5"	13' 4"
	9' 4"	11' 0"	15' 4"	17' 2"	16' 3"
	7' 8"	10' 7"	13' 0"	19' 2"	18' 11"
Rows of girts..........	1	2	3	4	5

REDUCTION

The carpenter is often required to divide a given space, which may be dimensioned in feet and inches, into an equal number of spaces. When planning a stairway he has to divide the vertical distance from one floor to the next one above into equal divisions. Locating the position of surface hardware is also a spacing problem.

This type of problem is best solved by reducing the compound number into the terms of the smaller unit, solving the problem, and then converting back to the larger one.

Problems

136. How many pieces of lumber 1′ 9″ long can be cut from a stick that is 16′ 8″ long?

FIG. 36.—An outside stairway.

137. What will be the spacing for seven hooks on a closet wall that is 10′ 8″ long?

138. A certain part of a framed building requires a number of pieces of 2 × 4 cut to 1′ 5″ long. How many of such pieces can be cut from a 2 × 4, 20′ long?

139. The wall of a cloak room in a school building is 18′ 9″ long. If 24 coat and hat hooks are used, how far apart will they be spaced?

140. A certain job requires a number of pieces of stock that are 11″ long. How many can be cut from a piece of lumber 14′ 8″ long?

141. The distance from floor to floor in a certain building is exactly 9′ 11″. It is planned to build an outside stairway to connect these floors. There will be **17** equal risers in the stairway. What will be their width? Figure 36 illustrates an outside stairway.[1]

142. What is the total run of a stairway that has ten steps in it, if the tread run is exactly 10″? Figure 37 illustrates tread run.

143. What will be the width of the risers in a stairway constructed in a building that is 8′ 9″ from floor to floor? The plans call for 15 risers.

[1] For a detailed description of stair mathematics and stair layout, see Wilson and Werner's "Simplified Stair Layout," Delmar Publishers, Inc., Albany, N.Y.

144. What will be the total run of a stairway that has 17 risers in it, if the tread run is 11″?

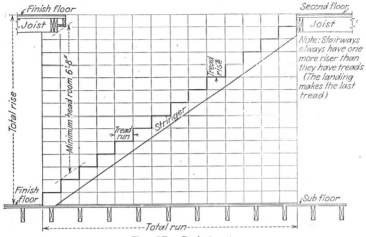

Fig. 37.—Stair terms.

A stairway always has one more riser than tread.   This is because the second floor serves as the last step.

145. What is the tread rise in a stairway for a building that is 12′ 8″ from floor to floor if the plans call for 19 risers?

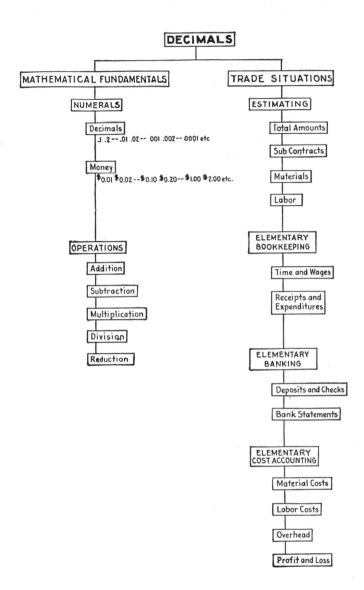

DECIMALS

MATHEMATICAL FUNDAMENTALS

NUMERALS

Decimals
.1 .2 -- .01 .02 -- .001 .002 -- .0001 etc

Money
$0.01 $0.02 -- $0.10 $0.20 -- $1.00 $2.00 etc.

OPERATIONS

Addition

Subtraction

Multiplication

Division

Reduction

TRADE SITUATIONS

ESTIMATING

Total Amounts

Sub Contracts

Materials

Labor

ELEMENTARY BOOKKEEPING

Time and Wages

Receipts and Expenditures

ELEMENTARY BANKING

Deposits and Checks

Bank Statements

ELEMENTARY COST ACCOUNTING

Material Costs

Labor Costs

Overhead

Profit and Loss

MATHEMATICAL CHECK-UP

DECIMALS⁴

Decimals.

- 1. Add 4.387, .0002, 102.01, 7693, and 999.897.
- 2. Subtract 698.437 from 779.5376.
- 3. Multiply 73.767 by 1.0028.
- 4. Divide .1728 by .144.
- 5. $25.00 per MB.F.[1] = what price per board foot?
- 6. Change 65,207 bd. ft.[2] to Mbd. ft.[3]
- 7. Change 27.3 cu. yd. to cubic feet.
- 8. Change 392 cu. ft. to cubic yards.
- 9. 435 bd. ft. at $35.50 per Mbd. ft. = how much?
- 10. How much will 4,250 bd. ft. cost at $38.25 per Mbd. ft.?

Money.

- 11. Add $29.29, $44.04, $176.75, $998.98, $16.00, and $1.75.
- 12. Subtract $4,976.39 from $10,000.09.
- 13. Multiply $785.29 by 18.
- 14. Divide $9,497.80 by $19.75.
- 15. Change $69.70 per 1,000 to price per board foot.
- 16. Change $.125 per board foot to price per 1,000.
- 17. Change $9.48 per dozen to price per piece.
- 18. Change $.47 per piece to price per dozen.
- 19. Change $.29 per piece to price per 50.
- 20. Change $25.75 per 50 to price per piece.

[1] MB.F. = 1,000 board feet.
[2] bd. ft. = board feet.
[3] M = 1,000.
⁴ See p. 163

44

CHAPTER III

DECIMALS

The mathematics the carpenter uses is divided very clearly into two distinct classes, as already indicated in the previous chapter. On the job, the measurements are for the purpose of locating certain parts of the building, or the building itself may have to be located on the lot. The spacing problem is always prominent during the process of construction. Again, the carpenter divides distances into an equal number of parts; and he is continuously figuring the sizes of innumerable pieces of lumber. The tools used for this layout work are the 3-ft. rule, the steel tape, and the steel square.

In addition to this constructional mathematics there is another field of work for the carpenter to learn if he aspires to direct work or to take full responsibility for the completion of different kinds of buildings. This work includes a knowledge of take-off methods: that is, taking off a bill of lumber or hardware; finding the cost of this material; and estimating the amount of labor necessary to do the work required. Very often he will have to itemize parts of the building for other crafts. An elementary knowledge of the methods used in balancing a bank account and in keeping a time book is a very desirable asset.

This chapter will deal with these divisions of the carpenter's mathematics. The basis of measurement in estimating costs is the dollar rather than the 3-ft. rule. The problems, therefore, will provide experience in the use of decimals.

ADDITION

Problems

146 to 150. A contractor checks over his time book at the end of a job and finds that he has paid out the following amounts each week to his men. What was the total amount paid each week?

Problems	146	147	148	149	150
Employees	1st week	2d week	3d week	4th week	5th week
William Berry..................	$31.58	$24.35	$16.90	$27.62	$46.58
John Detrick....................	36.40	32.61	37.89	.....	16.90
James Crawford.................	.....	.....	46.45	18.13	29.47
Harold Hess....................	11.00	22.00	34.56	33.77	9.10
George Black...................	19.35	.....	.....	54.68	45.79
Patrick Mullins.................	27.50	.....	43.50	27.25	33.00
George Squires.................	.....	.....	31.54	52.00	9.74
Lee Raby......................	48.00	36.30	42.90	33.26	44.68
John Zikratch..................	31.60	.....	28.00	17.43	35.90
Frank Arnold..................	3.25	5.50	19.88	27.65	45.99
Ben Ross......................	12.68	22.63	.....	31.95	43.92

151. What is the cost of the hardware listed in Fig. 38?

INVOICE

BLUEMLE & GIBSON
Established in Nineteen-Fifteen

HARDWARE · · CHINA · GLASSWARE · SPORTING GOODS

6354 PACIFIC BLVD. · LAfayette 1689 · HUNTINGTON PARK, CALIFORNIA

SOLD TO James A. Mc Arthur
1732 S. Rita Street

Date June 10, 19__

Your Order No.

Terms Net

QUANTITY	DESCRIPTION	PRICE	AMOUNT	TOTAL
1½ pr.	4"x4" D. B. Butts	.44	.66	
1 pr.	glass push plates	.60	.60	
1 pr.	3½" x 3½" N. P. butts	.28	.28	
8 pr.	3½" x 3½" D. B. butts	.26	2.08	
8	D. B. Door stops	.07	.56	
20 pr.	# 628 2½" x 2½" N. P. butts	.24	1.92	
4 pr.	# 628 2½" x 2½" D. B. butts	.22	.88	

FIG. 38.—Hardware bill.

152. A cement contractor purchased cement, sand, and rock for a sidewalk job. What did his material cost him? His bill was as follows:

62 sacks cement..................................$39.45
21 yd. of sand.................................. 44.10
28 yd. crushed rock............................ 70.00
52 empty sacks................................. 5.20

It is customary to charge for cloth sacks which contain the cement. Whenever these sacks are returned, credit is given at the approximate rate of 10¢ each.

153. What is the total cost of a bill of hardware that a contractor received for repairs on a building? The itemized bill follows: 6 3

Nails..$ 9.66
Locks.. 16.40
Drawer pulls................................... 3.45
Cupboard catches.............................. 2.00
Hinges, 2″ × 2″ butts.......................... 1.75
Bolts, carriage................................ 2.34
Screen wire.................................... 21.89
Door bumpers.................................. .75
Coat and hat hooks............................ 3.60
Handles....................................... .65
Elbow catches................................. .20
Window lifts.................................. 1.50
Window locks................................. 1.30

154. If the itemized list of extras on an interior cabinet job amounted to the following items, what was the total cost of the mill work? 4 3

Contract......................................$346.63
24 lin. ft. picture moulding................... .97
38 lin. ft. base-board......................... 1.36
One pair CC doors............................ 4.50
3 small drawers............................... 1.60
4 large drawers............................... 8.40
4 pc. 1″ × 12″ × 14′ shelving stock............. 2.24
Band sawing 4 brackets........................ 1.25
One set-up for moulding....................... 1.25
Delivery charges.............................. 1.50

The term "CC door" means china closet door. The term "set-up" refers to the work necessary to grind special knives and set them in the machine ready to make the moulding. The term "extras" means additional material necessary to complete the job which was not included in the original contract.

155. The bill for the sheet-metal work on a residence was as follows. What was the total cost of the sheet metal? 3 2

Lining bread drawers..........................$ 3.25
Two conductor heads.......................... 2.50
70 lin. ft. 3″ × 4″ gutter...................... 10.50
Roof safe for stove vent...................... 3.40
200 lin. ft. flashing.......................... 6.68
36 lin. ft. valley tin......................... 2.89

156. If the bids for materials and labor on a garage 20′ × 24′ were as follows, what was the total bid of the contractor?

Lumber	$74.47
Cement	17.65
Sand and rock	11.60
Painting	37.29
Sheet metal	13.92
Wiring	19.40
Labor	31.68
Profit	20.90

157. What is the total of the bid as shown in Fig. 39?

158. What was the cost of the hardware on an addition to a library if the itemized bill of the Oneonta Hardware Store was submitted thus?

4 pair 3″ loose-pin ball bearing butts	$ 3.50
3 transom catches	2.25
20 pair 4½″ × 4½″ wrought steel dull brass butts.	35.00
11 inside locks complete (two bit keys to each lock). .	66.18
5 Corbin door checks, size C	41.00
11 door bumpers, 3″	3.85
3 solid brass bolts, 8″	4.40

Hardware for a public building is usually made of solid brass, owing to its hard usage, and hence is more expensive. The hardware for an ordinary five-room house does not cost nearly so much.

159. What was the total bid of Mr. Wells for the construction and material necessary for a four-room bungalow? Excavating, $39.87; lumber, $363.00; fireplace, $73.00; plumbing, $359.28; sheet metal, $36.83; shingling, $56.28; wiring, $77.81; heating, $39.43; plastering, $289.67; painting, $267.23; millwork, $289.99; hardware, $58.40; hardwood floors, $131.62; electric fixtures, $48.97; liability insurance, $27.16; miscellaneous, $19.30; profit, $231.67.

160. A contractor received estimates for materials with which to construct 38 built-in cabinets. How much did they cost?

1,840 bd. ft. of lumber	$126.10
19 dozen pairs of hinges	42.17
19 doz. cupboard turns	51.62
2 qt. cold glue	.87
13 doz. drawer pulls	9.43

HENRY BERTCH
BUILDER

GENERAL ESTIMATE

DATE August 2, 19____

OWNER Norman Parkins

LOCATION South Pasadena, California   FLOOR AREA 1162 SQ. FT.

ARCHITECT Wilbur Harrison

No.	ITEMS	NOTATIONS	ESTIMATED COST	ADDITIONS AND DEDUCTIONS	REVISED COST	DIFFERENCE
1	PREPARATION	Permits	17 00			
2	GRAD. & EXC.		121 63			
3	CEMENT WORK		=432=21=		527 94	
4	REIN. STEEL					
5	MASONRY	Brickwork	=201=72=		245 38	
6	CAST STONE					
7	ROUGH LUMBER		1312 42			
8	MILL WORK		926 13			
9	FIN. LUMBER		644 46			
10	SASH & DOORS	in millwork				
11	SCREENS	included in millwork				
12	ROLL SCREENS					
13	STEEL SASH & GL.					
14	PLATE GLASS					
15	FRAMING	labor	701 16			
16	FINISHING	labor	387=21		422 21	
17	COMPLETING					
18	MISC. LABOR					
19	SHINGLING					
20	INSURANCE	Compensation	50 00			
21	HDW. FLOORS		237 53			
22	RGH. HDWE.	.	76 45			
23	FINISH HDWE.		146 63			
24	WROT IRON		37 86			
25	STRUCT. STEEL					
26	COMPO. ROOF		236 49			
27	TILE ROOF					
28	WATER PROOF					
29	PLASTERING	Exterior	538 42			
30	PAINTING (and Decorating)	Interior	483 36 747 21			
31	PLUMBING		942=27=		867 81	
32	SEWER & CESS.	included in plumbing				
33	HEATING		374 59			
34	SHEET METAL		246 39			
35	WIRING		134 59			
36	LIGHT FIXT.		123 48			
37	TILE AND MARBLE		189 16			
38	MISC. ITEMS	Drayage, phone, etc.	64 00			
	Insulation		=316=82=		365 28	
	Sprinkling System (front yard only)		72 00			
	Window Shades	.	64 32			
	Garage Complete		327 41			

IMPORTANT Check with all guides when listing materials. Check list for special items. Check specifications. Re-check additions before completing bid.	TOTAL COST			
	GROSS PROFIT	864 52		
	BOND (not required)			
	BID			

FIG. 39.—A typical bid outline.

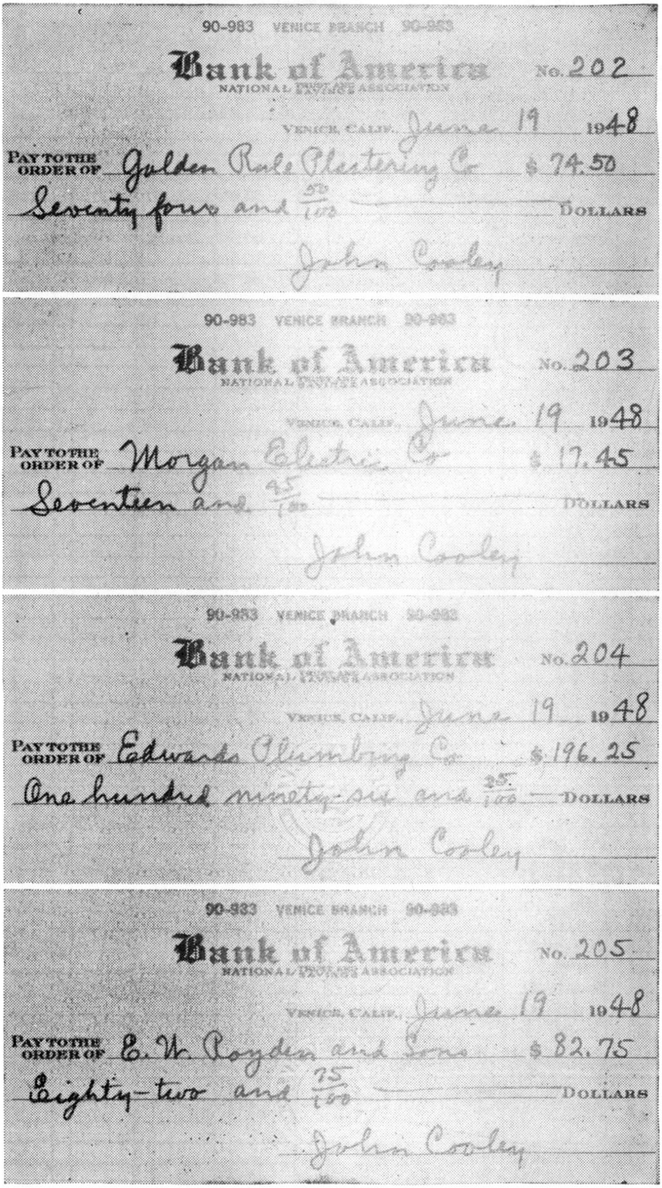

FIG. 40.—Illustrating problem 161.

161. If on the completion of a repair job a contractor pays the amounts shown in Fig. 40 to the different mechanics and subcontractors who assisted in the work, how much was paid out?

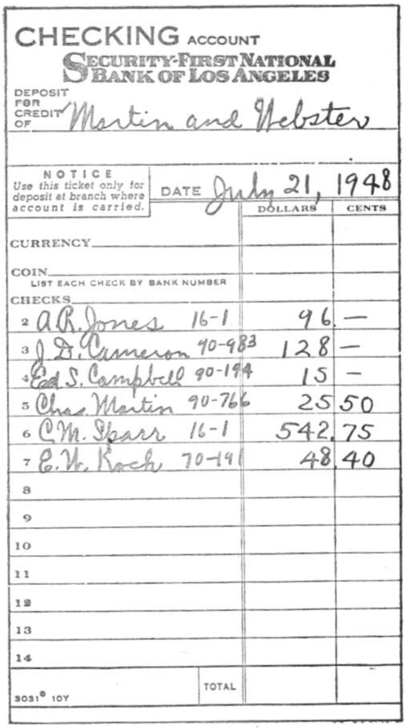

CHECKING ACCOUNT
SECURITY-FIRST NATIONAL BANK OF LOS ANGELES
DEPOSIT FOR CREDIT OF Martin and Webster

NOTICE Use this ticket only for deposit at branch where account is carried.

DATE July 21, 1948

		DOLLARS	CENTS
CURRENCY			
COIN			
CHECKS (LIST EACH CHECK BY BANK NUMBER)			
2 A. R. Jones	16-1	96	—
3 J. D. Cameron	90-483	128	—
4 Ed. S. Campbell	90-194	15	—
5 Chas. Martin	90-766	25	50
6 C. M. Sparr	16-1	542	75
7 E. W. Koch	70-191	48	40
8			
9			
10			
11			
12			
13			
14			
3031® 10Y	TOTAL		

FIG. 41.—Bank deposit slip.

162. A contractor has a bank balance of $1,457.68. He receives a number of checks for work performed which he deposits in his bank. What will his bank balance be after the deposits are made? The amounts of the checks are: $231.56, $687.90, $34.68, $3,573.84, $54.45.

163. A contractor has a bank balance of $538.35. If he deposits checks as shown on the deposit slip in Fig. 41, what is his new balance?

164. If a workman deposited four checks as shown in Fig. 42, what was the total amount of his deposit?

165. A contractor's bank balance is $3,426.38. His payroll for a week is as follows:

Carpenters	$326.16
Bricklayers	183.98
Plasterers	462.87
Laborers	89.28
Painters	231.29

He receives a check during the same week for $567.72. What was his net bank balance at the end of the week?

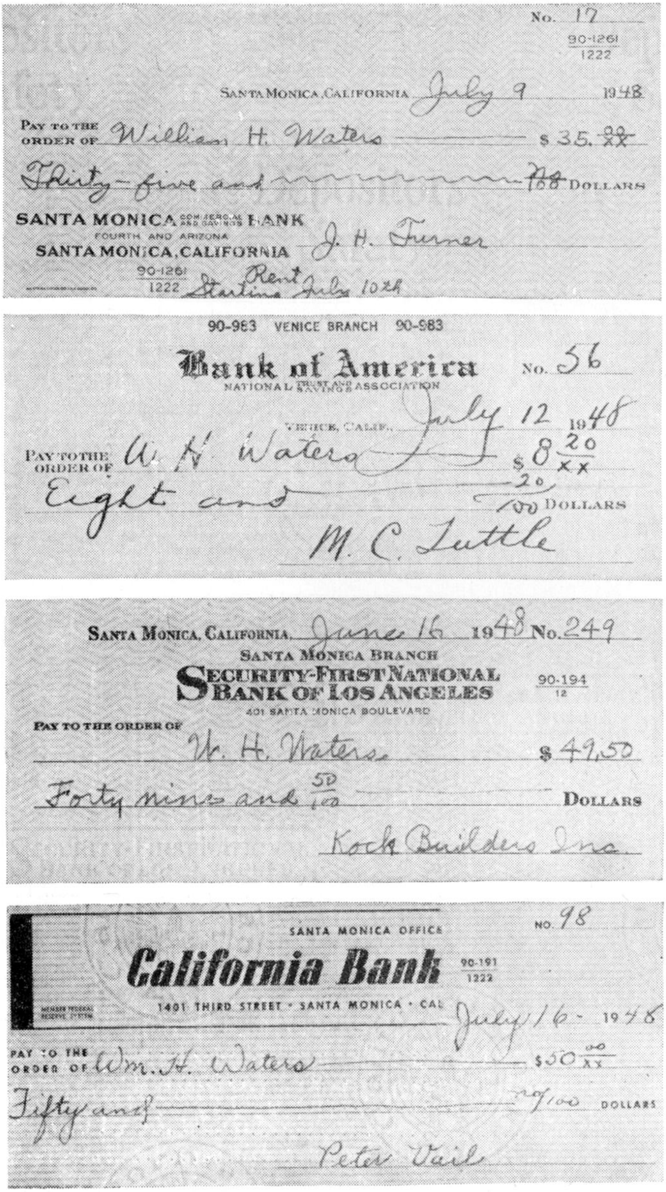

FIG. 42.—Typical bank checks.

SUBTRACTION

Problems

166. A contract for the lumber required for a five-room dwelling amounted to $438.29. During the construction period the builder required additional lumber to the amount of $58.77. When the job was completed he returned some material and received credit to the

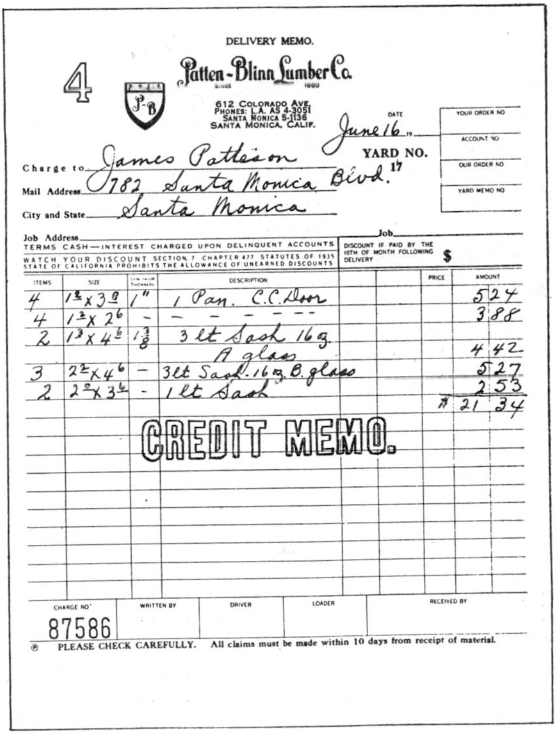

DELIVERY MEMO.

4 Patten-Blinn Lumber Co. Since 1880

612 Colorado Ave. Phones: L.A. AS 4-3051 Santa Monica 5-1136 Santa Monica, Calif.

Date June 16, 19

Your Order No. | Account No. | Our Order No. | Yard Memo No.

YARD NO. 17

Charge to James Patteson

Mail Address 782 Santa Monica Blvd.

City and State Santa Monica

Job Address Job

TERMS CASH—INTEREST CHARGED UPON DELINQUENT ACCOUNTS

WATCH YOUR DISCOUNT SECTION 7 CHAPTER 477 STATUTES OF 1935 STATE OF CALIFORNIA PROHIBITS THE ALLOWANCE OF UNEARNED DISCOUNTS

DISCOUNT IF PAID BY THE 10TH OF MONTH FOLLOWING DELIVERY $

ITEMS	SIZE	THICKNESS	DESCRIPTION	PRICE	AMOUNT
4	$1^2 \times 3^0$	1"	1 Pan. C.C. Door		5 24
4	$1^3 \times 2^6$	–	– – – – –		3 88
2	$1^3 \times 4^6$	$1\frac{3}{8}$	3 lt Sash 16 oz. A glass		4 42
3	$2^2 \times 4^6$	–	3 lt Sash 16 oz. B. glass		5 27
2	$2^0 \times 3^4$	–	1 lt Sash		2 53
				$	21 34

CREDIT MEMO.

CHARGE NO. 87586 | WRITTEN BY | DRIVER | LOADER | RECEIVED BY

PLEASE CHECK CAREFULLY. All claims must be made within 10 days from receipt of material.

FIG. 43.—Lumber yard credit slip.

amount of $21.34. What was the net cost of the lumber. Figure 43 illustrates the credit slip.

167. The cost of 110 sacks of cement for a foundation for a house was estimated at $82.60. Additional cement was purchased to do some extra work that the owner desired. This totaled 31 sacks and cost $21.70. When the job was completed the contractor returned eight sacks of cement for which he received credit for $5.60. He also received credit for all empty sacks returned which amounted to 8¢ each. What was the net cost of the cement?

168. The contract for the lumber on a Monterey chalet type house amounted to $689.67. The millwork bid amounted to $538.73. The contractor required additional lumber which amounted to $63.51, and additional millwork which cost him $34.50. He returned 341 bd. ft. of lumber when the job was completed and received a credit slip of $10.23. His millwork credit came to $13.48. What was the total net cost of the lumber and millwork?

It is usually possible to return the pieces of framing stock which are left on the job provided they are in good condition and have not been used. A planing mill will likewise take back mill stock if it has not been made to a special size or shape.

169. A cement contractor's estimate for concrete work for a bungalow court called for the following number of sacks of cement for the different parts of the building and walks:

Eight foundations.......	320 sacks	$236.80
Eight garage floors......	112 sacks	82.88
Sidewalks..............	78 sacks	59.72
Aprons................	56 sacks	41.34

When the job was completed his bill showed that he had purchased 35 additional sacks of cement at a cost of $22.50. He returned 11 sacks of cement and was given credit to the amount of $7.70. For each empty sack returned he was credited with 9¢. What was the cost of the cement?

The term "apron" refers to the flat piece of cement that is laid directly in front of the garage entrance.

170. A mill cabinet estimate for interior finish was as follows:

Doors..	$162.78
Windows.....................................	97.22
Casement sash...............................	26.38
Interior trim.................................	84.73
Shelving stock...............................	27.69
Drawer stock................................	18.52

When the job was completed the contractor received a credit of $14.27 on the doors, $3.25 on the sash, $6.29 on the interior trim. He ordered more shelving that cost him $6.26, and a light of glass to replace a broken one cost $3.75. What was the net amount of the bill?

171. The bids for a brick building, when opened, were found to be too high, therefore, concrete was substituted for brick. What will Mr. McGrath's bid be if he takes out $4,732.50 for the brick and adds $3,221.89 for the concrete work? His original bid amounted to $24,745.67.

172. Mr. White's total bid for the construction of an eight-room two-story house was $11,358.69. Before submitting this bid to the owner he received a new subcontract estimate on the heating which was $53.51 less than the one he first used. Likewise, on his plumbing he saved $37.52. By making these reductions on his original estimate he is able also to reduce his figure for profit $24.56. What was the amount of his revised bid?

173. An architect found it necessary to change the specifications for materials to be used in the construction of a school house, as the contractors' bids were all over the estimated cost. Mr. Weldon made a new bid with the following changes: What was his new bid?

Original bid..............................	$67,894.47
Omitted on excavations....................	1,358.38
Saved on plumbing fixtures.................	324.00
Omitted bleachers.........................	1,539.02

When bids are found to be too high a common method used to reduce the cost of the proposed building is to omit certain parts, or substitute a different grade of materials.

174. A 16-room school plant was estimated to cost $137,659.49. This was found to exceed the total amount of available money by nearly $35,000. The architect revised the plan, omitted one wing of the plant and used select common red brick in place of face brick. For the latter change the contractor allowed the sum of $18,987.27. Omitting one wing reduced the cost $13,409.38. The heating man lowered his bid $398.49. These three reductions lowered the contractor's profit $461.78 and the architect's fees $2,463.60. What was the new estimated cost of the school plant?

Architects' fees are based on a certain percentage of the total cost of the building. If he is to superintend the construction of the job also, an additional percentage is added to his regular fee which covers the drawing of the plans and the writing of the specifications.

175. An original bid of $38,427.16 was reduced on account of certain omissions on the job. These amounted to $6,139.49. Extras amounted to $1,564.27. What was the cost of the job?

176. A contractor buys an auto truck for $1,589.70. His bank balance for the month of April is $1,029.50. He deposits one check for $321.00 and another for $890.57. In addition to paying out the check for the truck, his payroll checks amount to $204.58. What is his bank balance on the first of May?

177. A contractor receives $231.77 for doing a piece of work. He gives one of his carpenters a check for $32.46 and another $35.88. His material costs him $129.68. How much did he make on the job?

178. Mr. Coons' bank statement on the first of January showed that he had $350.48 in the bank. During the month he paid out the following checks: $38.68, $98.76, $47.09, $65.04, $54.23, $9.68. His deposits were $65.83, $98.65, $357.89. What was his balance on the first on February?

179. What is the bank balance in the following account? Balance on first of August, $2,789.40: deposits $345.78, $398.00, $34.85, $87.74, $3,876.00, $308.03; paid out $35.65, $18.04, $654.78, $43.00, $45.09, $542.89.

180. A contractor's bank balance is $3,561.75. He deposits checks as follows: $21.63, $14.29, $609.28, $176.39. He draws out checks for the following amounts: $729.62. $43.39, $389.46, $53.54. What was his bank balance after these transactions were completed?

RECONCILEMENT OF ACCOUNT WITH

Security-First National Bank of Los Angeles

CHECKS OUTSTANDING

NUMBER	AMOUNT

TO PROVE THE BALANCE AS SHOWN
ON YOUR STATEMENT:

Sort the checks numerically or by date issued.

Check off on the stubs of your check book each of the checks paid by the bank and make a list of the numbers and amounts of those still outstanding in the space provided at the left; to the sum of the outstanding checks add the balance as shown in your check book.

List below all deposits which do not appear on the statement, and add to this total the balance as shown by the statement.

The two results should agree, and if so, the statement rendered is correct.

	DEPOSITS	
	NOT	
TOTAL CHECKS OUTSTANDING	CREDITED	
BALANCE AS PER CHECK BOOK	BANK BALANCE AS PER STATEMENT	
TOTAL	TOTAL	

See agreement with depositors printed in your pass book.
For every charge (or debit) appearing on the statement a corresponding voucher (cancelled check or debit ticket) will be found enclosed herewith.
If any items appearing on this statement are not clear the Bank will be pleased to furnish full detail upon request.
Kindly return immediately any checks that do not belong with this statement.

FIG. 44.—Form for reconcilement of account.

An important problem that arises monthly with any person who has a checking account is that of finding out if his check-book balance agrees with the monthly bank statement. A number of factors enter into the problem, such as mistakes in addition or subtraction in the check book and the fact that some checks may have been written that have not arrived at the bank (known as outstanding checks); occasionally, also, a deposit is made in the bank after the statement for that month has been made up (known as deposits not credited).

Figure 44 shows a Reconcilement of Account form that is sometimes printed on the back of the monthly bank statement to help the depositor reconcile his balance with the bank balance.

FIG. 45.—Illustrating problem 183.

Each of the following five problems is to be solved by the use of this form. Note carefully the directions as given on the form, working each step as indicated.

181. M. R. Smith receives his bank statement. In reconciling his account he finds the outstanding checks are as follows: check 15, $6.00; 17, $9.00; 21, $7.76; 25, $8.32. Deposits not credited at the bank are: Jan. 30, $77.50; Jan. 31; $24.64. The balance in the check book was $590.29. The bank statement balance was $519.23. Determine whether the accounts agree.

182. A contractor receives his bank statement from the bank and notes that the balance is $229.34. His own balance in his check book is $536.00. In proving his account he finds that the following checks have not arrived at the bank: 982, $36.00; 991, $5.69; 993, $48.65:

995, $28.00.   He also noted that the following deposits were not credited on his statement: $175.00 and $250.00.   Is his check book balance correct?

183. Mr. Johnson goes to the bank and obtains his bank statement on Jan. 30, which shows a balance of $771.65.   He finds that checks 3 and

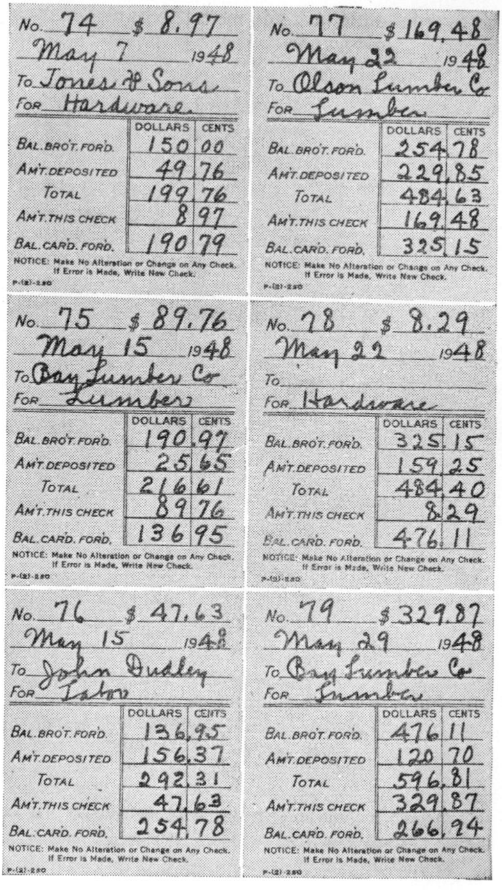

No. 74 $ 8.97		
May 7 1948		
To *Jones & Sons*		
For *Hardware.*		
	DOLLARS	CENTS
BAL. BRO'T. FOR'D.	150	00
AM'T. DEPOSITED	49	76
TOTAL	199	76
AM'T. THIS CHECK	8	97
BAL. CAR'D. FOR'D.	190	79

NOTICE: Make No Alteration or Change on Any Check. If Error is Made, Write New Check.

No. 77 $ 169.48		
May 22 1948		
To *Olson Lumber Co*		
For *Lumber*		
	DOLLARS	CENTS
BAL. BRO'T. FOR'D.	254	78
AM'T. DEPOSITED	229	85
TOTAL	484	63
AM'T. THIS CHECK	169	48
BAL. CAR'D. FOR'D.	325	15

NOTICE: Make No Alteration or Change on Any Check. If Error is Made, Write New Check.

No. 75 $ 89.76		
May 15 1948		
To *Bay Lumber Co*		
For *Lumber*		
	DOLLARS	CENTS
BAL. BRO'T. FOR'D.	190	97
AM'T. DEPOSITED	25	65
TOTAL	216	61
AM'T. THIS CHECK	89	76
BAL. CAR'D. FOR'D.	136	95

NOTICE: Make No Alteration or Change on Any Check. If Error is Made, Write New Check.

No. 78 $ 8.29		
May 22 1948		
To		
For *Hardware*		
	DOLLARS	CENTS
BAL. BRO'T. FOR'D.	325	15
AM'T. DEPOSITED	159	25
TOTAL	484	40
AM'T. THIS CHECK	8	29
BAL. CAR'D. FOR'D.	476	11

NOTICE: Make No Alteration or Change on Any Check. If Error is Made, Write New Check.

No. 76 $ 47.63		
May 15 1948		
To *John Dudley*		
For *Labor*		
	DOLLARS	CENTS
BAL. BRO'T. FOR'D.	136	95
AM'T. DEPOSITED	156	37
TOTAL	292	31
AM'T. THIS CHECK	47	63
BAL. CAR'D. FOR'D.	254	78

NOTICE: Make No Alteration or Change on Any Check. If Error is Made, Write New Check.

No. 79 $ 329.87		
May 29 1948		
To *Bay Lumber Co*		
For *Lumber*		
	DOLLARS	CENTS
BAL. BRO'T. FOR'D.	476	11
AM'T. DEPOSITED	120	70
TOTAL	596	81
AM'T. THIS CHECK	329	87
BAL. CAR'D. FOR'D.	266	94

NOTICE: Make No Alteration or Change on Any Check. If Error is Made, Write New Check.

Fig. 46.—Check book stub information for problem 184.

4, as shown in Fig. 45 are not in, but after making allowance for this fact when proving his statement his own balance still does not agree with the bank balance.   All deposits are included in the statement. He figures over his stubs and finds he made several errors in subtraction, addition, and carrying forward. Write out a new set of stubs similar to the original and prove that the bank balance is correct.

184. The August bank statement for Mr. Hall shows a balance of $293.50. Checks numbered 76 and 78 which are shown in Fig. 46 were

CHECKING ACCOUNT WITH											
Walter R. Roberts					***Venice***		BRANCH				
1692 Nowita St.					**SECURITY-FIRST NATIONAL BANK OF LOS ANGELES**						
Venice					This account does not bear interest						
MAY 2 4	1948	C		1	6	7	—	JUN 2 8 1948	C		6 5 70
MAY 2 6	1948	C			5	78	JUN 2 9 1948	C	2 5 0 15		
MAY 2 8	1948	C		1 4	93	JUL 2 1948	C	4 0 0 —			
JUN 3	1948	C		8 3	75	JUL 7 1948		2 5 50			
JUN 4	1948	C		9 6	30	JUL 1 5 1948	C	1 74 —			
JUN 5	1948	C	7 2 0	—	JUL 1 7 1948		3 5 0 —				
JUN 7	1948	C	5 6 0	—	JUL 1 9 1948	C	1 0 9 25				
JUN 8	1948	C	4 0	50	JUL 2 2 1948	C	6 5 35				
JUN 1 1	1948	C	7 5	25	JUL 2 3 1948	C	7 5 25				
JUN 1 2	1948	C	2 8	—	JUL 2 4 1948	C	1 2 5 —				
JUN 1 5	1948	C	4 7	—							
JUN 1 7	1948	C	9	—							
JUN 2 1	1948	C	2 7 2	—							
JUN 2 4	1948	C	1 5	—							
JUN 2 6	1948	C	8 2 12								

FIG. 47.—Typical pages from a pass book.

not accounted for on the statement. Allowing for this fact he still finds that the balance in his check book is "off" $29.36. Write out a new set of stubs and prove that the bank balance is correct.

185. Figures 47, 48 and 49, illustrate a pass book, the stub end of a check book, and a bank statement.

Cancelled checks were returned as follows:

209	Cooley & Sons............	$210.00
210	C. W. Freeman...........	75.50
211	Allen's Hardware..........	24.87
212	Price Bros...............	15.29
213	Hammond Lumber Co......	695.28
214	Myself only..............	274.24
216	Service Building Co........	160.00
217	J. W. Smith..............	88.45

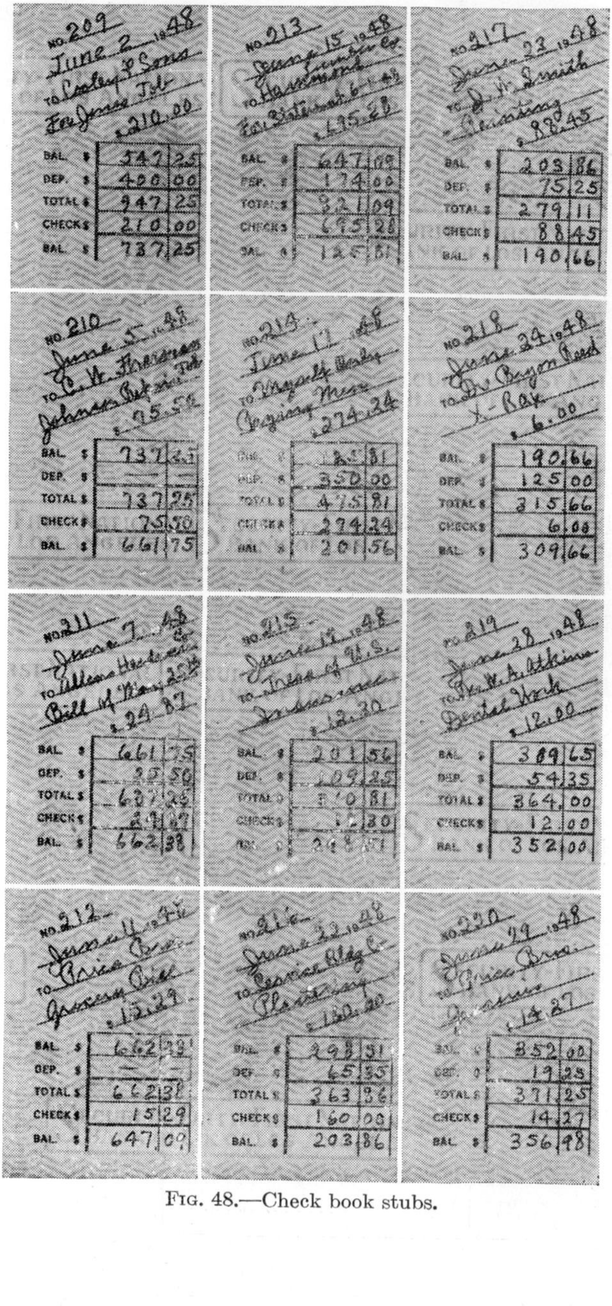

FIG. 48.—Check book stubs.

SHEET NO.

Ledger Sheet
COMMERCIAL ACCOUNT
SECURITY-FIRST NATIONAL BANK OF LOS ANGELES

Walter R. Roberts
1692 Nowita St., Venice, Calif.

OLD BALANCE	CHECKS	CHECKS	CHECKS	DEPOSITS		NEW BALANCE
				BALANCE BROUGHT FORWARD	JUN 30 '48	547.25
547.25	210.00 –			400.00	JUL 2 '48	737.25 *
737.25				25.50	JUL 7 '48	762.75 *
762.75	75.50 –				JUL 8 '48	687.25 *
687.25	24.87 –				JUL 10 '48	662.38 *
662.38	15.29 –				JUL 14 '48	647.09 *
647.09				174.00	JUL 15 '48	821.09 *
821.09	695.28 –	274.24 –		350.00	JUL 17 '48	201.57 *
201.57				109.25	JUL 19 '48	310.82 *
310.82				65.35	JUL 22 '48	376.17 *
376.17				75.25	JUL 23 '48	451.42 *
451.42				125.00	JUL 24 '48	576.42 *
576.42	160.00 –				JUL 25 '48	416.42 *
416.42	88.45 –				JUL 30 '48	327.97 *

FIG. 49.—Bank statement.

Reconcile the balance as shown in the check book with the balance on the bank statement.

MULTIPLICATION

Problems

186. A two-story house requires 35 double-hung window frames. A carpenter agreed to build them for an average of 75¢ each. How much did he earn?

The term "double-hung" denotes a window that has two parts, each one of which slides vertically and is usually balanced with sash balances.

187. An apartment house contains 12 apartments. To what does the finishing labor for the whole job amount if the interior finish work in each unit costs $138.80?

188. A contractor built a bungalow court containing eight units. The framing labor on each unit amounted to $184.50 and the finish labor $167.35. What was the total carpentry bill?

189. A carpenter receives pay at the rate of $8 per day of 8 hr. What will be the cost of the finishing labor on seven door openings if his time is divided as follows?

Setting one jamb............................. 30 min.
Casing both sides of this jamb................. 45 min.
Hanging the door .... 1 hr.
Fitting the lock .... 30 min.

190. What is the cost of 12 casement sash at $2.45; 9 one-panel inside doors at $4.35; and 22 cabinet doors at $1.65?

191. What will be the cost of the cement floor of a garage that is 12' wide and 18' long, at 17¢ per square foot?

192. Find the cost of excavating a cellar that is 33' wide, 45' long, and 5' deep. The price is 34¢ per cubic yard.

193. What will be the estimated cost of a house that has a floor dimension of 28' × 52' at $3.40 per square foot?

This method is only a "guesstimate" and is for approximate cost only. As proof of the variableness of this process note the following: A building 20' × 20' contains 400 sq. ft. of floor and 80 ft. of perimeter. A building 10' × 40' contains 400 sq. ft. of floor and 100 ft. of perimeter.

194. A bungalow court contained 12 units or apartments. Each one has a basement or cellar 5' × 9'. Owing to the fall or slope of the ground, three of them were 5' deep, three of them 7' deep, and the remaining ones 6' deep. What did the excavating cost at $1.55 per cubic yard?

195. At an estimated cost of $2.87 per square foot, what is the cost of the house that is 34' wide and 47' long?

196. What will be the cost of 28 lin. ft. of valley flashing 14″ wide at $.46 per lin. ft.?

Valley flashing is the material placed at the intersection of the two parts of the roof and is illustrated in Fig. 50. At this point the shingles cannot overlap, hence the flashing is used to prevent leaks and must be placed before the shingles are laid.

197. How much will 321 cu. ft. of concrete cost at 43¢ per cubic foot?

Concrete is estimated by either the cubic yard or the cubic foot. The cubic foot basis is preferable in house construction; the cubic yard is too large a measuring unit for an average house foundation, which contains only a few cubic yards.

198. Among other expenditures in the construction of a large building there are two items for lumber. One item is for 27,500 bd. ft. at $32.50 per M, and the other is 68 MB.F. at $43.00 per M. What is the cost of the lumber?

It is customary to state the cost of lumber on the basis of 1,000 bd. ft., which is written MB.F., M being the Roman numeral for thousand.

199. A builder buys D.F.K.D. T.&G.Flg. (Douglas fir kiln-

Fig. 50.—Valley flashing.

dried, tongue and grooved flooring) in five lots as follows: 2,460 bd. ft., 1,500 bd. ft., 750 bd. ft., 1,875 bd. ft., and 230 bd. ft. What was the cost of the material at 9½¢ per board foot?

200. What is the cost of the concrete for a foundation for a large piece of machinery? The plans show the sizes to be 12′ wide, 17′ long, and 5′ thick. The cost per cubic foot is 33¢.

Figure the cost of each of the following hardware bills. The prices as given indicate the cost per unit, which is the pair, the dozen, the box, the ball, etc. If no unit is given then the cost is based on the piece.

201. 3 pair 3½ × 3½ loose-pin butts, brass finish.... @ $ 28
1 inside mortise lock...................... @   .70
3 doz. door bumpers....................... @ 1.10
4 clothes line reels....................... @   .65

202. 10 lb. 8d common nails...................... @ $ .06
16 pair hinges, butterfly, old copper finish...... @   .15
22 drawer pulls............................. @   .20
8 elbow catches............................ @   .06
1 doz. drawer locks, each........ .... @   .50
4 cupboard turns.......................... @   .20
8 forbes catches........................... @   .15
2 balls twine.............................. @   .25
4 boxes ¾" No. 10 screws f.h. (flat head) bright @   .14
203. 3 pair hinges, 4" × 4", old copper finish...... @ $ .80
4 pair hinges............................. @   .60
11 drawer pulls............................ @   .40
3 elbow catches........................... @   .16
½ dozen drawer locks, each.................. @ 1.00
2 cupboard turns.......................... @   .40
8 forbes catches........................... @   .15
1 ball twine.............................. @   .50
4 boxes ⅜" screws f.h. bright................ @   .14
204. Find the total of the bill in Fig. 51.

BLUEMLE & GIBSON
Established in Nineteen-Fifteen

HARDWARE   -   CHINA   -   GLASSWARE   -   SPORTING GOODS
6384 PACIFIC BLVD. - LAfayette 1689 - HUNTINGTON PARK, CALIFORNIA

INVOICE

SOLD TO   J. C. Martin & Sons
729 So. Rita St. Huntington Park

Date   June 14, 19__

Your Order No.

Terms Net

QUANTITY	DESCRIPTION	PRICE	AMOUNT	TOTAL
8	Inside mortise locks, solid brass escutcheons	.85		
8 pr.	3"x3" L.P. brass butts	.22		
8	casement window fasteners, sgle	.25		
6	brass door bumpers, 3"	.08		
25 lbs	8d finish nails	.07		
3 boxes	½" #5 R. H. brass screws	.23		
1 quart	Le Pages glue	.45		
4 lbs	1" # 18 wire brads	.20		
30 sheets	sandpaper # 00	.05		
18	machine bolts, 5" x ½"	.11		
12 sets	shelf rests, ¼" steel dowel	.15		
6	elbow catches, steel	.05		

FIG. 51.—Hardware bill.

3 3

205. 7 outside mortise door locks................. .... @ $2.45

84 six-pound sashweights, per pound.......... @   .04

60 sash pulleys, per dozen................... @ 2.35

1 set sliding door track complete............. @ 3.95

2 sets castors (wood wheels) per set (4 castors

per set)................................... @ 1.85

1 dozen pair push plates, glass, pair.......... @   .95

DIVISION

Problems

206. A contractor pays $19.38 for 646 lin. ft. of $2\frac{1}{2}''$ sprung picture moulding. What is the price per linear foot?

The term "sprung" has reference to the fact that this kind of moulding is made from $1''$ thick stock in such a way that it has the appearance of being sprung away from the wall and looks like a heavy moulding. Figure 52 represents this kind of a moulding.

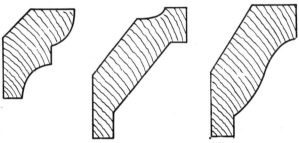

Fɪɢ. 52.—Typical sprung mouldings.

207. The cost of 568 lin. ft. of base-shoe is $8.79. What is the price paid per foot?

Base-shoe is used to fill in the space between the bottom edge of the base-board and the top of the finished floor and is shown in Fig. 53.

208. How much will a piece of $\frac{3}{8}'' \times 1\frac{1}{2}''$ 18' 0'' round cornered door stop cost if a contractor pays $16.10 for 644 lin. ft.?

209. What will be the cost of "moulding" eight lights of glass with a $\frac{1}{2}'' \times \frac{3}{4}''$ glass bead? The size of the glass is $12''$ by $18''$. A bill for 78 lin. ft. amounted to $1.17.

210. A garage floor is $16' \times 22'$ in size; the ribbons (see Fig. 20) are $2'$ wide and 104' long. What is the cost per square foot for this concrete work if the low bid was $95.68?

211. A house when completed cost $5,582.80. What was the average cost per square foot of floor space if the house contained 1,642 sq. ft.?

212. A house $28' \times 42'$ was estimated to cost $3,822. What would be the cost per square foot?

213. Four units of a motor court cost $7,022.40. Each unit contained 616 sq. ft. of floor space. What was the average cost per foot?

214. Each of six units of a motor inn were 12′ × 18′ in size. Four others were 22′ × 26′. What was the average cost per foot if the 10 units cost $9,581?

215. The total cost of three houses was estimated to be $17,107.20. Each house was 36′ × 48′. What is the estimated cost per square foot of floor area?

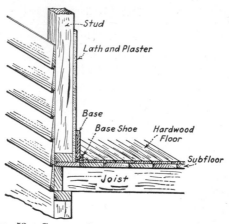

Fig. 53.—Cross-section of a framed floor and wall.

216. How much is the cost per yard of excavating 168 yd. of dirt if the total cost is $221.76?

217. A basement is 21′ × 20′ × 9′ deep. The cost of excavating was $121.80. How much did it cost per cubic yard?

218. A ditch 3′ wide, 6′ deep, and 567′ long cost $347.76. What was the cost per cubic yard?

219. Two wings of a school building were 24′ wide and 82′ long. Each required a basement, one of which was 5′ deep and the other 7′ deep. What was the contractor's price per cubic yard if his bid for the job of excavating was $1,100.96?

220. What is the cost per cubic yard for excavating a basement for a school that is 117′ wide and 148′ long? The depth of the excavation work, as shown on the blueprint, was 6′. The total cost of the work was $3,020.16.

221. If 432 bd. ft. of roof sheathing cost $28.08, what is the price per foot?

Roof sheathing is the term applied to the lumber which forms the flat surface of a roof and on which is nailed or laid the wood or composition shingles. The illustration in Fig. 54 shows a roof prepared for wood shingles.

222. The cost of 5,648 bd. ft. of framing lumber was $197.68. What was the cost per M?

223. An apartment house required 3,235 bd. ft. of shelving which cost $106.82. The inside trim cost $234.08, and required 2,128 bd. ft. The gum trim cost $297.00 and 850 bd. ft. were ordered. What price per foot was paid for each kind of material?

FIG. 54.—A roof sheathed ready for wood shingles.

224. A house 32′ wide and 56′ long required subfloor material that cost $68.99. Allow 308 bd. ft. of material for waste in laying, as the stock was laid diagonally, as illustrated in Fig. 55. What was the cost per board foot?

FIG. 55.—Laying subfloor diagonally.

Subfloor, usually 1″ × 6″ or 1″ × 8″, is laid directly on the floor joists and the hardwood floor is laid over it. Laying it diagonally is supposed to increase the strength of the building, but the primary motive in laying it that way is to make it possible to lay the hardwood floor in either direction of the room. A finish floor should never be laid in the same direction as the subfloor stock, for the result will be an uneven floor.

225. The dimensions of a house are 38′ × 54′. What is the cost per 1,000 of the siding stock to close in the frame of the house if the contractor ordered 2,140 bd. ft. of stock and paid $154.08 for the material.

226. Overtime on a rush job amounted to $38.76. How much did each of six men receive if all were paid at the same rate of wage?

227. A man does a repair job and receives altogether $75.80. Of this amount $34.80 was paid out for material. How much did he earn per hour if he worked 5½ eight-hour days doing the job?

228. A contract for the construction of a factory required that the building be completed by a certain date. Due to bad weather the foreman and superintendent could not keep up to the schedule. In order to gain time the contractor required the men to work overtime. At what rate per hour did he pay if the overtime pay for one week for 24 men amounted $648. Each man put in 18 hr. extra.

It is standard practice on a large building to "map out" in advance just when each kind of work should start and finish. By this procedure it is possible to get a fairly good estimate as to when the building should be completed. Of course, there may be many delays such as rainy weather and slow deliveries of materials.

229. A contractor did a repair job for which he received $456.20. Of this amount $123.45 was for material and $47.50 was profit. The carpenters received $213.25 and the painters the balance. How much did the three carpenters earn per hour if they worked 9½ days? What did the two painters receive per hour if they worked 5 days on the job?

230. A job is figured to cost $3,468. Of this amount $494 was paid out for wages. How much per hour did the carpenters earn if four of them worked 17 eight-hour days?

REDUCTION

The carpenter has many types of reduction to do, such as changing hours to their equivalent value in dollars and cents; changing linear feet of material, such as rope, into pounds; and changing a number of items into dozens. The following problems will furnish practice in these types of reduction.

Problems

231 to 235. Each of these problems represents a page out of a time book. Compute the wages due each person and the total amount of labor cost:

231. Time: Week ending Dec. 31, 1947.

Name	M T W T F S	No. days	Price per day	Amount $ ¢
Elmer Simons.............	8 8 8 8	....	$ 7	
E. Spence................	4 8 8 8 8 4	....	8	
Frank Jones.............	8 8 8 8 8 8	....	4	

232. Time: Week ending July 23, 1948.

Name	M T W T F S	No. days	Price per day	Amount $ ¢
S. Hamilton..............	8 8 8 8 8 4	....	$ 8	
James Brown	8 8 8 4 4	....	6	
William Black............	8 8 8 8 8 8	....	5	
F. Springer..............	8 8 8 8 8 8	....	8	
Thomas Murray...........	7 8 8 9 8 8	....	10	

233. Time: Week ending Aug. 4, 1947.

Name	M T W T F S	No. days	Price per day	Amount $ ¢
Will Fox..................	8 8 8 8 8 8	....	$ 8	
J. Dunlap.................	7 4 8 9 8 8	....	8	
Jack Fraley...............	8 8 8 5	....	7	
Howard Cody..............	6 8 4 8 4	....	6	
F. Anders.................	8 8 8 8 8	....	9	
R. Jones..................	8 8 8 8 8 8	....	8	
Robert Smith..............	8 8 8 8 8 8	....	7	

234. See Fig. 56, which is a typical page out of a time book.

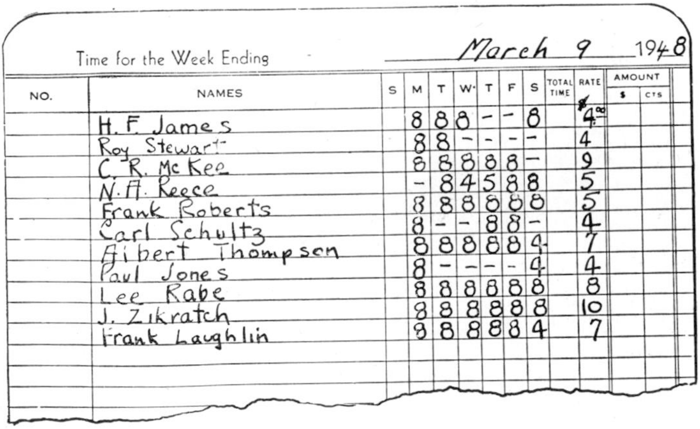

NO.	NAMES	S	M	T	W	T	F	S	TOTAL TIME	RATE	AMOUNT $	CTS
	H. F James		8	8	8	–	–	8		4⁰⁰		
	Roy Stewart		8	8	–	–	–	–		4		
	C. R. McKee		8	8	8	8	8	–		9		
	N. H. Reece		–	8	4	5	8	8		5		
	Frank Roberts		8	8	8	8	8	8		5		
	Carl Schultz		8	–	–	8	8	–		4		
	Hibert Thompson		8	8	8	8	8	4		7		
	Paul Jones		8	–	–	–	–	4		4		
	Lee Rabe		8	8	8	8	8	8		8		
	J. Zikratch		8	8	8	8	8	8		10		
	Frank Laughlin		8	8	8	8	8	4		7		

Time for the Week Ending *March 9* 1948

Fig. 56.—Page out of a time book.

235. Time: Week ending June 3, 1948.

Name	M	T	W	T	F	S	No. days	Price per day	Amount $ ¢
Robert Gold........	4	4	8	8		8	....	$ 4	
Charley Hill........		6	8	5	5	8	....	5	
Jim Burke..........			8	8	8	8	....	3	
Wilbur Skinner.....		8	8	8	8	.	....	9	
Walter Simon.......		8	4	4	6	2	....	7	
Louis Brown........		3	6	8	8	8	....	6	
Sidney Mellon......		8	4	8	8	8	....	10	
James Crocker......		8	4	8	8	8	....	5	

236. What will be the cost of 12 hanks (one bundle) of No. 7 sash cord at $1.05 per pound?   One bundle weighs 23 lb.

Sash cord is used for hanging double-hung windows and is manufactured in sizes 6, 7, 8, 9, 10, and 12.   The larger the number, the heavier the cord.   Allow four cords to a window, each one being 1 ft. longer than the window.   A hank of sash cord will contain 100 lin. ft. and is shown in Fig. 57.   In modern residential construction, the sash balance has replaced the sash weight.   However, repair jobs still require sash cords to match the old work.   Public school buildings require sash *chain* and sash weights if the sash are double hung.

237. How much will it cost for the hanks of sash cord for 14 double-hung windows 2′ 6″ × 6′?   Figure the hanks at $1.45 each.

Fig. 57.— A hank of sash cord.

238. What will 32 hanks of sash cord cost at $1.10 per pound?   One bundle, containing 12 hanks, weighs 22 lb.

239. What will the sash cord cost for eighteen 3′ 0″ × 6′ 0″ double-hung windows at $1.98 per hank?

240. A blueprint shows sixteen 3′ 0″ × 4′ 6″ windows and six 2′ 0″ × 3′ 6″ windows.   How much did the sash cord cost for these?   Add 1′

Fig. 58.—A wire fence.

to each window to get the length of each piece of cord.   One hank costs 75¢.

241. What will be the cost of the 1″ hexagon wire for a fence that is 5′ high and 70′ long? The price per 5′ roll (150 lin. ft.) is $12?

242. What will be the cost of poultry netting for fencing a back yard that is 50′ × 55′? The fence will be 4′ high, and 1″ hexagon mesh, 20 gage wire will be used. The price per 150 lin. ft. roll is $12.

243. A wire fence is 330′ long. How much will the wire cost if a roll 6′ wide and 150′ long is worth $16.50? The fence is 6′ high. Figure 58 illustrates a typical fence.

244. A rancher has 14 poultry yards to enclose with a wire fence which is to be 6′ high. What will it cost him if he uses ¾″ mesh wire that is worth $18 per roll. The poultry yards are 12′ wide and 18′ long. A roll contains 150 lin. ft.

245. A fence is 6′ high and 240′ long. What did the wire cost if a 6′ roll (150 lin. ft.) is worth $16.

246. Forty 6″ × ⅜″ carriage bolts are required to bolt down the mudsill of a house. How much will they cost at $4.50 per 100? Figure 59 shows a piece of mudsill bolted down.

Fig. 59.—Bedding and bolting mudsill down to concrete foundation.

247. Twelve platforms are required that are each 5′ wide, 8′ long, and 2′ high. How much will the bolts cost that fasten the legs if two bolts are used for each leg and each platform requires six legs? Bolts are worth $3.75 per 100.

248. The floors of 35 units of a motor court require 22 bolts each to fasten them to the foundation. How much will they cost at $4.75 per 100?

A   B

Fig. 60.—(a) Carriage bolt. (b) Machine bolt.

249. A shop building requires six roof trusses, each truss having sixteen 4½″ machine bolts at $3.80 per 100 and eight 6½″ bolts at $5.60 per 100. Find the cost of the bolts needed.

The difference between a machine bolt and a carriage bolt is that the latter has a square shoulder directly below the head which prevents the bolt from turning in the wood, while a machine bolt has a square head which can be held with a wrench. These bolts are illustrated in Fig. 60.

250. A special frame construction job requires 16 doz. bolts, which are worth $4.25 per 100. How much will the bolts cost?

251. What will be the cost of 60 lb. of 8d common nails at $3.35 per keg of 100 lb. and 40 lb. of 20d common at $3.64 per 100 lb.?

The letter "d" is an abbreviation for the English term "penny." Many persons are puzzled to understand what the terms "four penny," "six penny," and "ten penny" mean as applied to nails. One explanation is that "four penny" means 4 lb. to each 1,000 nails; "six penny" means 6 lb. to each 1,000 nails, and so on. It is an old English term and meant at first "ten pound" nails (the thousand being understood), but the old English clipped it to "ten-pun," and from that it degenerated until "penny" was substituted for "pounds."

252. What will the nails cost to frame 3,000 bd. ft. of rough lumber if 15 lb. of each kind of nail are required to frame 1,000 bd. ft. The nails are worth $3.80 per 100 lb. for the 8's and $3.45 per 100 lb. for the 16's.

253. Figure the cost of 185 lb. of lath nails (2d fine blue) at $3.60 per keg; 130 lb. of shingle nails (3d common) at $3.20 per keg; 60 lb. of wall-board nails (1¼" No. 12) at $3.40 per keg; and 80 lb. of cement nails at $3.80 per keg. A keg weighs 100 lb.

The term "cement" refers to a nail that has been coated with cement in order to make it hold better. It is generally used on the siding (or rustic) lumber that is nailed on the exterior walls of a frame building.

254. How much will the nails cost to do the following work? 9,756 bd. ft. of framing—15 lb. of 8d common and 15 lb. of 16d common per Mbd. ft.; 2,480 bd. ft. of flooring—25 lb. 8d box per Mbd. ft.; 1,600 bd. ft. of siding—25 lb. 8d cement per Mbd. ft. The 8d common are worth $3.40 per keg, the 16d common $3.60, the 8d box $3.15, and the 8d cement $3.50.

255. What is the cost of 70 lb. of 8d box nails if a keg (100 lb.) costs $3.45?

256. If lumber is worth $54 per 1,000 bd. ft., how much are 252 ft. worth?

257. If 3,570 bd. ft. of interior finish costs $385.56, what is the price per M?

258. What is the total cost of 196 bd. ft. of flooring at $78 per M and 385 bd. ft. of oak at $520 per M?

259. A contractor bought 650 bd. ft. of flooring and 428 bd. ft. of T. & G. ceiling and his bill totaled $32.34. What price per M did he pay for the lumber?

260. What is the cost of 648 bd. ft. of siding at $67 per M?

261. A contractor receives a quotation on mortise locks for inside doors at $11.40 per dozen. How much will nine locks cost?

262. A hardware salesman gave a price of $16.32 per dozen pairs for ball-bearing wrought-steel hinges 3½" × 3½". What would be the cost of 38 pairs?

Ball bearing hinges are not generally used in residence work but are an advantage in public buildings owing to the many hundreds of times that a door may be opened or closed during the day.

263. A motor court contains 16 separate units. One-half of these units require 18 drawer pulls and 9 drawer locks for each unit, and the remainder require 22 pulls and 13 locks each. What will be the cost at 75¢ per dozen for the pulls and $1.25 per dozen for the locks?

264. Figure the cost of the hardware for an apartment house of four units. Each unit requires the following: 12 pair hinges, 12 mortise locks, 16 sash lifts, 16 sash locks and 10 door bumpers. The price per dozen for each kind of hardware is: hinges, $3.00; locks, $9.50; sash lifts, $4.20; sash locks, $4.60; and bumpers, 80¢.

265. Sash lifts are worth $2.40 per dozen; sash lock, $2.60 per dozen; casement fasteners, $3.20 per dozen; and parliament butts, $4.40 per dozen. What is the total cost of 17 sash lifts, 28 sash locks, 20 casement fasteners, and 16 pairs of parliament butts?

266. How much will an apprentice earn in 52 weeks at 60¢ per hour? Figure 8 hr. per day and 5½ days per week. During this time he loses 15 days for rainy weather and a total of 11 days' time between jobs.

267. How much pay will a carpenter receive during the construction of a house if the framing took 3 weeks and 4 days and the interior finish 2 weeks and 5 days? He receives $8 per day of 8 hr. Figure 5½ days per week.

268. Which mechanic will average the larger daily wage, the brick-layer who earns $11 per day working 192 days or the carpenter who works 270 days at $8 per day?

A fair comparison of the different building trades is obtained by finding out not what is paid the mechanic in each trade per day, but what his earnings will average over a year's time. A full year's work will contain 365 days minus 52 Sundays and 4 holidays. Sometimes a higher paid mechanic will have considerable time off between jobs. In fact, this is one of the reasons why a trade may require high daily wages.

269. What is the total wage expense for the construction of a motor court? One man worked 4 days, and three men 5 days each on *each* unit at $.90 per hour. The court contained 36 separate units. They all worked 8 hr. per day and 5½ days per week.

270. What is the labor cost for erecting a large warehouse? Eight carpenters work 3 weeks at $7 per day; two helpers work 15 days at $3.50 per day and the foreman who was paid $10 per day worked 4 weeks. The work day was 8 hr. long and they worked 5 days per week.

Several kinds of sand are required in the operations of building construction. Some sands are screened, other kinds unscreened. In order to secure a clean material for plastering purposes washed sand is purchased. This sand is cleaned by a process which washes out all of the dirt and other foreign substances. For concrete work a material known as concrete gravel is used: this is a coarse sand with 2″ rocks mixed throughout.

It is the practice in some communities to sell sand by weight, the unit of measurement being the ton. Other communities sell by the cubic yard, and on this basis many of the estimating tables give the amount of sand to use for a certain volume or capacity. It is necessary, therefore, to be able to change or convert cubic yards of sand into tons.

271. How much will 16 cu. yd. of plastering sand weigh if 1 cu. yd. weighs 1.3 tons?

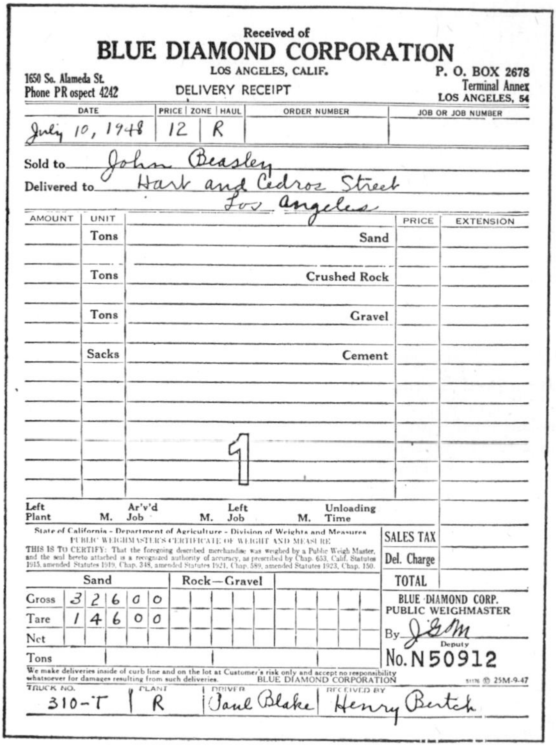
Received of
BLUE DIAMOND CORPORATION
LOS ANGELES, CALIF.
1650 So. Alameda St.
Phone PR ospect 4242
DELIVERY RECEIPT
P. O. BOX 2678
Terminal Annex
LOS ANGELES, 54

DATE	PRICE	ZONE	HAUL	ORDER NUMBER	JOB OR JOB NUMBER
July 10, 1948	12	R			

Sold to John Beasley
Delivered to Hart and Cedros Street
Los Angeles

AMOUNT	UNIT		PRICE	EXTENSION
	Tons	Sand		
	Tons	Crushed Rock		
	Tons	Gravel		
	Sacks	Cement		

1

Left Plant M. Ar'v'd Job M. Left Job M. Unloading Time

State of California - Department of Agriculture - Division of Weights and Measures
PUBLIC WEIGHMASTER'S CERTIFICATE OF WEIGHT AND MEASURE
THIS IS TO CERTIFY: That the foregoing described merchandise was weighed by a Public Weigh Master, and the seal hereto attached is a recognized authority of accuracy, as prescribed by Chap. 653, Calif. Statutes 1915, amended Statutes 1919, Chap. 348, amended Statutes 1921, Chap. 589, amended Statutes 1923, Chap. 150.

SALES TAX
Del. Charge
TOTAL

	Sand	Rock—Gravel	
Gross	32600		
Tare	14600		
Net			
Tons			

BLUE DIAMOND CORP.
PUBLIC WEIGHMASTER
By J G M
Deputy
No. N50912

We make deliveries inside of curb line and on the lot at Customer's risk only and accept no responsibility whatsoever for damages resulting from such deliveries. BLUE DIAMOND CORPORATION 25M-9-47

TRUCK NO.	PLANT	DRIVER	RECEIVED BY
310-T	R	Paul Blake	Henry Bertch

Fig. 61.—Weigh bill.

272. Compute the cost of the sand as shown on the weigh bill, Fig. 61, at $1.62 per ton.

Gross weight is the combined weight of sand and the truck. The term "tare" means all weight above the actual weight of the commodity being hauled.

273. What is the cost of 23 cu. yd. of screened plastering sand at $1.58 per ton if 1 yd. weighs 1.35 tons?

274. A material dealer quotes a price of $1.39 per ton for concrete gravel. For the foundation of a hotel a contractor figures that he will need 525 cu. yd. What will the gravel cost him? Estimate 1.35 tons per yard.

275. What is the cost of the sand contained in a bin 12' × 16' × 8' if 1 cu. yd. weighs 1.4 tons and the dealer's quotation is $1.46 per ton?

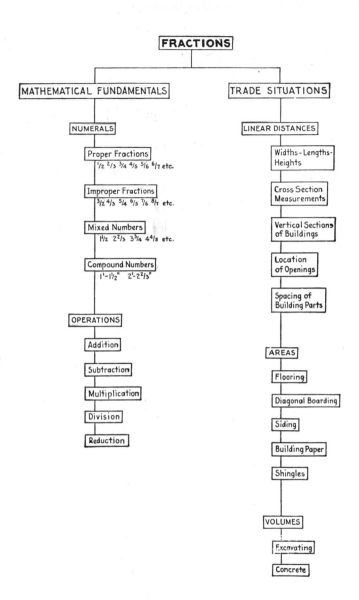

FRACTIONS

MATHEMATICAL FUNDAMENTALS

NUMERALS

Proper Fractions
$1/2$ $2/3$ $3/4$ $4/5$ $5/6$ $6/7$ etc.

Improper Fractions
$3/2$ $4/3$ $5/4$ $6/5$ $7/6$ $8/7$ etc.

Mixed Numbers
$1\frac{1}{2}$ $2\frac{2}{3}$ $3\frac{3}{4}$ $4\frac{4}{5}$ etc.

Compound Numbers
$1'-1\frac{1}{2}''$ $2'-2\frac{2}{3}''$

OPERATIONS

Addition

Subtraction

Multiplication

Division

Reduction

TRADE SITUATIONS

LINEAR DISTANCES

Widths - Lengths - Heights

Cross Section Measurements

Vertical Sections of Buildings

Location of Openings

Spacing of Building Parts

AREAS

Flooring

Diagonal Boarding

Siding

Building Paper

Shingles

VOLUMES

Excavating

Concrete

77

MATHEMATICAL CHECK-UP
FRACTIONS[1]

Proper Fractions.

Numerals: $\frac{1}{2}$, $\frac{2}{3}$, $\frac{3}{4}$, $\frac{4}{5}$, etc.

1. Add $\frac{1}{2}$, $\frac{1}{16}$, $\frac{3}{4}$, $\frac{5}{8}$.
2. Subtract $\frac{9}{16}$ from $\frac{3}{4}$.
3. Multiply $\frac{1}{8}$ by $\frac{2}{3}$.
4. Divide $\frac{5}{8}$ by $\frac{3}{16}$.
5. Change $\frac{3}{8}''$ to sixteenths.
6. Change $1\frac{2}{16}''$ to fourths.
7. Change $\frac{3}{4}'$ to inches.
8. Change $10''$ to a fractional foot.
9. Change $\frac{5}{8}$ cu. yd. to cubic feet.
10. Change 18 cu. ft. to fractional cubic yards.

Improper Fractions.

Numerals: $\frac{3}{2}$, $\frac{4}{3}$, $\frac{5}{4}$, $\frac{6}{5}$, etc.

11. Add $\frac{3}{2}$, $\frac{5}{4}$, $\frac{9}{8}$, $1\frac{5}{8}$.
12. Subtract $\frac{9}{4}$ from $2\frac{1}{8}$.
13. Multiply $\frac{7}{4}$ by $1\frac{7}{16}$.
14. Divide $1\frac{9}{16}$ by $\frac{5}{4}$.
15. How much is $\frac{9}{8}$ divided by $1\frac{7}{16}$?
16. $\frac{7}{8} \div \frac{3}{2} =$ what?
17. Change $\frac{129}{16}$ to a mixed number.
18. Change $5\frac{7}{16}$ to an improper fraction.
19. Change $\frac{5}{4}'$ to feet and inches.
20. Change $\frac{29}{16}$ to lowest terms.

Mixed Numbers; Fractions.

Numerals: $1\frac{1}{2}$, $2\frac{2}{3}$, $3\frac{3}{4}$, $4\frac{4}{5}$, etc.

21. Add $3\frac{1}{2}$, $4\frac{5}{16}$, $2\frac{1}{8}$, $3\frac{3}{4}$.
22. Subtract $8\frac{25}{32}$ from $10\frac{3}{4}$.
23. Multiply $2\frac{5}{8}$ by $19\frac{3}{4}$.
24. Divide $18\frac{1}{8}$ by $5\frac{3}{4}$.
25. Change $35\frac{5}{8}'$ to inches.
26. Change $21''$ to feet.
27. Change $3\frac{3}{4}$ doz. to number of pieces.
28. Change 215 pcs. to dozens.
29. Change $1\frac{2}{3}$ cu. yd. to cubic feet.
30. Change 225 cu. ft. to cubic yards.

Compound Numbers; Fractions.

Numerals: $1'\ 1\frac{1}{2}''$, $2'\ 2\frac{2}{3}''$, etc.

31. Add $2'\ 2\frac{1}{2}''$, $5'\ 6\frac{3}{4}''$, $8'\ 9\frac{5}{16}''$.
32. Subtract $5'\ 3\frac{1}{8}''$ from $10'\ 2\frac{9}{16}''$.
33. Multiply $5'\ 2\frac{3}{8}''$ by 24.
34. Divide $18'\ 6\frac{1}{2}''$ by 4.
35. Change to square inches $7'\ 5\frac{1}{2} \times 2'\ 4\frac{1}{2}''$.
36. Change to cubic feet $9'\ 6\frac{1}{2} \times 7'\ 8\frac{1}{2}'' \times 10'\ 0''$.
37. Change to square feet $10'\ 6\frac{1}{2}'' \times 15'\ 8\frac{1}{2}''$.
38. Change $16'$ to number of pieces $1'\ 9\frac{3}{4}''$ long.
39. Change $17\frac{5}{8}'$ to feet and inches.
40. Change $9'\ 5\frac{1}{2}''$ to feet (mixed number).

[1] See p. 169.

CHAPTER IV

FRACTIONS

A good builder or architect, when planning a building, will always try to keep the main dimensions in even feet as 30′, 38′, 46′. This is to economize in the use of lumber, for lumber is sold on the "even-foot" basis. Hardwoods are the exception to this rule owing to their value and scarcity, for the lumberman always gets as much as he can out of the rough log. This is in keeping with the problem of the National Committee on Wood Utilization, United States Department of Commerce. The department has published a pamphlet called "The Short-length House," stressing the fact that in many places on a building short lengths of lumber can be used to advantage.

Fig. 62.—Raising a framed wall.

It is not always possible, however, to follow this idea in its entirety. Many dimensions on a building will be in terms of feet and inches. Again, among the innumerable number of pieces required during the construction of a house, there are, of necessity, various lengths and sizes which must be cut to a fractional part of an inch. Therefore, the following pages will stress the use of fractions as applied to the carpenter's work, either on the job or off the job, including lumber bills, quantities of materials, etc.

ADDITION

A stud is one of the vertical members of a framed building. A group of studs when correctly placed, forms a wall or partition as shown in Fig. 62.

Problems

276. If a stud is $3\frac{5}{8}''$ wide and the lath and plaster on each face of a partition is $\frac{3}{4}''$ thick, how thick is the finished wall?

This information is essential in determining the width of stock to order when making a window or door frame.

277. What is the "over-all" thickness of a brick wall that is made by placing two bricks endwise and allowing $\frac{3}{8}''$ thickness of plaster on the inside and $\frac{1}{2}''$ on the outside face? The brick measures exactly $8\frac{3}{4}''$ long and the mortar joint between the bricks amounts to $\frac{3}{8}''$.

278. How wide will the jamb stock be for a window frame that is to fit into a framed wall? The size of stock used is $2'' \times 8''$ S1S1E.[1] Lath and plaster amount to $\frac{3}{4}''$ on the inside of the building, and the exterior is covered with siding which is $\frac{5}{8}''$ thick.

Sometimes in constructing brick buildings it is necessary to place strips of wood in a vertical direction on the inside face of the wall on which metal lath or some special building material can be fastened. These strips, which are called "furring," are placed $12''$ on center.

279. How thick will a brick wall be from outside face to inside face if the wall is $21''$ thick, furring stock $\frac{3}{4}''$, metal lath $\frac{1}{4}''$, and plaster $\frac{5}{8}''$?

These furring strips are fastened to the brick wall by removing some of the mortar between the bricks at various places on the wall and then driving a wedge in the hole. The wedge is then sawed off flush and the furring strip nailed to it.

280. What is the over-all width of a double wall that is made to receive a sliding door? The space between each wall is $3\frac{3}{4}''$; the width of the studs for one wall is $3\frac{5}{8}''$ and for the other wall $5\frac{1}{2}''$. The lath and plaster on the face of each wall is standard thickness, which is $\frac{3}{4}''$.

The term "underpinning" means all the members of a framed building that are below the floor joists, as illustrated in Figs. 63 and 64. The vertical members on outside walls are known as "studs" (see Fig. 64). The height of the underpinning will vary with each building. The basis or beginning point from which the carpenter plans his measurements for floor heights is the first floor level, so that

[1] See Table 1, dimension lumber, Chap. IX.

he has to figure the height of the underpinning, the width of the floor joists, and the thickness of the floors in order to find out the exact height of the finished floor.

Fig. 63.—First-floor joist supports: pier, pier blocks, post and girder.

281. How far is it from the lower edge of a floor joist that is sized (ripped) to $5\frac{1}{2}''$ wide to the top side of the subfloor which is nailed on the floor joist? The floor stock is $1\frac{3}{16}''$ thick.

Fig. 64.—Underpinning studs.

282. A piece of mudsill (see Fig. 59) is $1\frac{7}{8}''$ thick. The floor joist that rests on the sill is $9\frac{1}{4}''$ wide, the subfloor $1\frac{3}{16}''$ thick and the oak floor $\frac{3}{8}''$ thick. What is the distance from the top of the concrete foundation to the top of the finished floor?

283. The specifications for a five-room, one-story residence call for $2'' \times 8''$ floor joists sized to the standard width (see Table 1, Chap. IX).

The subfloor stock is ⅞″ thick and the hardwood floor ¾″. What is the over-all measurement of subfloor, hardwood floor, and joists?

The concrete foundation for an average residence is not always built up to the joist line of a building. Studs are used to make the floor the desired height. A horizontal plate is nailed to the studding and makes a support for the joists. This construction is often used when the lot is not level.

284. How far is it from the top of a foundation to the top of a finished floor as shown in the sketch, Fig. 65?

The length of the studs or posts "*A*" will vary with each building and are made to suit the height required for the first floor.

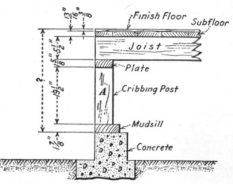

FIG. 65.—A typical section through under-pinning and first floor.

285. A factory floor is built by placing 2″ × 6″ stock S1E on edge and then covering this floor with 1″ stock S1S to 1³⁄₁₆″. The supporting girder which carries the floor is 6″ × 8″ sized to 7⅝″. What is the distance from the under side of the girder to the top of the finished floor? Consult the lumber table in Chap. IX for the width of the sized 2″ × 6″ dimension stock.

In order to check up or estimate the number of yards of plastering required on the exterior of a house, the plasterer must know the height of the wall from the foundation to its top. In addition, the carpenter often uses this measurement in planning some of his measurements, and the painter will use it when figuring the cost of painting.

286. How far will it be from the top of the subfloor to the top of a framed wall if the stud is 8′ 11″ long and each plate is 1¾″ thick? One plate is used at the bottom and two at the top.

287. What is the total height of a wall from the top of the foundation to the top of the wall? The mudsill is 1¾″ thick, the floor joists 9¼″

wide, the subfloor $1\frac{3}{16}''$ thick, the bottom plate $1\frac{5}{8}''$ thick, the stud
7' $10\frac{1}{2}''$ long, and the top plates (two) $1\frac{5}{8}''$ each?

288. Figure 66 shows two methods of erecting a two-story house.
In the left illustration each story is framed separately (known as Western

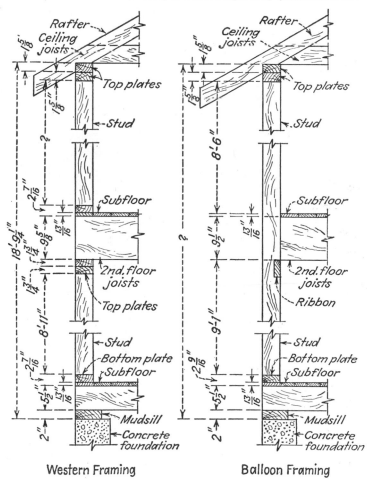

Western Framing   Balloon Framing

Fig. 66.—Types of framing.

framing), the first story naturally being raised first, then the second-
story joists and floor, and finally the second-story studding. The other
type of construction is known as Balloon framing. In it the studs are
cut the full length from the bottom to the top. The ribbon (see drawing)

is the piece of 1″ × 4″ notched into the edge of the studding, and it supports the second-story joists.   What is the measurement from the foundation to the top of the wall as shown in the Balloon framing?

289. What is the length of the second story stud, in Fig. 66, Western framing?

290. What is the total height of a framed wall from the mudsill to the top of the top plates if the several dimensions of each part are as follows: width of joists 5⅝″; subfloor stock 1³⁄₁₆″ thick; plate stock (allow for three) 1¾″ each; length of studs 7 ′ 11¼″; length of firewall stud 1′ 10″;

Fig. 67.—A framed wall showing firewall construction.

thickness of plate on the firewall stud 1⅝″?   Figure 67 illustrates the firewall.

The term "firewall" designates that part of the wall that extends above the surface of the roof, originally named from its use to stop a fire from traveling from one building to another when buildings were built close together.   The firewall was always brick. Since the advent of the flat-roof frame house the same type of construction is used although of lumber instead of brick.   Hence, the same terminology applies.

291. In some types of frame construction bolts are used in order to increase the strength of the finished frame.   Roof trusses are often built and held together at the main points of stress with bolts.   How long a bolt will be required to fasten a piece of wood that is 1¾″ thick to a second one that is 3⅝″ thick?   Allow ½″ for the nut, ⅛″ each for two washers.

292. The specifications for an apartment house require that the bolts that fasten the mudsill to the concrete foundation be imbedded in the concrete 3½″.   The sill is 1⅞″ thick and the nut is ⅜″ thick.   How long a bolt will have to be purchased?[1]

293. A main member of a roof truss is 3¾″ thick.   The plans require that a piece of stock 1⁹⁄₁₆″ thick be fastened on each side of the truss. What length bolt will be used?   The bolts will have to be machine bolts

[1] The minimum length of bolt in most building ordinances is 10″.

and not carriage bolts as a $\frac{5}{16}''$ thick iron washer is to be placed under both the head and the nut of the bolt. Allow $\frac{1}{2}''$ for the nut.

294. Figure the length of the bolts required at A and B in Fig. 68.

The horizontal members of the truss are called "chord." They are built up of several pieces of equal thickness.

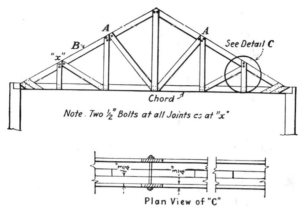

Note. Two $\frac{1}{2}''$ Bolts at all Joints as at "x"

Plan View of "C"

Fig. 68.—A bolted roof truss.

295. A girder for a factory is built up by bolting several pieces of framing stock together. How long will the carriage bolts have to be if the four center members are each $1\frac{3}{4}''$ thick? The outside pieces are $2\frac{1}{4}''$ thick. Figure 69 is a cross-section of this girder.

As stated previously in this chapter, lumber is usually sold on the even-foot-length basis. Therefore, if a number of pieces of stock of different lengths are required, the carpenter or builder must first of all find the total length of these pieces and then select a piece (or pieces) of stock of the nearest even-foot length. While lengths can be secured up to 40' and longer on special orders, the average length used in the building industry is from 8' to 24'.

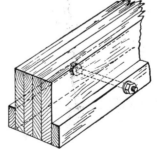

Fig. 69.—A built-up girder.

296. What length of lumber will be purchased to make the following shelves: 1 pc. 3' $9\frac{1}{2}''$ long, 1 pc. 2' $6\frac{1}{8}''$, and 1 pc. 5' $11\frac{1}{4}''$?

297. In repairing a building an odd-sized window was required. The dimensions of the window were 2' $7\frac{5}{8}''$ wide and 5' $9\frac{1}{4}''$ long.

What length of stock would be purchased to make a window frame if the same size stock was used on the four sides of the frame? Allow $3\frac{1}{4}''$ additional on the side pieces of the frame in order to have sufficient stock to make the joints.

298. What length of $3'' \times 4''$ stock would have to be purchased to make six underpinning posts? The lengths are $3'\ 6\frac{1}{8}''$; $2'\ 7\frac{3}{16}''$; $1'\ 8\frac{1}{4}''$; $11\frac{1}{2}''$; $2'\ 4''$; and $1'\ 10\frac{3}{8}''$.

299. A builder receives an order to make forms for some concrete slabs. There are four sizes of slabs: $14\frac{1}{2}'' \times 26\frac{1}{4}''$, $27\frac{1}{8}'' \times 31\frac{3}{4}''$, $18'' \times 27\frac{5}{8}''$, and $11\frac{1}{4}'' \times 42\frac{1}{2}''$. What lengths of $1'' \times 6''$ stock will have to be purchased for each form?

300. What is the length of stock to order to make the following bill of material: 1 piece each of the following lengths, $3'\ 4\frac{1}{8}''$, $2'\ 6\frac{3}{16}''$, $1'\ 9\frac{5}{8}''$, and $7'\ 8\frac{1}{2}''$?

SUBTRACTION

Problems

301. A board is $11\frac{3}{4}''$ wide. How wide will it be if $3\frac{5}{16}''$ are ripped off?

302. Two shelf cleats are required, one of which is $1\frac{7}{8}''$ wide and the other $2\frac{3}{16}''$ wide. A piece of door-jamb stock, wide enough for a $2'' \times 4''$ partition that is plastered both sides, is also needed. The stud is $3\frac{5}{8}''$ in width; the plaster is $\frac{3}{4}''$ thick. How much will remain from a board $11\frac{1}{4}''$ wide, allowing $\frac{1}{4}''$ for all saw cuts?

303. A carpenter required 3 pieces of stock of different widths to construct a cabinet. The first was $2\frac{1}{4}''$ wide, the second $3\frac{5}{16}''$, and the third $4\frac{1}{4}''$. If $\frac{1}{4}''$ was allowed for all saw cuts, how much remained from a board that was $11\frac{1}{2}''$ wide?

304. A board is $13\frac{1}{2}''$ wide. The foreman on the job gave an apprentice carpenter the job of ripping off a $\frac{7}{8}''$ piece, a $1\frac{1}{4}''$ piece, a $2\frac{7}{16}''$ piece, and a $3\frac{3}{4}''$ piece. How much remained of the original board if $\frac{1}{16}''$ was allowed for each saw cut?

305. A cabinet $6'\ 4\frac{3}{4}''$ long is built in a room that has an inside measurement of $11'\ 2\frac{1}{8}''$. What is the length of the remaining space?

"Stepping" or "tread stock" is the name given to material used for the steps of a stairway. It is milled S4S with one edge rounded or "nosed" to give a finish to the front edge of the tread. If Douglas fir lumber is used it is vertical or "edge" grain, as this grain will never sliver or become rough when the tread becomes worn. Hardwood is superior material and is selected to match the hardwood flooring.

In planning a stairway the tread run, which is the width of tread stock minus the amount it projects beyond the riser (see Fig. 37) is often determined on the basis of the exact width of the finished tread.

306. What is the tread run of a stairway if the stepping is 13¼′ wide, the projection of the tread ½″, and the mould under the projection ¾″ wide?

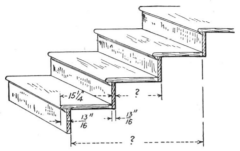

Fig. 70.—Typical section through a set of steps.

307. What is the tread run of the steps as shown in Fig. 70?

308. The net width of a stepping board is 11″. What is the total tread run of two treads if the tread projection is ⅜″?

309. What is the total run of the steps as illustrated in Fig. 70?

310. If the width of the tread stock is 9¼″, the thickness of the moulding is 1³⁄₁₆″, and the tread projection is ½″, what is the tread run?

311. In the 3′ 0″ × 7′ 0″ door in Fig. 71, what is the width of the stiles? Note that the size of the panel is given to the bottom of the groove (see section *A–A*).

A cross-section of the door stile is made by drawing a line across the stile and marking it *A-A*. If a drawing has a group of section lines that are marked *A-A*, *B-B*, *F-F*, etc., the carpenter looks on the plan for a detail drawn to a larger scale than the main plan and designated *A-A*, *B-B*, *F-F*, etc.

312. What is the length of panel *a*? The top rail is the same width as the stiles. The lower panel is 28½″ long, and the grooves for the panel the same as *A-A*.

313. What is the length of the lower panel in Fig. 71, if ½″ is allowed at each end of the panel for the groove? See previous problem.

314. What would be the width of the two upper panels if the mullion in the door as illustrated was increased in width to 5½″ with a panel groove of ⁷⁄₁₆″ depth?

315. What is the size of the panel stock for a 2′ 8″ × 6′ 8″ one-panel door as shown in Fig. 72.

The top rail of a door is always the same width as the stiles.

316. What will be the inside depth of a drawer if the lumber from which it is made is 7½″ wide and a ⅜″ groove is plowed in ½″ from the bottom edge of the drawer stock? Figure 73 is a cross-section of a drawer side and bottom.

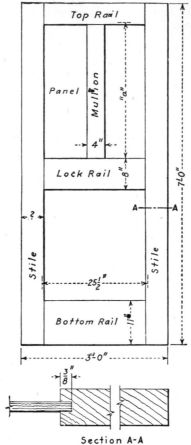

Section A-A

Fig. 71.—A typical interior door.

317. If a drawer side is 5⅛″ wide, the drawer bottom ¼″ thick, and the groove ⅝″ from the bottom, how deep is the drawer?

318. A large drawer requires a heavy bottom that is 1³⁄₁₆″ thick. The drawer side is 9¹⁄₁₆″ wide and the groove for the bottom is ⅞″ from the bottom of the drawer. A box 6¹¹⁄₁₆″ deep is placed in the drawer. How much clearance will there be between the top of the box and the top edge of the drawer?

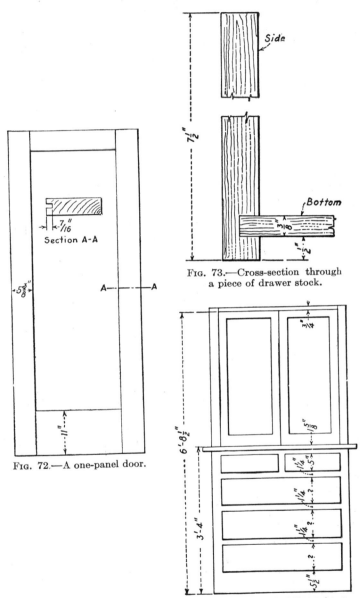

Section A-A

Fig. 72.—A one-panel door.

Fig. 73.—Cross-section through a piece of drawer stock.

Fig. 74.—A typical linen closet.

319. A carpenter is given an order to make a drawer that will hold a number of different size trays. The trays are $2\frac{1}{4}''$, $3\frac{5}{8}''$, $4\frac{7}{16}''$, and $1\frac{1}{2}''$ thick. How much clearance will there be after the trays are in

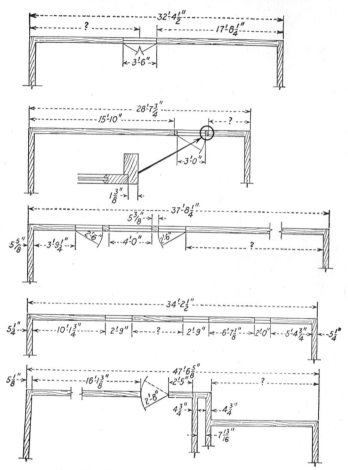

Fig. 75.—Typical parts of a floor plan.

the drawer if the width of the drawer side is $13''$ net, the thickness of the bottom is $\frac{3}{8}''$, and the amount of stock below the bottom is $\frac{9}{16}''$?

320. What is the depth of the drawers for a linen closet as shown in Fig. 74, all large drawers to be same depth?

321 to 325. Find the missing dimensions in the parts of a floor plan shown in Fig. 75.

MULTIPLICATION

When a builder or estimator is figuring the quantity of material necessary to cover a given area, it is always necessary to know how much more stock to add than will actually cover the area in question. More stock is added on account of the fact that lumber will always measure a trifle smaller than given dimensions owing to shrinkage, and also on account of the waste that will be incurred when the stock is cut to fit the space. A third reason is that some of the stock may have been milled away in the planing mill when it was made to a required shape. Emphasis should again be given to the fact that lumber sizes are based on the sawmill practice of cutting the green lumber to net sizes.

Subfloor stock is laid either straight (right angles to the floor joists) or at a 45-deg. angle (see Fig. 55). This material is usually ordered S4S, and $1'' \times 6''$ lumber is used. For subfloor laid straight, add 20 per cent or 1.5 to floor area to be covered. For subfloor laid diagonally, add 30 per cent or $\frac{3}{10}$ to floor area to be covered. For any given area, the increase is based on the next whole number to the exact number of square feet of floor area.

In the following problems the $1'' \times 6''$ subfloor stock is all S4S.

Problems

326. How many board feet of subfloor will be required for a house that is $32' \times 52\frac{1}{2}'$ in size? The floor is to be laid straight.

327. A house is $38' 3'' \times 32'$ in size. It is to be covered with subfloor laid diagonally, excepting a back porch $7' \times 9' 6''$, which will not require subfloor but is to be covered with T. & G. flooring. How much subfloor stock should be ordered. Size of stock is $1'' \times 6''$.

It is interesting to know that subfloor, which is usually surfaced only on one side so as to keep the stock as thick as possible, will rarely cup or warp if the rough side is laid up.

328. A house plan shows a foundation size of $28' 6'' \times 44' 8''$. The specifications call for a subfloor to be laid diagonally over the entire surface, excepting the kitchen, breakfast room, back porch, and bathroom. How many board feet of subfloor will be required to cover the remaining surface? Figure 76 shows a house under construction with the subfloor on part of it. The bathroom is $7' 0'' \times 8' 0''$ in size; the other three rooms cover an area $18' 0'' \times 18' 6''$ in size.

329. A motor court contains 14 individual units, each of which is $18'$ wide and $22'$ long. A small back porch in each is $4' 5''$ wide and $6' 0''$ long. How many M bd. ft. of 1×6 subfloor stock was ordered? It was to be laid straight. No subfloor is required on the back porch.

330. How many board feet of subfloor will be used for a house that is 28' × 46'? The specifications call for the floor to be laid diagonally.

Fig. 76.—Subfloor laid diagonally and pine flooring laid straight.

Matched flooring, that is, stock that has a tongue on one edge, as illustrated in Fig. 77, will not cover a given area without adding to the surface to allow for the waste incurred in milling. A piece of 1″ × 4″ stock will measure on its face only 3¼″ after it is milled into flooring. To allow for this waste and also the end waste when laying, ¼ must be added to a given area if 1″ × 4″ flooring is used. If 6″ flooring is used, ⅙ is added.

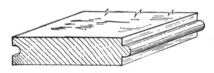

Fig. 77.—Tongue-and-groove flooring.

331. A cottage has a foundation size of 25' × 28'. How many board feet of 1″ × 4″ T. & G. flooring will be required to lay the floor?

332. The first floor of a two-story house measures 26' × 39' and the second floor 24' × 31'. How many board feet of 4″ flooring will be needed for the job?

333. A motor court contains 12 units, each of which is 22' × 27'. The owner plans to cover all of the floors with linoleum, which permits him to use No. 2 pine flooring. On 5 of the units he used 4″ stock and on the other 7 he used 6″ stock. How much of each size of flooring stock was ordered?

334. A contractor secured the contract to build a motel consisting of 24 units. Eight of them were 16' × 23', nine were 18' × 26', and the balance were 14' × 20'. How much did he pay for the flooring, using 1″ × 4″ T. & G. stock at $57 per M bd. ft.?

335. A barn 64′ wide and 112′ long requires a matched floor for the loft, which is 38′ × 112′. How much lumber will be ordered if 1″ × 6″ T. & G. stock is used, and it is laid straight?

Siding is the name of the lumber stock used to finish the exterior of a building; sometimes it is known as rustic. As in the case of the flooring the material will not cover a space equal to the original size from which it is made, owing partly to shrinkage, but mostly to the shape of this siding. It is milled so that the lower edge of one board will fit over the top edge of the board below it, as shown in Fig. 78.

A 1″ × 6″ piece will cover only 5″; 8″ stock covers 7″; 10″ covers 9″, etc. Therefore, for the 6″ add ⅕; for 8″ add ⅐; for 10″ add ⅑, etc., as the additional material required is based on what the board **covers** and not on its original size.

This rule applies only to a surface that has no openings. This situation is not a common one, however, in building construction. Naturally, less stock will be required in a wall that has a number of doors and windows in it. Experience has proved that adding ⅙ for 6″ instead of ⅕ (as suggested above) will give the amount of stock required when there are openings. For other widths, the same principle applies: ⅛ for 8″; ¼ for 4″; ⅒ for 10″, etc. One could, of course, deduct the actual area of all of the openings, and then apply the rule first given to the remaining area.

Fig. 78.— Rabbetted siding or rustic.

336. A frame store building is 30′ wide and 110′ long and has a flat roof. How many square feet of 1″ × 6″ siding will it take to cover the two sides and rear wall? The walls are 12″ high. Deduct 120 sq. ft. for openings. No siding is required on the front as it will be finished in brick. Since 6″ siding covers only 5″, ⅕ of the area of the wall to be covered will have to be added.

337. How many square feet of 1″ × 4″ redwood siding will be required for a house that is 28½′ × 47½′. The walls are 11′ high. Deduct 170 sq. ft. for openings. Allow 80 sq. ft. of siding extra for gables.

338. A contractor receives a contract to build fourteen 8′ × 12′ garages for a motel. The fronts are all open. The wall heights are 8′. How much will 4″ novelty siding cost to cover the walls at $43 per M bd. ft.?

339. A motel court contains 12 units each of which is 24' × 30' in size. How much 1" × 10" channel rustic will be required? Walls are 11' 6" high. For each unit deduct an amount equal to eight openings 2' 0" × 4' 6". Add 24 sq. ft. of rustic for the two gables of each building.

340. How much 1" × 8" siding will be ordered for a building that is 42' wide and 76' long? Deduct 216 bd. ft. for openings. Wall height is 14' 0".

341. What even-foot length of 2" × 4" stock is required to make 13 pieces for drawer guides each of which is 17¾" long?

342. What is the best length of stock to select to make 16 cripple studs each one of which is 9⅝" long?

343. In repairing a residence it was necessary to close in a hole in the floor that was 22½" × 26. If eight pieces of 4" flooring stock were laid lengthwise to cover the 22½" space, how long a flooring board was purchased?

344. A carpenter was required to mould in five lights of glass with a ⅜" glass bead. The size of each light was 6¼" and 9½". What length of moulding did he purchase?

345. How many linear feet of moulding will be required to make 22 frames that are each 6⅛" × 9½"?

346. What is the cost of 2⅓ doz. flush bolts that are ⅜" × 5" D.B. (dull brass) at $11.50 per dozen?

Dull brass has reference to the finish of the hardware. Other finishes are S.B. (sand brass), O.C. (old copper), S.C. (sanded copper), etc.

347. What is the cost of 3½ doz. ball tipped loose pin ornamental hinges, size 2" × 2½" A.C. (antique copper), at $4.15 per dozen?

348. How much will 2⅓ doz. mortise locks for inside doors cost at $25 per dozen? The finish is to be S.B. and the lock knobs are to be glass with long escutcheon plates.

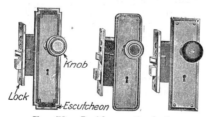

Door knobs can be secured in steel, bronze, and glass, each being in several different shapes and sizes. The term escutcheon means the brass plate screwed on the face of the door to form a finish and into which the key is fitted. Figure 79 indicates escutcheon plates.

Fɪɢ. 79.—Inside mortise locks.

349. The hardware specifications for a school house call for door checks on all of the classroom doors. What will be the cost of 4⅙ doz. at $7.45 each?

350. What is the cost of 3⅓ doz. sash locks at $2.49 per dozen?

351. It is estimated that 1,000 sq. ft. of framing lumber will require 15 lb. of 16d common nails and 15 lb. of 8d common nails. What will be the cost of the nails to frame 4½ M ft. of lumber at 5½¢ per pound?

352. A brick building contains 10 windows, each of which requires a steel lintel 6′ × 4½″ × 3″ (illustrated in Fig. 80). How much will the steel cost at 11½¢ per pound, if the lintel weighs 14.8 lb. per linear foot?

FIG. 80.—A steel lintel.

353. A contractor buys 240 ft. of ¾″ rope to be used to guy a gin pole. How much did it cost him at 25½¢ per pound if there are 6.1 ft of rope in 1 lb.? Count fractional pounds as whole pounds.

354. It takes 782 washers ⅞″ i.d. (inside diameter) to weigh 100 lb. How much will the washers cost for four roof trusses, each truss con-

FIG. 81.—Four pieces of three-ply panel stock. (*Photo by John D. Cress, Seattle. Courtesy, National Lumber Manufacturers Association, Chicago, Ill.*)

taining 30 bolts? Washers are worth 9½¢ per pound. Allow two washers to each bolt.

355. What is the cost of 165 lb. of nails on the basis of $4.60 per keg (100 lb.)?

356. Three-ply Douglas fir panels, 30″ × 72″ and good one side, are worth 8¾¢ per square foot. How much will 36 of these panels cost?

Three-ply panel stock is made good one side and good two sides. Good one side is usually used for drawer-bottom stock as only one side is exposed. This stock is known as D.B.S. (drawer-bottom-stock). The term "three-ply" refers to the number of layers of wood that have been glued together to make the panel. The advantage of this three-ply stock is that it will never split, as the grain in the center layer of wood runs in the opposite direction to that in the two outside pieces, as shown in Fig. 81.

357. A mill cabinet order includes 16 doors that require five panels, good two sides. Each panel is 30″ × 60″. What is the cost of the panels at 17½¢ per square foot?

358. A group of store fixtures requires 68 three-ply panels, oak on one side and birch on the other. The size of each is 30″ × 72″. How much did they cost at 28½¢ per foot?

On special orders, panel stock can be secured with a different kind of wood on each face. This enables the builder or architect to treat each face to conform to the finish desired. The interior of a show window might be finished in gum while the store itself might be in oak. Therefore, the necessity exists of securing stock with different woods on each face.

359. How much more will it cost to buy three-ply panel stock for 252 drawers, good two sides, instead of good one side? The price for good one side is 5½¢ per foot and for two sides 2¼¢ more. One piece of stock 30″ × 72″ will make three drawer bottoms.

360. A tool box is constructed by using three-ply stock for the two sides. The size of one side is 18″ × 24″. What is the cost of the paneling at 7½¢ per square foot?

361. How many bolts will it take to fasten down the mudsill of a house 28′ × 43½′ if they are placed 5′ 6″ o.c.?

362. How many bolts will be required for fastening down the mudsill for six units of a bungalow court? Bolts are placed 6′ o.c., and each unit is 28′ × 32′.

363. A frame store is 30′ wide and 134′ 6″ deep. If bolts for the sill are spaced 7′ o.c., how many will be required?

364. A motel contains 28 units, each one being 18′ × 22′. If bolts for the sill are spaced 5′, how many will be required?

365. How many bolts will be required for the lower chord of a roof (see Fig. 68) truss if the bolts are spaced 16¼″ o.c. and the truss is 54′ 2″ long? No bolts at ends.

DIVISION

Problems

366. How many boards of 6″ siding will it take to cover the side of a garage? Each board will lay 5¼″. The height of the wall is 8′ 2″. Count fractional boards as whole ones.

The advantage of knowing how far a group of siding boards will cover is seen when planning the height of a framed wall that is to be covered with this material. By first estimating the exact distance that the stock will cover, it is possible to change the height of the wall a trifle and by so doing save one board of siding for the entire distance around the building as only whole boards can be ordered.

367. A store requires a T. & G. partition so that each half of the store can be rented to different tenants. The building measures 78′ inside measurements. The boards are laid vertically. How many whole boards of 6″ stock will be required if one board of T. & G. ceiling material will lay 5⅛″? Figure 82 indicates a piece of T. & G. stock.

368. Four-inch novelty siding covers exactly 3⅛″. How many whole boards will it take to cover a wall that has a stud

FIG. 82.—Tongue-and-grooved ceiling.

length of 7′ 11½″, two top plates that are each 1¾″ thick, and a 2″ thick bottom plate?

369. A small store building is 16½′ wide and 20′ long. How many 20′ flooring boards will it take to cover the floor if each board will lay 3¼″?

370. Ten-inch siding will cover 9⅛″. How many boards will be required for a wall that is 16′ 2″ high?

371. How many risers will it take to go to the first landing of a stairway? The landing is 4′ 10½″ high and the tread rise is 6½″. (See Fig. 37).

372. The distance from floor to floor on a two-story house is 8′ 5½″. How many risers will there be in the stairway if the plans call for a 7¼″ rise?

373. A store building has a second story height of 14′ 10¾″. How many risers will be needed in the stairway? The tread rise is 6⅞″.

374. The blueprints for a two-story apartment house show the first story height to be 11′ 8⅛″. The stairway detail sheet in the plan shows a tread rise of 7⅜″. How many risers are in the stairway?

375. How many risers are there in a stairway for a building that has a second story height of 18′? The tread rise is 6¾″.

REDUCTION

See pages 176, 178, Chap. VIII.

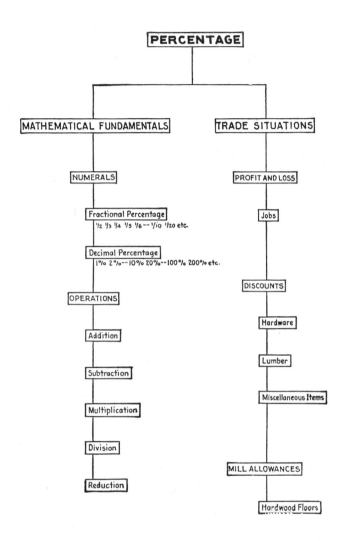

PERCENTAGE

MATHEMATICAL FUNDAMENTALS

NUMERALS

Fractional Percentage
½ ⅓ ¼ ⅕ ⅙ -- ⅒ ¹/₂₀ etc.

Decimal Percentage
1% 2%--10% 20%--100% 200% etc.

OPERATIONS

Addition

Subtraction

Multiplication

Division

Reduction

TRADE SITUATIONS

PROFIT AND LOSS

Jobs

DISCOUNTS

Hardware

Lumber

Miscellaneous Items

MILL ALLOWANCES

Hardwood Floors

MATHEMATICAL CHECK-UP

PERCENTAGE[1]

Percentage by Decimals.

1. Addition: cost = 100 per cent, profit = $37\frac{1}{2}$ per cent. Find selling price per cent.
2. Subtraction: loss = $23\frac{2}{3}$ per cent. Find selling price per cent.
3. Multiplication: cost = $72, per cent profit = 28. Find selling price.
4. Division: cost = $30, profit = $6. Find per cent profit on cost.
5. Division: Find cost; profit = $9, per cent profit on cost = 15 per cent.
6. Change $\frac{1}{8}$ to per cent; $\frac{2}{5}$ to per cent.
7. Change to price each: list price for 50 = $25, discount = 35 per cent.
8. Solve: selling price = $42, discount = $10.50. Find per cent discount on selling price.
9. Solve: list price = $24, discount = 15 per cent off the list. Find the cost.
10. Solve: list price = $12, discounts = 50, $16\frac{2}{3}$, and 2 per cent. Find cost.

Percentage by Fractions.

[1] See pp. 180 and 191.

100

CHAPTER V

PERCENTAGE

The mathematical processes involved in the use of percentage, when applied to the trade of carpentry, belong in a large measure to the field of the contracting carpenter and not to the foreman on the job. However, some of the best contractors have come up through the ranks, from apprentice to journeyman to foreman to superintendent to contractor. It is, therefore, for the purpose of giving the student experience and practice in some of the common and accepted methods of using and handling percentage problems that the following examples are given. For addition and subtraction problems see pages 182 and 183, Chap. VIII.

MULTIPLICATION

Problems

376. The estimated cost of a five-room cottage totals $4,261.38. The contractor adds 8 per cent for profit. What was the exact amount of his bid?

Adding a certain amount to the estimated cost of a building for profit is recognized as legitimate and fair for the contractor to do. There are so many items in the way of overhead for the contractor to pay that only by adding to the cost of a building is he able to make a financial return to himself. Some of the overhead items include bookkeeping costs, collection of money, telephone calls, labor spent in estimating costs and ordering materials. These items and many others of similar nature are all necessary and yet apart from the direct problem of actual construction of the building.

377. Contractor Smith adds 10 per cent to his estimated costs, while Mr. White adds 8 per cent. Which is the lower bid, and how much lower, if Smith's cost for a six-room Spanish residence is $5,271.48, while the other contractor's cost is $5,428.79?

378. A large contracting company submits a bid for a school house job. The estimated costs are $181,693.21. To this they add 3 per cent for overhead, and 9 per cent of the estimated cost plus the overhead for profit. What is the total amount of their bid?

379. To his estimate of $43,568.84 a contractor adds 2 per cent for incidentals and 8 per cent of the estimate and incidentals for profit. What was his bid?

101

380. A general contractor received a subcontractor's bid for the erection of a large store building. Some of the net costs were as follows: plumbing, $4,528.10; masonry, $6,278.43; electrical work, $1,829.71; heating, $2,372.17. His own actual costs, not including the four bids above, were $61,264.38. The plumber added 7 per cent, the mason contractor 11 per cent, the electrician 9 per cent, and the heating man 6 per cent. After these subbids, including the percentage, were added to his figure he added 12 per cent for profit. What was his bid?

Owing to the wide differences in conducting many types of building business there can be no definite percentage added to each bid. Each man's business requires a different percentage increase based on his overhead and the scope of the work.

381. A contractor builds a residence at a cost of $19,274.61. This cost also includes the price of the lot. Owing to a slow market for property he is forced to sell at 6 per cent loss. What did he receive for the property.

382. A contractor buys a lot for $1,845 and builds on it a home that cost $6,587. He sells it at a loss of 4½ per cent of his total expenditure. What is the selling price?

383. Owing to damage in shipping, a plumbing contractor is forced to reduce the price of a few fixtures. His original selling price for a standard bath tub complete was $34.80; for a pedestal lavatory 16″ × 24″, $21.38; and for a 20″ × 30″ sink $8.00. He makes a reduction of 15 per cent on the tub, 11 per cent on the lavatory, and 12 per cent on the sink. What would be the cost of each one of these fixtures?

384. A building contractor constructs a duplex at a total cost of $11,284.68. The value of the lot is $3,850.00. The owner holds the property for a year, during which time the value of the lot has increased 9 per cent. However, in order to make a sale, he is forced to reduce the price of his house and lot 8 per cent. What did he receive for the property?

385. A real estate company subdivides a large piece of property into city lots. Figure 83 is a typical subdividers map. The regular price for one lot in a certain block is $2,750.00. A contractor buys three lots and erects three houses, one costing $6,542.90, the second $7,178.45, and the third $5,421.00. He sells the first and third houses at a profit of 12 per cent, but is forced, owing to a shortage of cash, to sell the second at a loss of 18 per cent. How much did he gain or lose by the transaction?

386. A hardware firm sells nails at a discount of 28 per cent from the list price. What will be the cost of 540 lb. of 8d nails that are listed at 8¢ per pound?

It is customary in many lines of business to have a list price on which certain discounts are given. This enables the manufacturer or firm to print prices in their catalogues that will be usable even though the prices of the materials or goods fluctuate. The actual price is changed by giving a different discount.

387. What will be the total cost of 1,870 lb. of 16d nails at 7½¢ per pound list price, and 118 doz. bolts at a list price of 72¢ per dozen? The discount on the nails is 13 per cent and on the bolts 17 per cent.

Fig. 83.—Subdividers map. (*Courtesy, Los Angeles Investment Co.*)

388. In figuring the cost of a hardware bill a carpenter checks the prices in a hardware catalogue. He finds locks are listed at $34.00 per dozen; hinges, $4.80 per dozen pair; hooks, $1.80 per dozen; and casement fasteners, $4.60 per dozen. What will be the total cost of 5 locks, 5 pairs of hinges, 3½ doz. hooks, and 19 casement fasteners? The discount on the locks is 35 per cent; on the hinges, 30 per cent; on the hooks, 22 per cent; and on the fasteners, 18 per cent.

It is customary to quote prices on hardware by the dozen, 100 lb., gross, etc. The price per single unit is seldom given.

389. Nails are listed at $7.80 per hundredweight (cwt), ½″ × 6″ carriage bolts at $3.25 per 100, wire coat and hat hooks at $12.80 per gross, inside locks at $38.00 per dozen, and sash cord at $6.90 per dozen hanks. Figure the cost of the following bill of hardware:

> 1,250 lb. nails with a discount of 16 per cent
> 6½ doz. bolts, discount 22 per cent
> 5 doz. coat and hat hooks, discount 38 per cent
> 8 inside mortise locks, discount 52 per cent
> 3 hanks sash cord, discount 60 per cent

390. What is the cost of the hardware for a small repair job?
60 lb. finish nails at 7¢ per pound with 3 per cent discount
8 sash locks, $1.80 per dozen with 6 per cent discount
84 lb. sash weights, 5¢ per pound with 2 per cent discount
92 sq. ft. of screen wire 7½¢ per square foot with 2 per cent discount

391. A contractor purchases a large bill of hardware and is given a flat discount of 15 per cent and 5 per cent off. What did he pay for the hardware, the price quotation of which was $781.60?

In addition to the single discount allowed on some commodities or building materials, business practice often permits the giving of a second one. After the first discount (which is always the largest) is taken off, the second discount is figured on the remainder. In trade parlance the double discount is known as 10 and 2 off, 12 and 4 off, etc.

392. A hardware bill totals $345.69 with a discount of 5 and 3 off. What was the net cost of the material?

393. What will be the cost of the bolts for 26 roof trusses each one requiring 32 bolts? The list price per 100 is $14.50 with 10 and 2 off.

394. A large contractor needs 8 doz. square-point and 7 doz. round-point shovels. The list price for both kinds is $42 per dozen with 16 and 3 off. What did they cost?

395. The list price on common nails is $9.60 per 100 lb. (1 keg). If the contractor figures 30 lb. of nails per 1,000 bd. ft. of framing lumber, what will be the cost of the nails to frame 26,000 ft. of lumber? Discount is 12 and 3 off.

396. What will be the amount of the check for the bill illustrated in Fig. 84 if the contractor takes advantage of the 2 per cent trade discount and pays his bill before the tenth of the month?

A certain percentage off, if the bill is paid on or before a certain time, is a recognized business procedure. The method aids in the collection of bills and is really a premium for their prompt payment. A contractor who has sufficient capital (cash) on hand to take advantage of these discounts can make a considerable saving during a year's time.

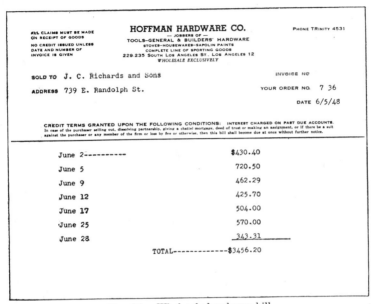

FIG. 84.—Wholesale hardware bill.

397. With 2 per cent discount allowance for cash, how much does a contractor save on a bill of $3,452.59?

398. The discount from the list for inside mortise locks is 16 per cent. What will 5½ doz. locks cost at $36.20 per dozen (list) with 2 per cent off for cash?

399. A contractor buys 75 sacks of cement at 80¢ per sack; 28 bundles of lath (1 bundle equals 100 lath) at $7.60 per 1,000; 58 sacks of plaster (1 sack equals 100 lb.) at $14.50 per ton. How much did he pay for these materials if he took advantage of 3 per cent off for cash?

400. What will be the cash price of 6½ doz. casement fasteners at $7.80 per dozen with 18 and 8 off; 3½ doz. drawer pulls at $5.60 per dozen with 11 and 3 off; 1 gross of hat hooks at $1.50 per dozen with 6 and 4 off; 1,400 lb. of 8d common nails at $6.65 per hundredweight with 8 and 4 off. The cash discount for the entire bill is 3 per cent.

401. How much ½″ × 2″ hardwood flooring will be required for an area 26′ × 34′? Owing to loss in milling add 28 per cent to the floor area.

Hardwood flooring is purchased on the basis of the original size of the rough stock, as illustrated in Fig. 85. Flooring $1\frac{3}{16}''$ thick measures $\frac{3}{4}''$ less *on its face* than the rough measurement; $\frac{3}{8}''$ and $\frac{1}{2}''$ flooring measures $\frac{1}{2}''$ less than the rough stock. The term

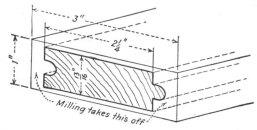

Fig. 85.—Illustrates the necessity for mill allowance when figuring T. and G. stock.

"face," when applied to flooring, means the net surface width of the stock, after it has been milled. A certain percentage must, therefore, be added. The following table will give the percentage of increase for some of the standard sizes of stock:

$\frac{3}{8}'' \times 1\frac{1}{2}''$ flooring, add 36 per cent
$\frac{1}{2}'' \times 2''$, add 28 per cent
$\frac{3}{8}'' \times 2''$, add 28 per cent
$\frac{1}{2}'' \times 1\frac{1}{2}''$, add 36 per cent
$1\frac{3}{16}'' \times 1\frac{1}{2}''$, add $52\frac{1}{2}$ per cent
$1\frac{3}{16}'' \times 2\frac{1}{4}''$, add 36 per cent

These percentages allow for end waste and milling waste. Fractional parts of a square foot must be counted as a full square foot.

402. What is the cost of the hardwood flooring for a residence 56′ × 74′? Stock is $\frac{1}{2}'' \times 2''$ clear quarter-sawed red oak. Cost is $99 per Mbd. ft.

There are two kinds of oak used for floors, white and red, designated as W.O. and R.O. There are four grades of flooring, namely, clear, select, No. 1 common, and No. 2 common. In addition, oak flooring is divided into two classes, quartered and plain; the difference is in the appearance of the stock, and is caused by the way the material is sawed from the log.

In the illustration, sections *A* and *B*, Fig. 86, are shown the two most common methods of quarter sawing to yield quarter-sawed stock. The upper three boards, section *C*, cut from the lower half are quarter-sawed also. The next board below, section *D*, will show a quartered figure near the edges, but toward the center will come under the classification of "bastard-sawed" since it shows neither a full-quartered nor a full-plain figure. The balance of boards below will show a plain-sawed surface. The "flash" or "flake" of quarter-sawed oak is caused when the saw cuts boards in such a way that the medullary rays (the white lines in the illustration) are parallel with the surface of the board, the cut going directly through the rays. However, a quartered figure will appear if the rays cut the surface of the board at any angle up to about 40 to 45 degrees, but the flake is not so large as in the case of a smaller angle or no angle at all.[1]

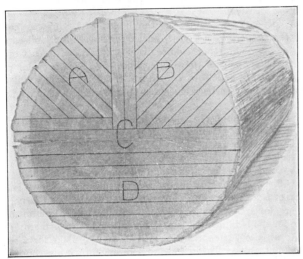

FIG. 86.—How lumber is quarter-sawed.

403. What is the cost of clr.qtd. (clear-quartered) R.O. flooring for a house that is 36′ 0″ wide and 46′ 0″ long? Deduct an area 12′ × 22′ for kitchen and back porch which will not be covered with hardwood flooring. The size of the stock is $1\frac{3}{16}″ \times 1\frac{1}{2}″$, and it is worth $119 per M.

404. A motor court contains nine units each being 28′ × 33′ in size. What was the cost of the $\frac{3}{8}″ \times 1\frac{1}{2}″$ sel.pln. (select-plain) W.O. flooring at $54 per M with 2 per cent off for cash?

405. What is the cost of the maple flooring for a lodge hall that is 92′ × 132′ in size? The contractor used $1\frac{3}{16}″ \times 2\frac{1}{4}″$ stock, and saved a reduction of 3 per cent for cash. The flooring was worth $126 per M.

DIVISION

Problems

406. A house that cost $6,586 was sold for $7,771.48. What was the percentage of profit?

407. What percentage of profit did a contractor make on a house that cost him $5,420.00 and was sold for $6,233.00?

[1] From E. L. Bruce, "Oak flooring."

408. A man invested $11,262 in a duplex. He retained it for a year, putting in shrubbery that cost him $319. At the end of the year he sold it for $12,970.72 What per cent profit did he make?

409. A lot cost $1,975.00 and a house $4,221.27. The taxes for the first year were $43.47. What per cent profit was made if the house was sold for $7,948.48?

410. A lot cost $3,475.00 and the house $9,128.45. A contractor retained the property for a year, paid out $356.40 for landscaping and $208.17 for taxes, and then sold it for $16,729.00. The cost of making the sale was 8 per cent of the selling price. Find his per cent profit?

411. A man has $7,830 to invest in a building. What will the contractor's costs have to be if he plans to make 8 per cent profit on the job?

412. A bond issue for a school building totals $254,587. Of this amount $45,389 is planned for furnishings. What amount of the balance is available for actual construction if the balance includes an architect's fee of 9 per cent for plans and superintendence?

413. A bond issue for a school building totaled $37,950. Of this amount, $6,500 is provided for interior furnishings. There is to be a deduction of 5 per cent from the total amount of the bond issue, less the furnishings, for architect's fees. What will be the net amount of money available for the building if 7 per cent is allowed for contractor's profit?

414. An architect is commissioned to draw the plans for a residence. The total amount available for the job, including his commission of 8 per cent for "plans and superintendence," is $17,850. He must allow for a contractor's profit of 6 per cent. What is the net amount of money available for actual construction work?

The terms "plans and superintendence" mean that the architect will draw the plans and specifications and also supervise the constructional work. A lower rate of percentage for architect's fees is charged if no superintendence work is required.

415. At an estimated cost of $3.25 per square foot of area, how many square feet of floor area can be planned for if the amount of money available for the job is $4,258? This amount must include architect's fees of 4 per cent and contractor's profits of 6 per cent.

REDUCTION

See page 190, Chap. VIII.

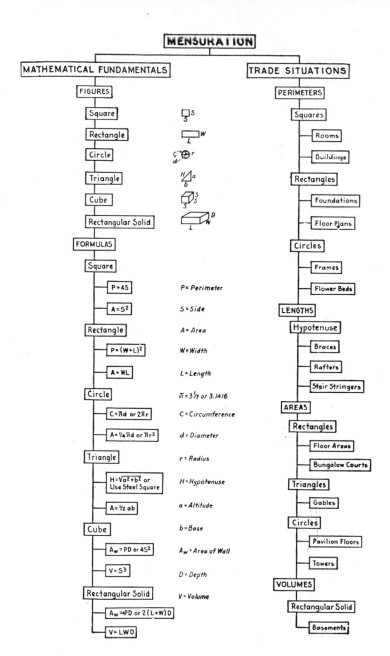

MENSURATION

MATHEMATICAL FUNDAMENTALS

FIGURES

- Square
- Rectangle
- Circle
- Triangle
- Cube
- Rectangular Solid

FORMULAS

Square
- $P = 4S$ — $P = Perimeter$
- $A = S^2$ — $S = Side$

Rectangle — $A = Area$
- $P = (W+L)^2$ — $W = Width$
- $A = WL$ — $L = Length$

Circle — $\pi = 3\frac{1}{7}$ or 3.1416
- $C = \pi d$ or $2\pi r$ — $C = Circumference$
- $A = \frac{1}{4}\pi d$ or πr^2 — $d = Diameter$

Triangle — $r = Radius$
- $H = \sqrt{a^2 + b^2}$ or Use Steel Square — $H = Hypotenuse$
- $A = \frac{1}{2} ab$ — $a = Altitude$

Cube — $b = Base$
- $A_w = PD$ or $4S^2$ — $A_w = Area\ of\ Wall$
- $V = S^3$ — $D = Depth$

Rectangular Solid — $V = Volume$
- $A_w = PD$ or $2(L+W)D$
- $V = LWD$

TRADE SITUATIONS

PERIMETERS

Squares
- Rooms
- Buildings

Rectangles
- Foundations
- Floor Plans

Circles
- Frames
- Flower Beds

LENGTHS

Hypotenuse
- Braces
- Rafters
- Stair Stringers

AREAS

Rectangles
- Floor Areas
- Bungalow Courts

Triangles
- Gables

Circles
- Pavilion Floors
- Towers

VOLUMES

Rectangular Solid
- Basements

MATHEMATICAL CHECK-UP

MENSURATION[1]

Figures: Square, rectangle, circle, triangle, cube, rectangular solid.
1. Square: side = 29′.   Find the perimeter.
2. Square: side = 12′.   Find the area.
3. Rectangle: width = 12′, length = 22′.   Find the perimeter.
4. Rectangle: width = 7′, length = 15′.   Find the area.
5. Circle: d = 16′.   Find the circumference.
6. Circle: d = 18′.   Find the area.
7. Circle: r = 6′.   Find the area.
8. Triangle: base = 12′, perpendicular = 9′.   Find the hypotenuse.
9. Triangle: base = 18′, perpendicular = 6′.   Find the area.
10. Cube: side = 8′.   Find the wall area.
11. Cube: side = 7′.   Find the volume.
12. Rectangular solid: length = 18′, width = 11′, depth = 9′.   Find the wall area.
13. Rectangular solid: length = 22′, width = 15′ depth = 7′.   Find the volume.
14. Find the hypotenuse of a triangle: base = 16′, perpendicular = 12′.
15. Find the perimeter of a square: side = 11′ 3″.
16. Find the perimeter of a rectangle: length = 15′ 4″, width = 9′ 2″.
17. Find the circumference of a circle: diameter = 15′.
18. Find the area of a square: side = 15′ 6″.
19. Find the area of a rectangle: length = 17′ 4″, width = 7′ 8″.
20. Find the area of a circle: diameter = 35′.
21. Find the area of a triangle: base = 15′ 6″, perpendicular 7′ 9″.
22. Find the wall area of a cube: side = 20′ 6″.
23. Find the wall area of a rectangle: length = 23′ 6″, width = 16′, depth = 10′.
24. Find the volume of a cube: side = 15′ 6″.
25. Find the volume of a rectangular solid: length = 17′ 6″, width = 11′ 6″, depth = 9′ 0″.

[1] See p. 192.

CHAPTER VI

MENSURATION[1]

There are a number of problems in carpentry which involve the process of figuring the *perimeter* of a rectangle or square, the *circumference* of a circle, the *area* of a square or triangle, the *hypotenuse* of a triangle, etc. These mathematical processes are known as mensuration. In this chapter each type will be discussed in detail. Where possible, the steel square will be used for solving the problems, as this tool has very fine mathematical possibilities in its application to mensuration, particularly in finding the hypotenuse of a triangle.

PERIMETERS

Squares.—The term "perimeter" means the distance around a square or rectangle. As a square is a geometrical figure having four sides of equal length, *the length of one side times 4 equals the perimeter.*

Problems

416. A room is 12′ × 12′ in size. What is the distance around it?

417. How many linear feet of curbing are there around a city block that is 330′ square?

418. A building is 26′ square. What is its perimeter?

419. A warehouse blueprint shows dimensions 87′ × 87′. How many linear feet of outside wall are there?

420. A new subdivision of a city has outside dimensions of 978′ × 978′. What is the distance around it?

421 to 425. What is the perimeter of the building outlines as shown in Fig. 87?

In a building outline, the *length of one side times 4, plus the length of each end wall of the offset, equals the perimeter.* Figure 88 illustrates the method. Dotted line *A* is the same length as line *B*.

426 to 430. Figure 89 illustrates five square buildings with one outside corner removed. What is the distance around each building?

[1] In connection with this chapter it is advisable to read the section on Mensuration in Chap. VIII, p. 192.

111

The **perimeter** for a building shaped as illustrated can be estimated—length of one side times 4.   The reason for this is shown in Fig. 90.   Dotted lines have the same dimensions as opposite full lines.

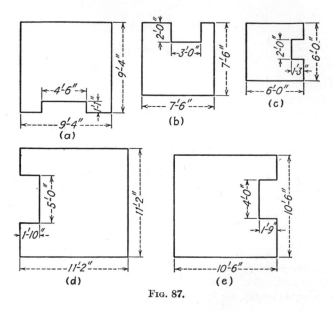

FIG. 87.

Rectangles.—A rectangle is a figure having two sides of equal length and two ends of equal length.   To find the distance around a rectangle: *the sum of the width plus the length, times 2 equals the perimeter.*

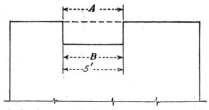

FIG. 88.—Proof of rule as applied to squares or rectangles with offsets.

431. What is the perimeter of a building 32′ × 48′?

432. A house 28′ 6″ × 42′ 6″ has how many feet of perimeter?

433. In constructing a double apartment house it was necessary to know the total distance around both buildings.   How much was it if each building was 38′ 6 ′ wide and 64′ 4 ″ long?

434. How many linear feet of outside wall are there in a building that is 68′ wide and 87′ long?

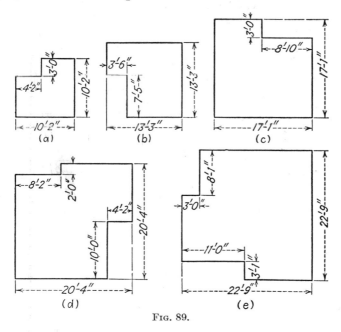

Fɪɢ. 89.

435. An auto camp contains 32 units, each of which is 18′ wide and 26′ long. What is the total number of linear feet of outside walls?

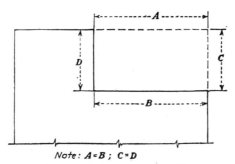

Note: *A = B ; C = D*

Fɪɢ. 90.—Proof of rule as applied to rectangle with one corner removed.

436 to 440. What is the perimeter of each of the buildings shown in Fig. 91? The rule for a building of this shape is: *the sum of the width plus* *the length (W* plus *L), times* 2, *plus twice the length of the end wall of the offset, equals the perimeter* (see Fig. 88).

441 to 445. What is the distance around the following L-shaped buildings as shown in Fig. 92? The rule is *the sum of the width plus the length, times* 2 *equals the perimeter* (see Fig. 90).

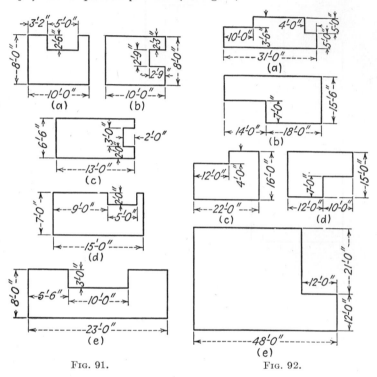

Fig. 91.   Fig. 92.

Circles.—The circumference of a circle is always found by multiplying the diameter by 3.1416 (known as *pi*, which is the Greek symbol for this number).

446. A baseball diamond is enclosed by a circular fence. If the diameter of the field is 148′, how long will the fence be?

447. If a silo is 8′ in diameter, what will be the distance around it?

448. How many linear feet of 1″ × 4″ will be required to make a form for a flower bed if the landscape plans show a diameter of 22′?

All circumferences should be increased to the next even foot if applied to lumber.

449. What will be the length of the glass bead for a semicircular transom sash as shown in Fig. 93? The glass is 4′ wide.

450. A large entrance to a public building is semicircular and is 8' 0" wide. What will be the length of the moulding for the circle top head of a door frame made to fit this opening?

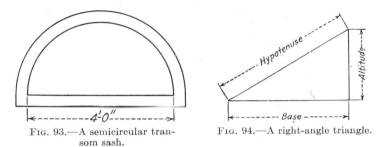

Fig. 93.—A semicircular transom sash.

Fig. 94.—A right-angle triangle.

LENGTHS

Hypotenuse.—The problem of finding the hypotenuse of a right-angle triangle, illustrated in Fig. 94, is a common one for the carpenter. The situations in which he requires it are illustrated in Fig. 95. The length of a piece of stock to make a brace, the length of a rafter, or the length of stock required to make the supporting member of a stairway, known in trade terms as a "stringer" or "horse" are problems that carpenters are constantly solving.

The usual mathematical rule for finding the hypotenuse of a right-angle triangle is: *the sum of the square of the base plus the square of the altitude equals the square of the hypotenuse.* The proof of this rule is illustrated in Fig. 96. Notice that the base of the triangle is 3" and the altitude is 4". Applying the rule: the square of 3 is 9 and the square of 4 is 16; 9 plus 16 equals 25, which is the square of the hypotenuse measurement. A study of the illustration will show 9 squares, 16 squares, and 25 squares, respectively. This mathematical rule will apply to any right-angle triangle.

Application of the Steel Square.—In carpentry the steel square is of considerable value and help in this problem. Figure 97 illustrates this tool. Notice that the shape of the steel square is such that it can readily be used to represent the base and altitude of a right-angle triangle. The shorter part of the square is called the "tongue," the longer part the "body," or "blade."

The process of finding a hypotenuse by using this tool is one of measuring across the square from two given numbers. The result will be the hypotenuse for that size triangle. In the problem of a triangle having a base of 3" and an altitude of 4", it will be found that

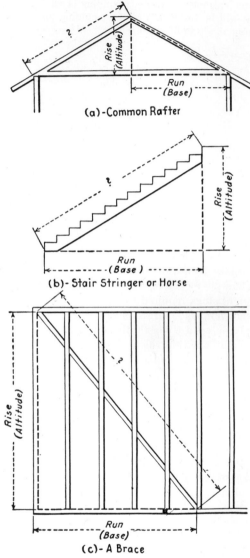

(a) - Common Rafter

(b) - Stair Stringer or Horse

(c) - A Brace

Fɪɢ. 95.—Trade situations requiring the finding of the hypotenuse of triangle by measuring across from 3″ on the tongue of the square to 4″ on the body of the square the length will be exactly 5″.

The simplicity of this method of solving problems is evidenced if a fraction is used for the base and altitude measurements. To

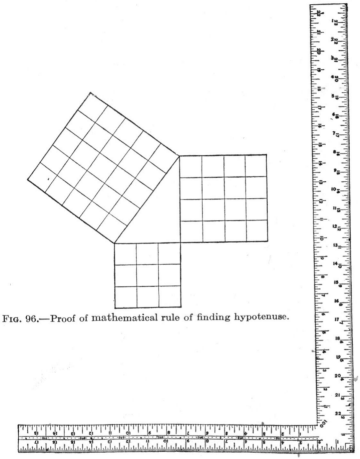

Fig. 96.—Proof of mathematical rule of finding hypotenuse.

Fig. 97.—A typical steel square.

illustrate: what is the hypotenuse of a right-angle triangle that has a base line of 6¼″ and an altitude of 9⅜″? Measuring across from these numbers on the square the answer is readily determined as 11¼″.

It should be noted that the figures on one face of the square are usually marked off into 12 divisions. By using a square so stamped the rule is to "let 1 in. represent 1 ft. and $\frac{1}{12}$ in. represent 1 in. Thus, 6'4" is represented as $6\frac{4}{12}$; 8'10" is $8\frac{10}{12}$ in., etc.

Fig. 98.—Steel square gages.   Fig. 99.—Illustrates the use of square gages.

To simplify the mathematical work, a pair of square gages, illustrated in Fig. 98, can be purchased at any hardware store. These are small tools that will clamp on one edge of the square at any desired position. The work of reading the hypotenuse is also simplified by using another steel square. Figure 99 indicates the method.

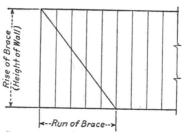

Fig. 100.—The run of a brace.

Braces.—Braces are used in a frame building to give it rigidity, the best angle being 45 deg. The term "run" of the brace means the length of the horizontal distance over which the brace "passes," as shown in Fig. 100.

Problems

451 to 460. Using the steel square, determine the actual and standard length[1] of stock required to make a brace for the following different height walls. The run of the brace is also given.

Problem	Height of the wall	Run of the brace
451	6' 0"	9' 0"
452	7' 0"	11' 0"
453	6' 4"	13' 0"
454	5' 2"	5' 8"
455	3' 8"	6' 6"
456	8' 0"	13' 0"
457	18' 0"	26' 0"
458	15' 2"	17' 4"
459	10' 3"	13' 7"
460	8' 4"	8' 4"

For dimensions that are too large to be measured on the square, divide each number by 2, measure as usual, and then multiply the answer by 2. Any reduction will do, provided the hypotenuse as measured is increased as much as the original figures were decreased.

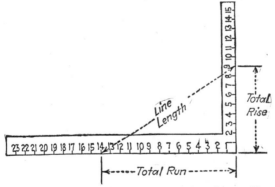

FIG. 101.—The steel square applied to the rafter problem.

Rafters.—The process of framing rafters is a subject that requires considerable study and a good background of building construction. The following problems will give the student experience in the application of the steel square to this very important problem.[2]

[1] See p. 203 for information on lengths of lumber.

[2] For a detailed explanation of rafter layout, see Wilson and Werner's, "Simplified Roof Framing," McGraw-Hill Book Co., Inc.

The diagonal or hypotenuse distance of the total rise of a roof and the total run of the common rafter illustrated in Fig. 101, will be the "line length" of the rafter. The overhang of the rafter must be added to this result to find the overall length of the rafter.

461 to 465. Using the steel square, determine the line length of the rafter for the following buildings.

Problem	Total run	Total rise
461	7′	2′ 8″
462	8′	2′ 0″
463	13′	4′ 4″
464	17′	8′ 6″
465	18′	12′ 0″

The span of a roof is twice the total run of the common rafter; or: the total run is always one-half of the span (see Fig. 102).

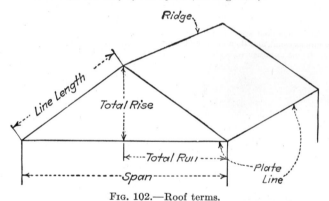

Fig. 102.—Roof terms.

466 to 470. In the following problems, what is the line length of the common rafters?

Problem	Span	Total rise
466	32′	8′ 0″
467	40′	20′ 0″
468	32′	10′ 8″
469	22′	5′ 6″
470	25′	18′ 0″

For problems in which the measurements are too large for the steel square see information in problem 460.

All framing lumber is ordered by the even-foot measurement except in special cases where short-length stock can be secured in odd-foot lengths. Therefore, in finding the length of stock for rafters the theoretical or line length must first be found and then converted into the nearest even-foot length of stock.

471 to 475. What length of lumber must be bought to make common rafters for buildings of the following sizes?

Problem	Span	Total rise	Overhang
471	28′	7′ 0″	1′ 6″
472	14′	4′ 8″	1′ 3″
473	16′	4′ 0″	0′ 8″
474	46′	11′ 0″	1′ 4″
475	27′	9′ 0″	2′ 8″

Stair Stringers.[1]—The stringer of a stairway is the piece of finish stock that is placed in a slanting position and into which risers and

FIG. 103.—A stair horse.

treads are fitted. If rough stock is used it is called a "stair horse"; in this case the treads and risers are nailed on top of the horse, as illustrated in Fig. 103.

[1] See footnote p. 41.

The length of stock required to make a stair stringer is measured on the square in the same way as the rafter. *The diagonal of the total rise and the total run of the stairway is the length of the stringer stock. Change to the nearest even-foot length of lumber.* The total rise is the vertical distance from the top of one floor to the top of the next floor above (see Fig. 37).

476 to 480. Using the square, determine the actual and standard length of stock required to make the stringer in the following problems.

Problem	Total rise	Total run
476	9′ 4″	8′ 0″
477	16′ 2″	12′ 8″
478	13′ 9″	11′ 7″
479	10′ 6″	13′ 4″
480	8′ 7″	4′ 5″

481 to 485. How long should the stock be to make stringers for the stairways with the following rise and run dimensions?

Problem	Total rise	Total run
481	5′ 4″	3′ 8″
482	7′ 6″	5′ 2″
483	3′ 9″	2′ 7″
484	12′ 0″	16′ 0″
485	11′ 3″	12′ 9″

AREAS
Squares.

Problems

486 to 490. How many square feet of floor area are there in each of the buildings represented in Fig. 87? To find the area of a surface the shape

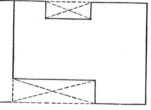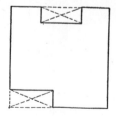

FIG. 104.

of these, *multiply the two over-all dimensions and deduct the offset area,* Figure 104 illustrates this method.

Rectangles.—The area of a rectangle is found by multiplying the width by the length, or $W \times L =$ area.

491 to 493. What are the areas of the following buildings?

Problem	Width	Length
491	18′	36′
492	28′	47′
493	56′	65′

494. A motor court contains 14 units, each 18′ 6″ × 26′ 6″. What is the total floor area?

495. How many square feet of floor area are there in three two-story apartment houses, each of which is 38′ wide and 76′ long?

496 to 500. What is the area of each of the buildings represented in Fig. 89? To find the area, multiply the width times the length and deduct the offset area (see Fig. 104).

For the mathematical practice involved, figure all dimensions as given. In trade practice, the estimator usually increases all fractional dimensions to the next half or whole foot before computing perimeters or areas. For detailed instructions on listing a bill of materials, see Wilson and Rogers' "Simplified Carpentry Estimating," Delmar Publishers, Inc., Albany, N.Y.

501 to 510. The buildings represented in Figs. 91 and 92 contain how many square feet each?

Triangles.—The area of a triangle, as represented in Fig. 105, is easily figured, for it can be converted into a rectangle which will have for its dimensions the same height but only one-half the width of the original triangle. Therefore, *multiply the altitude of the triangle by one-half of its width.* This will give the area. This problem applies to the end of a gable roof, as it is in the shape of a triangle.

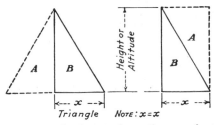

FIG. 105.—Illustrating how to figure the area of a triangle.

511. What is the area of the gable end of a roof that has an altitude of 6′ and a span of 18′?

512. A building is 30' wide and the ridge is 10' above the plate line (see Fig. 106). What is the area of the gable?

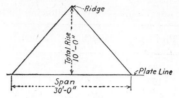

FIG. 106.—A gable end.

513. A gable roof has a height of 14' and a span of 16'. What is the area of both end gables?

514. How many square feet of wall space are there in the two gables of a roof if the ridge is 8' above the plate line and the building is 36' wide?

515. A gable roof has a span of 11' 6" and a rise of 7' 6". What is the area of the gable ends of the roof?

516 to 520. What is the area of the gables represented in the following problems?

Problem	Total rise	Span
516	6' 0"	38' 0"
517	4' 6"	22' 0"
518	7' 0"	27' 0"
519	19' 8"	46' 0"
520	14' 4"	32' 8"

Circles.—To find the area of a circle *multiply the radius squared by* π (3.1416) or *diameter squared by* $\frac{1}{4}$ π (.7854).

Convert all answers in the following problems to next whole foot.

521. What is the area of a pavilion floor that has a diameter of 16'?

522. How many square feet of floor space are there in a pavilion that is 32' in diameter?

523. A circle tower has a radius of 12'. What is the floor area?

524. How many square feet of floor area are there in a circular bandstand that has a radius of 22'?

525. A heavy machine requires a concrete base that is 13' in diameter. How many square feet of area are there in the base?

VOLUME

Rectangular Solids.—Volume mathematical problems must be solved when figuring the number of cubic yards or cubic feet of earth in a basement excavation or when finding the contents of a concrete form.

To find the volume, *multiply the width by the length by the depth*, being sure, however, that all measurements are in the same terms.

Problems

526. How many cubic feet of earth are there in a basement 8' wide × 16' long × 7' deep?

527. A concrete form is 2' wide, 7' high, and 684' long. What are the cubical contents of the form?

528. A building is 28' wide and 44' long. The excavation for the footing is 18" wide and 6" deep. How many cubic feet of earth were removed in digging the trench?

529. A large building requires a basement 9' deep, 78' wide, and 96' long. How many yards of earth are there to be removed?

It is customary, when figuring excavations, to figure them on the basis of the cubic yard and not the cubic foot. Therefore, *to change cubic feet to cubic yards divide by 27.*

530. An apartment house required a concrete foundation 8" thick and 3' high. The size of the building was 38' × 82'. How many cubic feet of concrete were there in the foundation?

531 to 535. What are the cubical contents of the basements represented in Fig. 91? Each has a depth as shown below:

Problem	Figure	Depth
531	A	5' 0"
532	B	6' 6"
533	C	4' 6"
534	D	9' 0"
535	E	7' 0"

536 to 540. Figure 92 represents several basement plans. How many cubic yards of earth are to be removed? The depths are as follows:

Problem	Figure	Depth
536	A	6' 6"
537	B	8' 4"
538	C	12' 0"
539	D	5' 8"
540	E	7' 6"

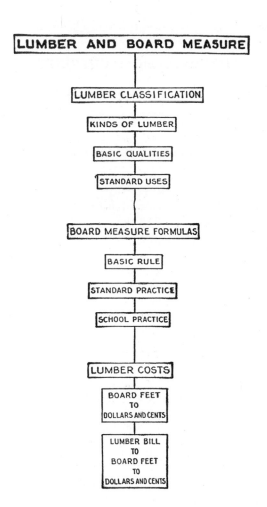

MATHEMATICAL CHECK-UP

LUMBER AND BOARD MEASURE

Board Measure.

One board foot: (1 bd. ft.) is 1″ thick, 1′ wide, 1′ long.

Find the number of board feet in the following problems: [2]

1. 14 boards 1″ thick, 12″ wide, 10′ long.
2. 8 boards 1½″ thick, 22″ wide, 16′ long.
3. 6 planks 2″ thick, 10″ wide, 14′ long.
4. 10 pcs. 2 × 6 × 12′ redwood mudsill.
5. 15 pcs. 1″ × 8″ × 14′ subfloor stock.
6. 25 pcs. ¾″ × 3″ × 12′ Douglas fir.
7. 1 pc. 2″ × 3″ × 20′ Douglas fir.
8. 60 lin. ft. of 1″ × 4″ redwood.
9. 250 lin. ft. of 1″ × 6″ sugar pine.
10. 150 lin. ft. of 2″ × 3″ redwood.
11. 72 lin. ft. of 1″ × 3″ Douglas fir.
12. 5 pcs. 1″ × 4″ × 42″ sugar pine.
13. 15 pcs. 1″ × 6″ × 30″ mahogany.
14. 27 pcs. 1″ × 12″ × 50″ oak.
15. 9 pcs. ½″ × 12″ × 32″ sugar pine.

Lumber Costs.

16. Find the cost of 24 pcs. 2″ × 8″ × 16′ @ $34 per 1,000.
17. Find the cost of 44 pcs. 1″ × 10″ × 20′ @ $37 per M.
18. Find the cost of 360 bd. ft. 1″ × 8″ Oregon pine S1S at $29.50 per M.
19. Find the cost of 34 pcs. ¾″ × 4″ × 44″ mahogany at $246 per M.
20. Find the cost of 160 lin. ft. 1″ × 8″ Douglas fir at $35.

[1] See p. 203.
[2] Fractional board foot counted as whole board foot if ½ or over.

CHAPTER VII

LUMBER AND BOARD MEASURE[1]

LUMBER CLASSIFICATION

The material which the carpenter uses for the greater part of his work is lumber. A basic knowledge of the uses of lumber, its durability, the many kinds that can be purchased, and other similar information is therefore of considerable value to him. Figure 107 illustrates lumber cross piled for air drying.

Chart V illustrates the specific qualifications for the more common woods that are in use in this country and also gives the general use as applied to house carpentry. The fact that

Fig. 107.—Lumber being cross piled for air drying. (*Courtesy, West Coast Lumbermen's Association, Los Angeles, Calif.*)

a wood is durable indicates that it has within itself some quality that makes it last. Redwood, cypress, and cedar are the best known materials for use as fence posts and mudsills where moisture may enter the wood.

[1] The table of lumber sizes on pp. 217–219 should be studied in connection with this chapter.

If strength is the qualification sought for, the southern pine or Douglas fir are most often used. These materials are,

LUMBER CLASSIFICATION

KINDS OF LUMBER	BASIC QUALITIES	STANDARD USES
CYPRESS RED WOOD CEDAR	DURABILITY (Water Resistance)	SILLS CHESTS OUTSIDE FINISH
SOUTHERN PINE AND DOUGLAS FIR	STRENGTH (Beauty)	FRAMING FLOORING INSIDE FINISH
YELLOW PINE WHITE PINE SOUTHERN PINE DOUGLAS FIR	WORKING QUALITIES (Painting Qualities)	INTERIOR FINISH AND CABINETS
OAK GUM BIRCH MAHOGANY.	WEARING QUALITIES (Beauty)	FLOORING AND INTERIOR FINISH

CHART V

FIG. 108.—Large bridge timbers. (*Courtesy, West Coast Lumbermen's Association, Portland, Ore.*)

therefore, popular for framing, bridge building, etc. Figure 108 shows a very large bridge timber.

For interior finish, the special qualifications desired are not durability or strength so much as good working qualities, capacity to "take" paint or varnish easily, and a grain that will look beautiful when finished. In this class are white pine, Pondosa pine, California white pine, southern pine, yellow pine, Douglas fir (formerly known as Oregon pine), and several of the hardwoods, such as gum, oak, mahogany, and birch.

Lumber used for floors must have for its particular qualifications good wearing qualities and also a grain that will look attractive after the floor is finished. Hence, the hardwoods, particularly oak and maple, are commonly used for this purpose. For the less expensive floor, vertical grained Douglas fir or southern yellow pine have splendid wearing possibilities.

Present-day Lumber Much Improved.[1]—The use of wood for building purposes is traditional. The colonists and pioneers built the walls of their homes and stock shelters of logs. Poles were used for joists and rafters, shakes for shingles and siding, and rough-hewn boards for floors.

The appearance of the sawmill brought in frame structures covered with rough boards applied vertically, the cracks being sealed with battens. The frames were of huge hewn timbers which were too large for the early saws. Where used, mouldings and finishing lumber had to be carved and smoothed with hand tools.

Later, larger saws and planing mills reduced hand labor. Framing timbers have been gradually reduced in size until today practically all small building frames are made of 2-inch lumber. Most finishing lumber now comes from the mill ready for use. Window and door frames are procured ready to set in place.

The lumber of today is more accurately sawed, planed, and graded; more closely adapted to specific uses; and available in greater variety of species than ever before. Cypress, redwood, and cedar for durability; southern pine and Douglas fir for strength; the softer pines for millwork; and the hardwoods for flooring or interior finish, all are brought together from far distant parts of the country to meet the requirements of the builder.

[1] From "The Uses of Lumber on the Farm" by the National Lumber Manufacturers Association. The Association publishes many other pamphlets of similar nature.

The forests of the northeastern and central states, though still producing important quantities of spruce, pine, hemlock, and hardwoods, have been depleted, partly to meet the nation's vast building requirements and largely to make way for millions of farms, and have given first place in lumbering to the southern and western states, which contain original forests sufficient to supply the nation for years to come.   New forests are growing to replace those standing.

Lumber Is a Durable Material.—Lumber, wisely used, is not only an economical material of many superior qualities, but also a most durable one.

Many of the wood houses built in the early days are still occupied, and in many instances by descendants of the original owners.   Why are these old structures still in use?   Because great care was taken in the selection of materials and in using them.   The occupants of these sturdy old houses are proud of the fact that they are living in the homes their great, great grandfathers built.

The Fairbanks house, at Dedham, Massachusetts, was built in 1636 by Jonathan Fairbanks.   It is maintained today by his descendants.   This house is accredited with being the oldest all-wood house in America.   It was built of white pine, left unpainted, and is a striking tribute to the durability of wood.

One hundred and sixty-nine years after Columbus discovered America, Samuel Moore, one of the early settlers, built a home of wood in Newton, a section of Queensborough, New York City.   That was 266 years ago.   Today there is no decay in the planks and beams of this quaint old structure with its gabled windows and shingled roof. The house is occupied by John Moore Perry, a descendant of Samuel Moore.   This house was the center of the British occupation of Newtown during the Revolution.

The name of no historic home is more familiar to American people than that of Mt. Vernon.   The original house was built in 1743 by Lawrence Washington, half brother of George Washington, who inherited the estate in 1752.   The latter remodeled and enlarged the house, completing the work in 1788.

The frame timbers of the house are of rough-hewn white oak, cut on the plantation.   Virginia pine, sawed at a near-by waterpower mill, was used for the sheathing and siding.   The laths were hand-split from red oak.   The roof was covered with cypress shingles.   When George Washington remodeled Mt. Vernon many of the cypress shingles, then half a century old, were turned over and used again. Not until 1913 was it necessary to reshingle the house.

Hundreds of other examples can be given of wood houses and other buildings that are still in good repair and constant use. Many are being preserved by historical and other associations, as is Mt. Vernon, for their historic value.

Care Will Insure Equal Durability of Present-day Structures.—It will be asked: Why are so many of the buildings of the last generation now old shacks unfit for use? Because no thought was given to the quality of materials used and the buildings were not kept in repair.

Many of our present-day construction methods are sources of dissatisfaction. The general practice is to get the building up with as little work and materials as possible. Corners are not sufficiently braced, sheathing and flooring are not tightly laid, nor sufficiently nailed. Continuous spaces are left inside the walls from basement to attic, and lumber is placed next to thin-walled chimneys. Many contractors and real-estate promoters skimp construction; and buildings, therefore, soon show cracks in the plastering, the floors sag and become uneven, doors and windows will not close properly.

With reasonable care all of this can be avoided. Many homes show none of these blemishes and illustrate the precautions which should be taken. Lumber is easily abused. It is also easy to use it wisely, effectively, and economically.

Some General Principles.

1. Foundation footings should be placed on solid ground, ordinarily below the frost line to prevent heaving and cracks. Good foundations must not be expected to correct unwise framing, nor the framework to take care of settling foundations.

2. The lasting qualities of wood vary with the part of the tree from which it is cut and with the species. Heartwood of any species lasts better than sapwood, where exposed to the weather and unprotected. Sapwood takes preservatives better than heartwood and treatment will double or triple its life. More treated lumber could be advantageously used in farm buildings.

3. The size of a piece of lumber has something to do with its lasting qualities. Large pieces, or timbers, are cut from the heart of logs. Inch boards, siding, etc., contain more sapwood because they are made from the outer cuts from the log.

4. Most retail yards carry timbers as large as 6″ × 6″; some carry larger. A 6″ × 6″ is large enough for most supporting posts in farm use. It is not large enough, however, for the ordinary girder, which will usually have to be built up of 2-inch planks of the required width. However, solid timbers are to be preferred, if available in suitable sizes and at comparable prices, because they are dressed larger **for**

specified standard sizes than the corresponding built-up girders, and, therefore, will be a little stronger.

5. Proper nailing increases the rigidity of structures. There is excellent foundation for the statement that 20 per cent more nails will increase the rigidity of a frame structure 50 per cent. Use 20d spikes for nailing joists, studs, and rafters. Ten-penny nails find relatively little use in general building. Eight-penny nails should be used for all inch boards—hurricane construction calls for 12d.

HOW TO ORDER LUMBER

The emphasis is continually being placed in these pages on the problems that the carpenter has to be familiar with in order to be able to make out a lumber bill for a five-room house. The general procedure practiced by many carpenters is to give the material bill to the lumber man organized in the order in which he constructs the house; that is, beginning with

Fig. 109.—Lumber on job ready for use.

the foundation, working on through the frame, and ending with the interior finish. This method has the advantage of making it very easy to select the materials needed on the job, as the first items on the bill will be the first ones used on the job. Figure 109 shows lumber on the job, ready for use.

The problem of computing the cost of a bill of materials belongs primarily to the lumberman. In order that the many items on a bill of lumber may be priced, he must first convert them into the units recognized by the lumber industry as the standard of measurement, namely, the board foot. After the total footage of each kind of material is known it can then be converted into its equivalent dollar-value. This process is indicated on Chart VII, page 145.

It is hardly possible for the carpenter to have a broad knowledge of the lumber industry, yet it is quite essential that he have a basic knowledge of it, including methods of ordering lumber and what information to give the lumber yard. It is customary to give first the thickness of the lumber, second the width, and last the length. It is also necessary to state:

1. How many pieces of lumber of each size are needed.
2. The grade of the lumber (see Fig. 112).
3. The kind of wood.
4. Whether it is to be rough, partly smooth, or surfaced on all four sides.

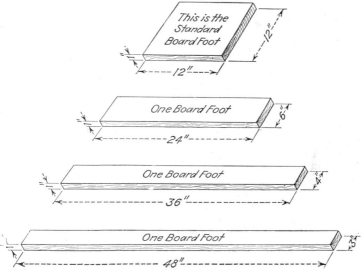

FIG. 110.—Various standard sizes of lumber containing one board foot.

BOARD MEASURE

The standard measurement for lumber is the board foot which is represented by a piece of lumber 1″ thick, 12″ wide, and 12″ long or *its equivalent volume*. A piece of 1″ × 6″ × 24″ would contain 1 bd. ft.; likewise, a piece of 1″ × 4″ × 36″, or 1″ × 3″ × 48″, etc., as shown in Fig. 110.

There are four methods of finding the number of board feet in a given size piece of lumber. Primarily, there is really only one, the others being variations of it. Chart VI outlines the four methods.

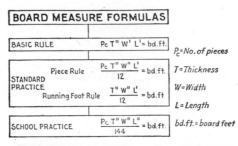

BOARD MEASURE FORMULAS

Finish sizes are computed according to the original rough sizes. See page 217.

Width in "uneven" inches, (except 3″ widths, 1″ × 5″ S4S and the hardwoods) are counted the next even inch width, as 1″ × 6½″ = 1″ × 8″.

Odd lengths are to be figured the next even foot length, except that 3′, 5′, 7′, 9′, and 11′ can be cut from twice their length.

Also students figure actual lengths used.

Thickness less than 1″ is counted as 1″.

Thickness over 1″ is counted 1¼″; 1½″; 2″; 3″; 4″; 6″; etc.

Fractional parts of a board foot are counted as whole board feet.

CHART VI

The basic rule for finding board feet is: *Multiply the number of pieces by the thickness expressed in inches by the width expressed in feet by the length expressed in feet*, or:

$$\text{pc.} \times T'' \times W' \times L' = \text{bd. ft.}$$

It should be emphasized that although inches are apparently being multiplied by feet, such is not the case. The thickness, while expressed in inches, is really a unit thickness, the unit in all cases being 1 in.; a piece of lumber 2″ thick being 2 units thick, 3″ lumber 3 units, 1½″ lumber 1½ units, etc. The board foot measurement of lumber less than 1″ nominal thickness is based on the surface dimensions except in special cases such as thin stock which is often made by resawing a 1″ or thicker stock.

Lumber can be purchased 1″, 1¼″, 1½″, 2″, 3″, 4″, 6″ thick, etc. In terms of widths, the standard widths are 3″, 4″, 5″, 6″, 8″, 10″, etc.[1] Hardwoods are usually sold in random widths because of their scarcity and because they are generally cut up into short and narrow pieces for various industrial uses.

Variations of the Basic Rule.—The width of lumber is usually given in terms of inches and not of feet. Hence, the basic rule will have to be modified to take care of this situation. Dividing the width of a board by 12, if expressed in inches, will convert it to feet; therefore,

$$\text{pc.} \times T'' \times \frac{W''}{12''} \times L' = \text{bd. ft.}$$

This is what might be called standard lumber-yard practice, although the lumber man has a short-cut method which is a series of tables in which the total footage for any given number of pieces for any given size is tabulated for quick reference.[2]

Another method commonly used is a satisfactory rule for narrow stock and is what could be called "running-foot practice." In this case the thickness and the width are multiplied together and divided by 12″. The resulting fraction is then multiplied by the length or total number of linear feet of the stock. Expressed as a short rule this becomes:

$$\frac{T'' \times W''}{12''} \times L' = \text{bd. ft.}$$

In many cases the mathematical operation can be done mentally and gives the fractional number of board feet per linear foot of stock determined. The following table gives the number of board feet per linear foot for several of the commonly used widths of stock:

---

[1] 5″ widths in 1″ finish stock only.
[2] See Table 11, p. 221.

Size stock	Board feet per linear foot
1″ × 2″	⅙
1″ × 3″	¼
1″ × 4″	⅓
1″ × 6″	½
1″ × 8″	⅔
2″ × 3″	½
2″ × 4″	⅔
2″ × 6″	1
2″ × 8″	1⅓

The fourth possibility is based on the problem of converting a piece of lumber to board feet when the length is given in inches. This is *not* standard commercial practice but is a common problem in school shopwork in which the student is required to figure the total footage of material for some project he has made. Therefore:

$$\text{pc.} \times \frac{T'' \times W'' \times L''}{12'' \times 12''} = \text{bd. ft.}$$

This is known as school practice.

Summary of Rules.—For convenience, these board-measure rules are grouped as follows:

1. The basic rule—pc. $\times T''' \times W' \times L' = $ bd. ft.

2. Piece rule—pc. $\times T'' \times \dfrac{W''}{12''} \times L' = $ bd. ft.

3. Running-foot rule— $\dfrac{T'' \times W''}{12''} \times L' = $ bd. ft.

4. School practice, inch rule— $\dfrac{T'' \times W'' \times L''}{12'' \times 12''} = $ bd. ft.

Problems

Work the following problems using the standard practice, piece rule: pc. $\times T'' \times \dfrac{W''}{12''} \times L' = $ bd. ft.[1]

541. How many board feet of lumber are there in 10 pieces 2″ × 6″ × 16′ redwood mudsill?

[1] See footnote, p. 128.

542. A motor court requires 28 pieces 2″ × 8″ × 14′ redwood sill. How many board feet of lumber are there in the order?

543. Twenty-two pieces of 2″ × 8″ × 18′ cypress contain how many board feet of lumber?

544. A fence requires 68 pieces 4″ × 4″ × 7′ cedar posts. How many board feet of lumber are there in the posts?

545. In enclosing a large lot the contractor used 148 pieces 4″ × 4″ × 8′. How many board feet of lumber were there in the posts?

546. A contractor figures that a certain job requires 72 pieces 2″ × 4″ × 18′ for ceiling joists. How many feet of lumber are needed in the joists?

547. In constructing a large bridge 18 pieces 10″ × 10″ × 24′ were used. These pieces contained how many board feet of lumber?

548. A contractor's order for material for a small job was as follows: 28 pieces 1″ × 8″ × 16′; 5 pieces 1″ × 4″ × 10′; 32 pieces 1″ × 6″ × 16′; 12 pieces 2″ × 10″ × 18′. How many board feet of lumber were in the order?

549. How many board feet of lumber are there in 26 pieces 2″ × 6″ × 32′ floor joists and 180 pieces 1″ × 8″ × 16′ subfloor stock?

550. A warehouse job requires 64 pieces 8″ × 8″ × 12′ for posts and 38 pieces 10″ × 14″ × 18′ for girders. How many board feet of lumber are there in this material?

551. How many board feet of lumber are there in the following items: 52 pieces 2″ × 3″ × 22′ braces; 63 pieces 1″ × 10″ × 16′ shelving stock; 38 pieces 1″ × 4″ × 20′ sheathing?

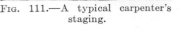

Fig. 111.—A typical carpenter's staging.

552. A contractor ordered material for a staging, a typical one being illustrated in Fig. 111. How many board feet of stock did he buy? His bill of materials follows: 26 pieces 2″ × 4″ × 20′ for posts; 18 pieces 1″ × 8″ × 14′ for ledgers (horizontal pieces); 22 pieces 1″ × 6″ × 16′ for braces; 15 pieces 2″ × 12″ × 16′ for planks.

553. How many board feet of lumber were there in a fence that required 172 pieces 1″ × 12″ × 16′; 52 pieces 4″ × 4″ × 7′; and 78 pieces 2″ × 4″ × 22′?

554. A contractor's order for framing stock was as follows: 72 pieces 2″ × 4″ × 8′; 162 pieces 1″ × 4″ × 14′; 46 pieces 2″ × 6″ × 18′; 107 pieces 1″ × 10″ × 16′; and 27 pieces 1″ × 3″ × 12′. How many board feet of lumber are there in the bill?

555. In constructing a small garage the contractor ordered: 58 studs 2″ × 4″ × 10′; 6 plates 2″ × 4″ × 18′; 12 braces 2″ × 4″ × 12′; 8 sills 3″ × 4″ × 16′. What is the total "footage" of the bill?

The term "footage" is often used when considering the total number of board feet of stock in a lumber bill. It is another expression for total board feet.

556. For the door jambs for the interior finish of a residence 18 pieces 1¼″ × 6″ × 18′ were ordered. These pieces contained how many board feet?

557. In making up a bid a contractor ordered 10 pieces 1½″ × 10″ × 18′ to be delivered to the planing mill for special milling. How many board feet of lumber were in the order?

558. How many board feet are contained in 28 pieces 1¼″ × 12″ × 16′ and 14 pieces 1½″ × 8″ × 14′?

559. For constructing some built-in cabinets the contractor ordered the following bill of materials: 8 pieces 1¼″ × 8″ × 18′, No. 2 clr. Douglas

FIG. 112.—Number 2 common grade white fir. (*Courtesy, Western Pine Association, Portland, Ore.*)

fir; 15 pieces 1″ × 10″ × 14′, No. 3 clr. factory California pine for shelving, S4S; and 8 pieces 1¼″ × 3″ × 12′, Douglas fir S4S. How many board feet of materials in these items? Figure 112 illustrates the California pine.

560. A set of shelving for a store required the following materials: 38 pieces 1″ × 12″ × 18′ yellow pine S4S; 56 pieces 1″ × 8″ × 14′; 24 pieces 1″ × 4″ × 10′. How many board feet of stock were in the order?

Work the following problems using the standard practice, running-foot rule: $\dfrac{T'' \times W''}{12''} \times L' = $ bd. ft.[1]

561. How many board feet are there in 248 lin. ft. of 2″ × 4″ Douglas fir plate stock? Figure 113 illustrates bottom plates being nailed on.

562. A frame apartment building required 84 lin. ft. of 2″ × 10″ header joists. How many board feet of lumber is this?

563. For the belt course of a two-story house 118 lin. ft. of 1″ × 8″, 118 lin. ft. of 1″ × 12″, and 118 lin. ft. of 1″ × 4″ redwood stock were ordered. How many board feet of lumber were there in the belt course?

564. In constructing a motor court the contractor ordered 262 lin. ft. of 1″ × 6″ stock for the ridge boards. How many board feet of lumber did he receive?

565. An eight-unit apartment house requires 438 lin. ft. of 2″ × 4″ firestop. How many board feet of lumber are there in this material?

Fig. 113.—Cutting and nailing bottom plate.

Work the following problems using the school practice, inch rule:

$$\frac{T'' \times W'' \times L''}{12'' \times 12''} = \text{bd. ft.}[1]$$

566. In constructing certain pieces of furniture a school-shop student used the following pieces of lumber: 8 pieces 1″ × 8″ × 36″; 4 pieces 1″ × 4″ × 54″; 16 pieces 1″ × 10″ × 42″. What is the total number of board feet?

567. The rough lumber list to make a cabinet includes the following items: 5 pieces 1″ × 4″ × 62″; 3 pieces 1″ × 3″ × 38″; 6 pieces 1″ × 8″ × 28″; 4 pieces 1″ × 2″ × 34″. How many board feet of lumber are there in the group?

568. In making five tables a woodshop student used the following materials: 20 pieces 3″ × 3″ × 30″; 10 pieces 1″ × 6″ × 24″; 10 pieces 1″ × 6″ × 42″; 15 pieces 1″ × 12″ × 48″. How many board feet of lumber are there in the order? A typical table is shown in Fig. 114.

[1] See footnote, p. 128.

569. How many board feet of lumber are there in the following list of materials that were used in making a cabinet: 8 pieces $1\frac{1}{4}'' \times 2'' \times 56''$; 12 pieces $1\frac{1}{4}'' \times 3'' \times 38''$; 18 pieces $1'' \times 16'' \times 24''$; 14 pieces $1\frac{1}{2}'' \times 6'' \times 18''$?

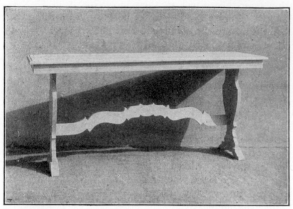

Fig. 114.—A woodshop project.

570. In making several chairs a woodshop student used: 4 pieces $1'' \times 8'' \times 32''$ mahogany; 8 pieces $1'' \times 3'' \times 26''$; 14 pieces $1'' \times 12'' \times 16''$. What is the total number of board feet of lumber?

BASIS FOR DETERMINING SIZES OF LUMBER

The basis for the size of a piece of lumber is determined by the sawmill cut. All lumber is cut to the "full-inch" size, such as $2'' \times 4''$, $2'' \times 6''$, $1'' \times 8''$, and $1'' \times 4''$, the lumber in each instance being cut to these dimensions. The lumber is "green" or wet after cutting so that when shrinkage takes place the lumber is smaller than its original size, the amount varying with the kind of wood, the length of time it has had to dry, and how it is dried, which is by either the air or the kiln method.[1]

As already noted, the board foot measurement of lumber less than $1''$ in thickness is based on the surface dimensions (as if $1''$ thick). Above $1''$ thickness lumber is cut to a number of different thicknesses.

The same rule applies to the width of a board; any board less than an "even-inch" width (excepting $3''$ widths, $1'' \times$

[1] See Fig. 107, p. 129.

5″ S4S and the hardwoods) is counted the next even-inch width above it. A board 1″ × 6½″ must be counted as 1″ × 8″; 11¼″ is figured as 12″; 4¾″ as 6″; etc.

The same principle is applied to the odd lengths of lumber. Any odd length must be figured the next even-foot length above it, except that 3′, 5′, 7′, 9′, and 11′ can be cut from twice their length. For woodshop practice in schoolwork it is customary for the student to figure his footage on the sizes of the stock he actually uses.

The table on page 217, Chap. IX, gives the sizes of the rough stock and also the dimension of the stock when milled in several different ways. These are now adopted nationally, which means that anywhere in the United States, from Maine to California, one can be sure of the exact size of a piece of lumber.

Problems

The problem of figuring board feet when the finish sizes of the stock are given is: *first convert the finish sizes to their original rough size* and then figure as usual.

571. How many board feet of lumber are there in 16 pieces ¾″ × 5½″ × 16′ redwood corner boards?

572. In taking off a lumber bill a contractor listed 21 pieces ¾″ × 3½″ × 14′ Douglas fir to be used for a special part of a number of window frames. How many board feet of lumber were there in these pieces?

573. An apartment house required 262 lin. ft. of ¾″ × 7½″ redwood S4S and the same amount of ¾″ × 9½″. How many board feet of lumber were there in this stock?

574. For the interior finish of a house a contractor ordered 324 lin. ft. ⅝″ × 5¼″ yellow pine base-board; 670 lin. ft. of ¾″ × 2½″ casing stock; and 124 lin. ft. of ⅜″ × 3¾″. How many board feet of lumber did he buy?

575. In constructing a cabinet a contractor ordered the following materials: How many board feet of lumber in the order?

4 pcs. 1″ net × 3½″ × 14′
11 pcs. ¾″ × 11¼″ × 12′
16 pcs. ¼″ × 5¼″ × 18′
12 pcs. 1¼″ net × 4″ net × 12′

The term "net" indicates that the lumber is to be finished the exact size as given. Therefore, the stock must be figured the next size above the dimensions required. In this case 4″ net will have to be made from 6″ board, 1¼″ net is made from a 1½″ piece of stock, etc.

576. How many board feet of lumber are there in:

5 pcs. ⅝″ × 3⅜″ × 38″
18 pcs. ½″ × 6¼″ × 52″
4 pcs. ¾″ × 10⅛″ × 18″

These pieces were used in constructing a small cabinet.

577. After a cabinet-making student had completed a project he reported that he had used the following materials. Find the number of board feet of lumber in his bill.

14 pcs. ¾″ × 5½″ × 26″
18 pcs. ¾″ × 7¼″ × 42″
10 pcs. 2½″ × 2½″ × 30″
8 pcs. ¾″ × 9¼″ × 48″

578. For the lumber required in making a chair the worker used:

4 pcs. 1½″ × 1½″ × 8″
32 pcs. ¾″ × 1½″ × 32″
6 pcs. ¾″ × 2⅝″ × 44″

How many board feet were there in these pieces? When pieces are small it is easier to convert all to the square inch content, add together and then divide by 144.

579. How many board feet of lumber are there in the following pieces?

26 pcs. 1¾″ × 1¾″ × 36″
4 pcs. ¾″ × 8″ net × 48″
2 pcs. ⅝″ × 4⅝″ × 24″

580. In constructing eight cabinets in a woodshop a student used the following materials:

22 pcs. 1¾″ × 3½″ × 28″
16 pcs. 9⁄16″ × 11⅜″ × 14″
6 pcs. 1¹⁄16″ × 5⅝″ × 32″
4 pcs. 1¼″ × 6⅛″ × 12″

How many board feet of lumber are there in the list?

HOW LUMBER IS PURCHASED

The basis for figuring the cost of lumber is in terms of 1,000 bd. ft., usually written MB.F., or $32.50 per M, $45.00 per M, etc.

The price varies according to the kind, grade, and size of the lumber. Naturally, hardwoods cost the most. A piece of lumber that is not clear, but has knots or other imperfections, has not the same value as a clear piece. Again, the short lengths of lumber are less expensive, although often they may be clear stock. Because of these variations it is not possible to find the total footage of a lumber bill and compute the cost by figuring it at one price per MB.F.

This problem essentially belongs to the lumberman, but a basic knowledge of this subject is worth while for the carpenter, as he is often required to estimate the cost of a number of board feet of lumber in an order.

Problems

To find the cost of a given number of board feet of lumber *multiply the total number of board feet by its cost per* 1,000 *and point off three places.* Fractional parts of a board foot are counted a full board foot.

LUMBER COSTS

BOARD FEET TO COST	$\dfrac{bd.ft. \quad \$}{1000} = COST$	$P = No. of pieces$
		$T = Thickness$
LUMBER BILL TO BOARD FEET TO DOLLARS AND CENTS	$\dfrac{Pc \, T'' W'' L'\$}{12 \quad 1000} = COST$	$W = Width$
	$\dfrac{T'' W'' L' \$}{12 \quad 1000} = COST$	$L = Length$
	$\dfrac{Pc \, T'' W'' L'' \$}{144 \quad 1000} COST$	$bd.ft. = board feet$
		$\$ = dollars per M.$

CHART VII

581. What is the cost of 564 bd. ft. of lumber at $33 per M?

582. In listing a lumber bill a contractor needed 245 bd. ft. of No. 1 common Douglas fir and 168 bd. ft. of redwood. What is the cost of the lumber if fir is worth $35.00 and redwood $72.50?

It is customary to state the cost of lumber as $34.00, $37.50, $29.00 etc., without stating that this means per M bd. ft.

583. In taking off a bill of materials for a house a contractor listed the following items:

22 pcs. 2″ × 8″ × 16′
47 pcs. 1″ × 6″ × 16′
45 pcs. 1″ × 10″ × 20′
66 pcs. 2″ × 6″ × 26′

What is the lumber worth at $36 per M?

584. In repairing a residence the carpenter ordered

> 560 bd. ft. of 1″ × 6″
> 28 pcs. 2″ × 10″ × 18′
> 134 pcs. 2″ × 3″ × 10′
> 98 pcs. 1″ × 4″ × 14′

What is the cost of this material if the lumber is worth $29.50?

585. A material list for a cabinet included these items:

> 18 pcs. ¾″ × 6½″ × 12′
> 4 pcs. 1¼″ × 3½″ × 16′
> 4 pcs. 1½″ × 5¼″ × 18′
> 4 pcs. 1″ × 12 ″ × 20′

Finish lumber is worth $110.   What did this lumber cost?

586. In figuring the material for a set of shelving for a store the contractor found that he needed the following items:

> 84 pcs. ¾″ × 9½″ × 18′
> 56 pcs. ¾″ × 10″ net × 14′
> 28 pcs. 1″ net × 4″ net × 20′

What did this material cost at $88 per M?

587. Mahogany is worth $246 per M.   What will the material cost for a library table that requires the following items?

> 4 legs 2½″ × 2½″ × 30″
> 2 end rails ¾″ × 6½″ × 28″
> 2 side rails ¾″ × 6½″ × 42″
> 1 shelf ⅝″ × 10½″ × 48″
> 3 pcs. for the top 1¼″ × 12″ × 48″

588. An oak piano bench required 1 piece ¾″ × 3½″ × 14′ and one piece 1″ net × 8″ net × 12′.   What did this material cost at $364 per M?

589. An interior finish job required 780 lin. ft. of ¾″ × 2½″ casing; 348 lin. ft. ⅝″ × 3½″ base-board; 68 lin. ft. ¾″ × 3¼″ apron stock; and 12 pieces ¾″ × 12″ × 18′ shelving.   What did this material cost if the price list on lumber showed finish stock to be worth $84?

590. The exterior finish of a house required 1,450 bd. ft. of rustic which was worth $68 per M.   What did this amount of stock cost?

591. The roof for an English house required 2,648 bd. ft. of 1″ × 4″ sheathing.   What is this worth at $34?

592. A house required 680 bd. ft. of hardwood flooring.   What did it cost at $210 per M?

593. A motor court contained 16 units.   Each unit required 3,450 bd. ft. of lumber.   What did the lumber cost for the job if the lumberman estimated the bill at an average of $31.50 per M?

594. In putting in the forms for a foundation a contractor ordered 1,500 bd. ft. of $1'' \times 6''$ stock and 250 lin. ft. of $2'' \times 4''$. At $29 per M what did this material cost?

595. A composition roof required 66 pieces $2'' \times 8'' \times 24'$ for rafters and 1,680 bd. ft. of $1'' \times 6''$ stock for sheathing. At $38.50 per M what did this material cost?

SECTION II

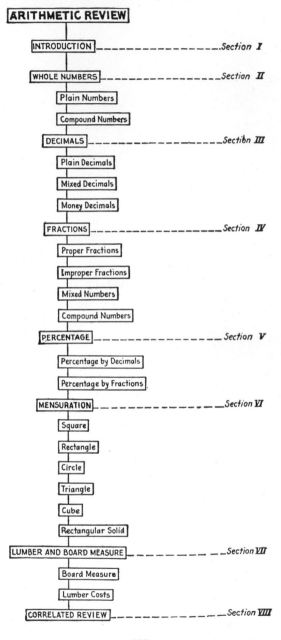

ARITHMETIC REVIEW

INTRODUCTION — — — — — — — — — — — — — — — Section *I*

WHOLE NUMBERS — — — — — — — — — — — — — — Section *II*

Plain Numbers

Compound Numbers

DECIMALS — — — — — — — — — — — — — — — — Section *III*

Plain Decimals

Mixed Decimals

Money Decimals

FRACTIONS — — — — — — — — — — — — — — — — Section *IV*

Proper Fractions

Improper Fractions

Mixed Numbers

Compound Numbers

PERCENTAGE — — — — — — — — — — — — — — — Section *V*

Percentage by Decimals

Percentage by Fractions

MENSURATION — — — — — — — — — — — — — — — Section *VI*

Square

Rectangle

Circle

Triangle

Cube

Rectangular Solid

LUMBER AND BOARD MEASURE — — — — — — — — — — Section *VII*

Board Measure

Lumber Costs

CORRELATED REVIEW — — — — — — — — — — — — — Section *VIII*

150

CHAPTER VIII

ARITHMETICAL REVIEW

I. INTRODUCTION

The basis for all mathematical calculations is an intelligent understanding of the fundamentals of arithmetic. The principles involved in these fundamentals are learned in the lower grades of school. Experience has proved, however, that many craftsmen, although skilled in the use of their hand-tools, have difficulty in making their daily calculations. This is due partly to lack of practice and drill. The purpose of this chapter is to provide material that will give a brief review of these basic principles.

The following facts concerning numbers are worth noting.

a. All numbers can be classified into two types: abstract and concrete. An abstract number is a plain number without a name, as 5, ¼, .5. A concrete number is one with a name, as 8″, 4 studs, 12 rafters.

b. Addition is the process of finding the sum of several numbers. If concrete numbers are used they must be alike, as adding 9″ to 10″; 4 joists to 16 joists; 6 doors to 14 doors.

c. Subtraction is a process of finding the difference between two like numbers.

d. Multiplication is a rapid process of addition.

e. Division is a rapid process of subtraction.

f. Reduction is a process of changing one number to another number without changing the real value, as changing ¼ to .25; 18″ to 1′ 6″.

All mathematical operations in Chaps. II to V, inclusive, can be classified into five groups; namely, addition, subtraction, multiplication, division, and reduction. In this chapter, also, these operations have been applied to the following types of numbers with their subdivisions: whole numbers, decimals, fractions, and percentage. The key chart outlines these divisions. The subjects of mensuration and board measure introduce the use of simple formulas as applied to the geometrical figures that are used in carpentry.

151

The review material can be used in several ways. It may serve as a means of "brushing up" a person's mathematical ability. This can be done by working one or two problems under each heading. A more thorough review can be accomplished, of course, by working all of the problems. Lastly the examples that have been solved are blocked off so that they may readily be found. A study of any one of these problems will indicate quickly the methods to follow in solving similar problems.

Each section of this review corresponds to the same numbered chapter (Sec. II is based on Chap. II, etc.). This will make it easy for reference. Each section is preceded by an outline chart showing the general arrangement.

II. WHOLE NUMBERS[1]

Whole numbers are numerals that do not contain decimals, fractions, per cent, etc. They are read by orders, as units, tens, hundreds, thousands, tens of thousands, hundreds of thousands, millions, etc.; for example, 9,784 is read nine thousand, seven hundred eighty-four; 34,921 is read thirty-four thousand, nine hundred twenty-one; 276,341 is read two hundred seventy-six thousand, three hundred forty-one. No "and" is used in the reading of whole numbers as its use indicates the location of the decimal point when reading decimals.

Plain whole numbers are numerals that do not contain units of more than one denomination, as 6, 27, 125, 3 ft., 11 students.

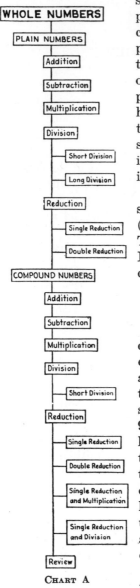

CHART A

[1] See p. 19.

Compound whole numbers are numerals that contain units of more than one denomination as 2 ft. 6 in., 29' 11'', 3 lb. 9 oz., 2 gross 3 doz., etc.

Plain Numbers: 1, 2, 10, 20, 100, etc.

ADDITION

Example: Add 376, 234, 128, and 859.

3 7 6	In order to be sure that the answer is correct, it is advisable
2 3 4	to add each column of figures twice, once upward and once
1 2 8	downward, thus: $9 + 8 + 4 + 6 = 27$ and $6 + 4 + 8 +$
8 5 9	$9 = 27$. The 7 is written down and the 2 added into the
1 5 9 7	next column.

Problems

The following four problems contain every possible combination that might occur in adding two figures. With sufficient practice the sums can be added mentally, reading off the 48 answers in about 25 seconds. Practice adding these and hand them in added correctly.

1. 7 2 7 1 9 6 8 4 5 7 6 5
   3 5 4 1 1 2 6 4 6 2 9 3

2. 5 1 6 5 8 8 6 9 5 1 4 5
   5 8 6 4 8 2 1 9 8 3 6 4

3. 7 3 6 3 7 4 9 3 8 1 5 4
   9 2 7 3 8 2 3 6 4 7 7 3

4. 4 8 4 2 7 9 2 3 4 5 1 1
   6 9 9 1 7 2 2 8 1 9 5 6

5. Add the following numbers: 128, 36, 45, 32, 98, and 876.
6. Find the sum of 8632, 9862, 5879, 7632, and 2934.
7. Add 4763, 7639, 1122, 9999, 7632.
8. Find the sum of 56, 78, 35, 43, 69, 77, 84, and 97.
9. How much is $4763 + 9876 + 3492 + 8632 + 7849 + 7837$?
10. Add 7692716, 4634728, 8724631, 9763416.

SUBTRACTION

Example: Subtract 897 from 1683.

```
1 6 8 3
  8 9 7
  7 8 6
```

One method of subtraction says 7 from 13 = 6 and then takes 1 away from 8 saying 9 from 17 = 8, etc. Another method says 7 from 13 = 6 and then adds one to 9 saying 10 from 18 = 8, etc.

A third method says 7 plus what number = 13? *Ans.* 6; and then adds 1 to 9 and says 10 plus what number = 18, answer 8, etc.

Problems

11. Subtract 38629 from 73420.

12. Subtract 98601 from 897999.

13. Take 62439 from 562498.

14. Solve the following examples in subtraction:

```
54    43    63    34    25
35    37    37    18    17
```

15. Subtract the following:

```
44    35    46    97    87
29    26    37    89    69
```

16. Subtract 354152 from 727196.

17. How much is 846564 less 649365?

18. Take 528589 from 670088.

19. Subtract 3900796 from 7084080

20. Take 543927 from 773695.

MULTIPLICATION

Example: Multiply 3762 by 125.

```
      3 7 6 2
        1 2 5
    1 8 8 1 0
    7 5 2 4
  3 7 6 2
  4 7 0 2 5 0
```

The 5 and 2 are multiplied together giving 10. The 0 is placed under the 5 and the 1 added into the next multiplication, as 5 × 6 = 30 + 1 = 31. The 1 is written under the 6 and the 3 carried to the next multiplication, etc.

Problems

21. Multiply 9635 by 825.
22. Find the product of 1934 and 2762.
23. How much is 6234 times 568?
24. Multiply 7273 by 1212.
25. Find the product of 3629 and 758.

When ciphers occur, this process may be shortened.

Example: Multiply 7644 by 50200.

7 6 4 4 5 0 2 0 0 ——————— 1 5 2 8 8 3 8 2 2 0 ——————— 3 8 3 7 2 8 8 0 0	This method saves the trouble of multiplying through by ciphers. When multiplying by the 2, it is important that the product of 2 × 4 or 8 be placed under the 2. Likewise, when multiplying by the 5 where the first product is 20, the 0 must be placed under the 5.

26. Multiply 1075 by 308.
27. Find the product of 762 and 9700.
28. How much is 7835 × 2050?
29. Multiply 97890 by 560.
30. How much is 70690 × 308?
31. Multiply 8763 by 9800.
32. Find the product of 7076 and 807.
33. Multiply 9878 by 250.
34. Multiply 8620 by 309.
35. Find the product of 70809 and 9090.

DIVISION

Short Division.

Example: Divide 2231 by 5.

5)2 2 3 1 ——————— 4 4 6⅕	The 5 is divided into 22, going 4 times with 2 left over; 5 is then divided into 23, etc. The remainder of 1 is placed over the divisor 5 making the answer 446⅕.

Problems

36. Divide 144 by 4.
37. How much is 266 divided by 5?

38. How many times is 8 contained in 7053.
39. Divide 984004 by 9.
40. Divide 763200 by 7.

Long Division.

Example: Divide 23570 by 62.

$\underset{\overline{}}{3\ 8\ 0}\ \ ^{5}\!\!/_{31}$ $6\ 2\overline{)\ 2\ 3\ 5\ 7\ 0}$ $\underline{1\ 8\ 6}$ $\underline{4\ 9\ 7}$ $4\ 9\ 6$ $\dfrac{10}{62} = \dfrac{5}{31}$	The 62 is divided into 235, going 3 times with 49 left over. The 7 is brought down and 62 is divided into 497, going 8 times with 1 left over. The 0 is brought down and since 62 will not divide into 10, a cipher is placed in the answer to show that it does not divide. The 10 placed over 62 gives $^{10}\!\!/_{62}$ which is reduced to $^{5}\!\!/_{31}$, making the answer $380^{5}\!\!/_{31}$.

41. Divide 1287 by 24.
42. How much is 29284 divided by 27?
43. How much is 697175 divided by 1765?
44. Divide 762534 by 729.
45. Divide 74520 by 648.

REDUCTION

Single Reduction—Higher to Lower Denomination.

Example: Change 15 ft. to inches.

$1\ 5'$ $\underline{1\ 2''} = 1'$ $3\ 0$ $1\ 5$ $\overline{1\ 8\ 0''}$	If there are $12''$ in $1'$ then in $15'$ there are 15 times as many inches as in $1'$, or $15 \times 12'' = 180''$. (Consult tables in Chap. IX when necessary.)

Problems

46. Reduce 25 ft. to inches.
47. Change 52 sq. yd. to square feet.
48. Reduce 5 sq. ft. to square inches.
49. Change 29 doz. to number of pieces.
50. Reduce 24 cu. ft. to cubic inches.

Single Reduction—Lower to Higher Denominations.
Example: Change 209 in. to feet.

$$1\ 7\ 5\!\!/_{12}\ \text{ft.}$$

$$1\ 2'')\overline{2\ 0\ 9''}$$

$$\underline{1\ 2}$$

$$8\ 9$$

$$\underline{8\ 4}$$

$$\underline{5}$$

$$12$$

If there are 12'' in 1', then there are as many feet in 209'' as there are 12's contained in 209'', or 209 ÷ 12 = 17$5\!\!/_{12}$ ft.

---

51. Change 144'' to feet.
52. How many square yards are there in 3,495 sq. ft.
53. Reduce 432 sq. in. to square feet.
54. Reduce 621 cu. ft. to cubic yards.
55. Change 262 pieces to dozens.

Double Reduction—Higher to Lower Denominations.
Example: Change 2 gross to number of pieces.

---

2 gross

1 2 doz. = 1 gross

2 4 doz.

1 2 pcs. = 1 dozen

4 8

2 4

2 8 8 pcs.

If there are 12 doz. in 1 gross, then in 2 gross there are 2 × 12 = 24 doz. And if there are 12 pieces in 1 doz., then in 24 doz., there are 12 × 24 = 288.

---

56. Change 5 gross to number of pieces.
57. Reduce 2 yd. to inches.
58. Reduce 7 gal. to number of pints.
59. Change 8 yd. to inches.
60. Change 2 cu. yd. to cubic inches.

Double Reduction—Lower to Higher Denomination.

Example: Change 864 pieces to number of gross.

pcs.   7 2 doz.
1 2)8 6 4 pcs.
    8 4
    ─────
     2 4
     2 4
     ─────
 	
doz.   6 gross
1 2)7 2 doz.
    7 2
	If there are 12 pieces in 1 doz., then there are as many dozen in 864 pieces as there are 12's contained in 864, or 864 ÷ 12 = 72 doz.
	If there are 12 doz. in 1 gross, then there are as many gross in 72 doz. as 72 ÷ 12 = 6 gross.

61. Reduce 1,008 pieces to number of gross.
62. Change 144″ to yards.
63. Reduce 96 pt. to gallons.
64. How many yards are there in 288 in.?
65. Reduce 46,656 cu. in. to cubic yards.

Compound Numbers: 1′ 1″, 1′ 2″, 1′ 3″, 1′ 4″ etc.

ADDITION

Example: Add 16′ 2″, 8′ 4″, and 29′ 11″.

16′ 2″ 8′ 4″ 29′ 11″ ───── 54′ 5″	Adding 2″ + 4″ + 11″ gives 17″. But 17″ = 1′ and 5″. Hence, 5″ is written down and the 1′ is added into the next column of feet giving 6′ + 8′ + 9′ + 1′ = 24′. The 4′ is written down and 2 added into the next column giving 2′ + 1′ + 2′ = 5′.

Problems

66. Add 5′ 2″, 7′ 6″, 3′ 2″, and 4′ 1″.
67. Add 12′ 7″, 16′ 9″, 21′ 3″, and 8′ 2″.
68. Add 2′ 7″, 0′ 9″, 1′ 8″, 5′ 6″, 3′ 3″, and 6′ 4″.
69. Add 12′ 9″, 15′ 7″, 16′ 4″, 9′ 2″, 11′ 1″, and 14′ 8″.
70. Add 27′ 9″, 35′ 4″, 23′ 2″, 15′ 7″, 40′ 6″, and 17′ 11″.

SUBTRACTION

Example: Subtract 10′ 6″ from 19′ 5″.

19′ 5″ 10′ 6″ ————— 8′ 11″	Since the 6″ cannot be subtracted from 5″, it is necessary to borrow 1′ (or 12″) from the 19′ and add this 12″ into the 5″, making 17″. Then 6″ can be taken from 17″, leaving 11″. The 10′ is then subtracted from 18′, leaving 8′.

71. Subtract 6′ 7″ from 10′ 11″.
72. Subtract 9′ 6″ from 15′ 4″.
73. Subtract 15′ 9″ from 18′ 6″.
74. Subtract 29′ 8″ from 35′ 0″.
75. Subtract 54′ 5″ from 60′ 6″.

MULTIPLICATION

Example: Multiply 9′ 5″ by 5.

9′ 5″ 5 ————— 47′ 1″	Multiplying 5″ by 5 gives 25″, which equals 2′ and 1″. The 1″ is written down and the 2′ added into the product of the 9′ × 5, or 9′ × 5 = 45 + 2 = 47′.

Multiplication of two compound numbers such as 3′ 2″ by 5′ 7″ is treated in the section on reduction of compound numbers.

76. Multiply 3′ 2″ by 3.
77. Multiply 12′ 6″ by 5.
78. Multiply 18′ 7″ by 3.
79. Multiply 25′ 6″ by 12.
80. Multiply 35′ 8″ by 16.

DIVISION

Short Division.
Example: Divide 8′ 6″ by 6.

6)8′ 6″ ————— 1′ 5″	Dividing 8′ by 6 gives 1′ and 2′ left over. The 2′ is reduced to 24″ and added to the 6″, making 30″ to be divided by 6, or 30″ ÷ 6 = 5″.

Division of two compound numbers such as 16′ 9″ divided by 3′ 4″ is treated in the section on reduction of compound numbers.

81. 6′ 9″ by 3.
82. Divide 12′ 6″ by 5.
83. Divide 28′ 6″ by 9.
84. Divide 60′ 0″ by 8.
85. Divide 133′ 10″ by 11.

REDUCTION

Single Reduction—Higher to Lower Denomination.
Example: Change 10′ 6″ to inches.

10′ 6″ 12″ = 1 ft. $\overline{}$ 120″ 6″ (added) $\overline{}$ 126″	The 10′ is multiplied by 12″, converting it to 120″. Then the 6″ is added, making 126″.

Problems

86. Reduce 15′ 3″ to inches.

87. Change 27′ 11″ to inches.

88. Reduce 52 sq. yd. 4 sq. ft. to square feet.

89. How many square inches are there in 3 sq. ft. 71 sq. in.?

90. Change 18 doz. 9 pieces to pieces.

Single Reduction—Lower to Higher Denominations.
Example: Change 41″ to feet.

3′
 12″)41″
   36
 $\overline{}$
   5″
 Ans. 3′ 5″
	Dividing 41″ by 12″ (equal to 1′) gives 3′ and 5″. It should be noted that the 5″ could be placed over 12″ giving the fraction of $\frac{5}{12}′$, or an answer of $3\frac{5}{12}′$. This type of problem was worked under reduction of plain numbers.

91. Change 67″ to feet.

92. Reduce 4,496 sq. ft. to square yards.

93. How many cubic yards are there in 63 cu. ft.?

94. Change 364 pieces to dozens.

95. Reduce 528 sq. in. to square feet.

Double Reduction—Higher to Lower Denomination.
Example: Reduce 2 yd. 1 ft. 7 in. to inches.

2 yd. 3 ft. = 1 yd. $\overline{}$ 6 ft. 1 ft. (added) $\overline{}$ 7 ft.	7′ 12″ = 1 ft. $\overline{}$ 84″ 7″ (added) $\overline{}$ 91″	Reduction from 2 yd. to 7′ and then from 7′ to 91″ involves two reductions worked the same as single reduction.

96. Reduce 8 yd. 2 ft. 9 in. to inches.

97. Change 3 gross 5 doz. 7 pieces to pieces.

98. Change 7 gal. 3 qt. 1 pt. to pints.

99. Reduce 5 yd. 1 ft. 11 in. to inches.

100. How many cubic inches are there in 1 cu. yd. 2 cu. ft. 3 cu. in.?

Double Reduction—Lower to Higher Denominations.

Example: Reduce 242″ to yards, feet, and inches.

20 ft. 12″)242″ 3′)20′ $\underline{24}$ $\overline{6\ \text{yd. }2'}$ $\overline{2''}$	Reducing 242″ to feet gives 20′ and 2″ left over. Reducing 20′ to yards gives 6 yd. and 2′ left over. Hence, *Ans.* 6 yd. 2 ft. 2 in.

101. Reduce 371″ to yards, feet, and inches.

102. Change 305 pieces to gross, dozen, and pieces.

103. Change 59 pt. to gallons, quarts, and pints.

104. Reduce 170 in. to yards, feet, and inches.

105. How many cubic yards, cubic feet and cubic inches are there in 95,045 cu. in.?

Single Reduction and Multiplication—Higher to Lower Denominations.

Example: Multiply 5′ 5″ by 7′ 9″

5′ 5″	7′ 9″	65″
$\underline{12'' = 1'}$	$\underline{12'' = 1'}$	$\underline{93''}$
60″	84″	195
$\underline{5''}$ (added)	$\underline{9''}$ (added)	585
65″	93″	6045 sq. in.

The 5′ 5″ is reduced to inches, equaling 65″; also the 7′ 9″, equaling 93″. The 65″ and 93″ are then multiplied, giving 6,045 sq. in.

106. Multiply 7′ 5″ by 2′ 7″.

107. Multiply 6′ 3″ by 12′ 4″.

108. Multiply 7′ 4″ by 15′ 8″.

109. Multiply 12′ 7″ by 18′ 8″.

110. Multiply 20′ 5″ by 30′ 3″.

Single Reduction and Division—Higher to Lower Denominations.
Example: Divide 12′ 10″ by 1′ 2″.

12′ 10″	1″ 2″	11 times
12″ = 1′	12″	14″)154″
24	12″	14
12	2″ (added)	14
144″	14″	14
10″ (added)		
154″		

Each length is reduced to inches and then the short length is divided into the longer length, going 11 times.

111. Divide 6′ 3″ by 1′ 3″.
112. Divide 12′ 6″ by 2′ 6″.
113. Divide 4′ 2″ by 2′ 1″.
114. Divide 18′ 9″ by 3′ 9″.
115. Divide 31′ 3″ by 6′ 3″.

REVIEW

116. Add 68′, 19′, 37′, 17′, 9′, 24′, 40′, 6′, 7′, and 15′.
117. Subtract 98732 from 1075400.
118. Change 984″ to feet.
119. Reduce 15 doz. 3 pieces to pieces.
120. Reduce 15 yd. 2 ft. to feet.
121. Change 78 pieces to dozens and pieces.
122. Reduce 982″ to feet and inches.
123. Add 6′ 3″, 9′ 5″, 15′ 1″, 29′ 7″, 14′ 6″, and 18′ 3″.
124. Change 5 doz. 7 pieces to pieces.
125. Multiply 17′ 3″ by 6.
126. Multiply 5′ 3″ by 9′ 5″.
127. Divide 8′ 9″ by 7.
128. Divide 75′ 0″ by 1′ 3″.
129. Subtract 8′ 9″ from 11′ 8″.
130. Change 54 ft. to yards.
131. Change 111 pieces to dozens and pieces.
132. Multiply 15″ by 67 pieces, and change to feet and inches.
133. Change 17 yd. to feet.
134. Change 1,152 pieces to gross, dozens, and pieces.
135. Reduce 5 cu. ft. to cubic inches.
136. Change 5 yd. 6 in. to inches.
137. Change 12 lb. 4 oz. to ounces and divide by 7 oz.
138. Divide 400 lin. ft. by 11 in.
139. Change 1,584 sq. ft. to square yards.
140. Subtract 28′ 9″ from 35′ 5″.

III. DECIMALS[1]

Decimals are numerals written at the right of the decimal point to represent values less than 1. They are read by orders as tenths, hundredths, thousandths, ten-thousandths, millionths, etc.; for example: .6875 is read six thousand eight hundred seventy-five ten-thousandths. The decimals commonly used are of three kinds, plain decimals, mixed decimals and money decimals.

DECIMALS

PLAIN DECIMALS

MIXED DECIMALS

MONEY DECIMALS

Addition

Subtraction

Multiplication

Division

Short Division

Long Division

Reduction

Single Reduction

REVIEW

CHART B

Plain decimals, or pure decimals, are numerals written only at the right of the decimal point and always represented values less than 1, as, .257 read two hundred fifty-seven thousandths.

Mixed decimals are made up of plain numbers and plain decimals or numerals written at both the right and the left of the decimal point, as, 345.67 read three hundred forty-five and sixty-seven hundredths.

Money decimals are mixed decimals written in terms of one denomination, dollars. In general usage they are read like compound numbers thus $12.45 is read twelve dollars and forty-five cents ($12-45¢) though technically it would be read as twelve and forty-five hundredths dollars. Carried to the third decimal place money decimals are also read as dollars, cents, and mills, thus $1.237 is read one dollar, twenty-three cents, and seven mills.

Plain decimals: .1 .2 .3 .01 .02 .001 .002 .0001, etc.
Mixed decimals: 1.1 2.2 10.01 20.02 100.001 200.002.
Money decimals: $0.01 $0.2 $0.03 $0.10 $0.20 $1.01 $1.02 etc.

[1] See p. 45.

ADDITION

Example: Add 62.34, 89.216, 702.3, and 620.1

```
   6 2. 3 4    Always keep the decimal points under each
   8 9. 2 1 6  other and add the same as with whole numbers.
   7 0 2. 3
   6 2 0. 1
 1 4 7 3. 9 5 6
```

Problems

141. Add 6.297, 73.61, .062, 396.20, .007, and 76.32.
142. Add .006, .053, .001, 100.01, 9.99, and 76.325.
143. Find the sum of $623. + $87.25 + $9,600.21 + $83.29.
144. How much is 1.006 + .0053 + .62 + .73 + 1.08 + 1.005 + 1.96.
145. Find the sum of 1.2 cu. yd. + 4.3 cu. yd. + 7.6 cu. yd. + 8.72 cu. yd.

SUBTRACTION

Example: Subtract 70.795 from 81.08

```
   8 1. 0 8    Always keep the decimal points under each other
   7 0. 7 9 5  and subtract the same as with whole numbers.
   1 0. 2 8 5
```

146. Subtract .090 from 1.117.
147. How much is 1.07 less .999?
148. Take away $5.065 from $7.05.
149. Subtract $896.23 from $995.105.
150. Take away 995623.889 from 1076512.69.

MULTIPLICATION

Example: Multiply 25.3 by .12.

```
  25.3   Point off    Set the numbers down and multiply the same
   .12   1 + 2 = 3    as for whole numbers.  Point off from the
   506   decimal      right as many decimal places in the answer
   253   places       as there are total decimal places in both of the
 3.036                numbers to be multiplied.
```

151. Multiply 62.31 by 2.35.
152. Find the product of 18.25 and .65.
153. Multiply .2972 by .029.

154. Multiply 19.25 by 45.875.

155. How much is 709.037 by 220.73?

In multiplying a whole number (25) by a decimal (.12) the answer (3.00) is less than the whole number. Also one decimal multiplied by another decimal (.12 × .14 = .0168) gives an answer less than either, but two mixed decimals, give an answer larger than either (4.2 × 2.1 = 8.82).

DIVISION

Short Division.

Example: Divide 19.44 by .6.

.6)19.44 — 32.4	Point off 2 − 1 = 1 decimal place.	The number of decimal places in the dividend (19.44) or 2 places, minus the number of decimal places in the divisor, (.6) or 1 place, gives the number of places to point off in the answer.

If the problem were .06)1944. the situation would call for pointing off 0 − 2 places which is impossible. So ciphers are added thus .06)1944.00 and the problem then calls for pointing off 2 − 2 = 0 places giving an answer 32400.

156. Divide 893.64 by .6.

157. Divide .1728 by 8.

158. Divide 52.8 by .05.

159. How much is 187.63 ÷ .007?

160. Find the quotient of 793.64 ÷ .09.

Another method of pointing off is that of moving the decimal point.

The divisor decimal point is always moved completely to the right, making the divisor a whole number. *The dividend decimal point must* then *be moved to the right exactly the same number of places that the divisor point was moved. The dividend decimal point is then moved straight down into the answer.* This method requires that the figures in the answer be kept in their proper positions below the figures in the dividend. Either method may be used in working Problems 156 to 160.

Long Division.

Example: Divide 19.44 by 1.2.

16.2 1.2)19.44 12 — 74 72 — 24 24 — x	Point off 2 − 1 = 1 decimal place.	The number of decimal places in the dividend minus the number in the divisor gives the number of decimal places to point off in the answer.

If the problem were .12)1944. the situation would call for pointing off 0 − 2 decimal places which is impossible; consequently ciphers have to be added thus .12)1944.00 which calls for pointing off 2 − 2 = 0 places giving an answer of 16200.

161. Divide 52.80 by 1.2.

162. Divide 20.736 by 144.

163. How much is 10.560 ÷ .024?

164. Divide .196 by 1.6.

165. Find the quotient of 3.99 ÷ .28.

Another method of pointing off is that of moving decimal points.

The divisor decimal point must always be moved completely to the right, making the divisor a whole number. *The dividend decimal point must* then *be moved to the right exactly the same number of places that the divisor point was moved. The dividend decimal point is then moved straight up into the answer.* This method requires that the figures in the answer be kept in their proper positions above the figures in the dividend. Either method may be used in working Problems 161 to 165.

REDUCTION

Single Reduction—Higher to Lower Denominations.

Example: Change 2.50 M bd. ft. to board feet.

2 . 5 0 M bd. ft. ___1 0 0 0 bd. ft. = 1 M bd. ft. 2 5 0 0 . 0 0 bd. ft. RULE: Move decimal point 3 places to the right.	The answer can be written without computation by simply moving the decimal point three places to the right thus: 2.50 M bd. ft. = 2,500 bd. ft.

166. Reduce 12.50 M bd. ft. to board feet.

167. Change .250 M bd. ft. to board feet.

168. How many board feet are there in 6.75 M bd. ft.?

169. Reduce 25.5 M bd. ft. to board feet.

170. Reduce 569. M bd. ft. to board feet.

Example: At $0.235 per board feet what is the price per M bd. ft.?

Multiply by 1,000 as illustrated above, or write by inspection thus: $0.235 per board feet = $235.00 per M bd. ft. RULE: Move decimal point 3 places to the right.	If 1 bd. ft. costs $0.235, 1 M bd. ft. (1,000 bd. ft.) will cost 1,000 times as much as 1 bd. ft. or 1,000 × $0.235 = $235.00.

171. Change $0.048 per board feet to dollars per M bd. ft.

172. Reduce $0.0725 per board feet to price per M bd. ft.

173. How much will 1 M bd. ft. cost if 1 bd. ft. costs $0.0375?

174. At $0.0295 per board feet what will 1 M bd. ft. cost?

175. Reduce $0.364 per board feet to dollars per M bd. ft.

Example: At $0.29 per piece what will 1 doz. cost?

$0.29 per piece 　12 pcs. = 1 doz. 　　58 　29 [$3.48 per dozen	If 1 pc. costs $0.29, a dozen, or 12 pcs., will cost 12 × $0.29 = $3.48

176. Reduce $0.41 per piece to price per dozen.

177. Change $0.095 per piece to price per box of 50.

178. How much will 1 doz. cost if one article costs $0.675?

179. Find the cost of 50 if one costs $0.0225

180. Change $2.625 to price per dozen.

Single Reduction—Lower to Higher Denominations.

Example: Change 3,750 bd. ft. to M bd. ft.

bd. ft.　　　　3 . 7 5 M bd. ft. 1 0 0 0.)3 7 5 0 . 0 0 bd. ft. 　　　　3 0 0 0 　　　　7 5 0 0 　　　　7 0 0 0 　　　　　5 0 0 0 　　　　　5 0 0 0	The answer can be written without computation by simply moving the decimal point three places to the left; thus, 3,750 bd. ft. = 3.75 M bd. ft.

Rule: Move decimal point 3 places to the left.

Problems

181. Change 5,550 bd. ft. to M bd. ft.

182. Reduce 17,295 bd. ft. to M bd. ft.

183. How many M bd. ft. are there in 8,075 bd ft.?

184. Change 620 bd. ft. to M bd. ft.

185. Reduce 895,700 bd. ft. to M bd. ft.

Example: Change $45 per M bd. ft. to price per board foot.

Divide by 1,000 as shown above or better write by inspection; thus, $45.00 per M bd. ft. = $0.045 per board foot Rule: Move decimal point 3 places to the left.	If 1 M bd. ft. or (1,000 bd. ft.) costs $45.00, 1 bd. ft. will cost as much as $45.00 ÷ 1,000 = $.045.

186. Change $62.50 per M bd. ft. to price per board foot.
187. Reduce $84 per M bd. ft. to price per board foot.
188. How much will 1 bd. ft. cost if one M bd. ft. costs $246?
189. Reduce $110 per M bd. ft. to price per board foot.
190. Change $364 per M bd. ft. to price per board foot.

Example: At $8.52 per dozen what is the price each?

.71 each
12)$8.52 per dozen
pcs.
  84
  12
  12
  x
	If 1 dozen or 12 pcs. costs $8.52, 1 pc. will cost as much as $8.52 divided by 12 or $0.71.

191. Change $3.48 per dozen to price each.
192. Reduce $1.75 per box of 50 to price each.
193. How much will one article cost if a dozen costs $54?
194. Change $42 per dozen to price each.
195. Reduce $2.82 per dozen to price each.

Review

196. Add .007, 76.95, .09, 9865. and 18.75.
197. Multiply 76.53 by .25.
198. Divide 8.764 by 16.
199. Subtract 93.62 from 184.50.
200. Reduce 9.25 M bd. ft. to board feet.
201. Divide 1723 by .09.
202. Change $67.50 per M bd. ft. to price per board foot.
203. Reduce 8,976 bd. ft. to M bd. ft.
204. Divide $10.91 by 144.
205. Reduce $9.72 per dozen to price each.
206. Change $0.0475 per board foot to price per M bd. ft.
207. Divide $86.00 by 1.5.
208. Change $0.34 per piece to price per dozen.
209. Subtract $176.98 from $865.43.
210. If a box of 50 bolts costs $2.39 what will one bolt cost?
211. Reduce $120.00 per M bd. ft. to price per board foot.
212. Add $1,763.25, $85.07, $96.39, $84.72, $0.25, and $0.79.
213. Change $18.95 per dozen to price each.
214. Multiply $79.86 by 49.
215. Reduce $9.57 for 50 articles to price each.

IV. FRACTIONS[1]

Whenever any number is divided into equal parts the parts are called fractions.

A fraction is always made up of two numbers, one written above the other with a horizontal line between. The upper number is called the numerator and the lower one the denominator as $\frac{5 \text{ numerator}}{10 \text{ denominator}}$. In this example the whole has been divided into 10 parts and the 5 indicates the number of these parts that are being used. The line between the 5 and the 10 always indicates that a division can be made.

If this division is performed the resulting answer is called a decimal fraction. In other words, a decimal may be another representation of the same fractional value. To illustrate: $\frac{3}{4}$ equals 3 divided by 4 which is .75. Therefore either the .75 or the $\frac{3}{4}$ represents the same part of the whole. Likewise, $\frac{5}{4}$, when reduced to a decimal fraction equals 1.25.

Fractions can be grouped into two classes, namely, proper and improper.

Fractions can be used with whole numbers or with compound numbers. When used with whole numbers the combination is called a mixed number.

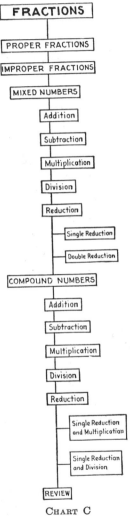

CHART C

A proper fraction always has a value less than one: for example, ⅝ is less than ⅜ or 1. The numerator is always less than the denominator.

[1] See p. 79.

An improper fraction always has a value equal to or greater than one: for example, $\frac{9}{8}$ is greater than $\frac{8}{8}$ or 1. The numerator is always equal to or larger than the denominator.

A mixed number is always made up of a whole number and a proper fraction, such as $2\frac{3}{8}$.

A fraction always expresses a certain part of a unit, as illustrated below where 1 whole inch, a unit is divided into fourths.

Proper fractions
$\left\{\begin{array}{l}\end{array}\right.$
$\frac{1}{4}''$..............equals one-fourth part of a whole inch
$\frac{2}{4}'' = \frac{1}{2}''$........equals two-fourth parts of a whole inch
$\frac{3}{4}''$..............equals three-fourth parts of a whole inch

Improper fractions
$\left\{\begin{array}{l}\end{array}\right.$
$\frac{4}{4}'' = 1''$........equals four-fourth parts of a whole inch
$\frac{5}{4}''$..............equals five-fourth parts of a whole inch
$\frac{6}{4}'' = 1\frac{1}{2}$........equals six-fourth parts of a whole inch
$\frac{7}{4}''$..............equals seven-fourth parts of a whole inch
$\frac{8}{4}'' = 2''$........equals eight-fourth parts of a whole inch

In many problems, especially in the answers, proper fractions have to be reduced to lowest terms. This may be accomplished as follows:

To reduce a fraction to its lowest terms divide both numerator and denominator by the same number, thus, to reduce $\frac{12}{16}$ to lowest terms:

$$\frac{12 \div 2 = 6}{16 \div 2 = 8} \quad \frac{6 \div 2 = 3}{8 \div 2 = 4} \quad \text{or } 4\overline{)\dfrac{12}{16}} = \frac{3}{4}$$

In many problems, especially in adding or subtracting, fractions have to be reduced to higher terms. This may be accomplished as follows:

To reduce a fraction to higher terms multiply both numerator and denominator by the same number, thus, to reduce $\frac{1}{4}$ to twenty-fourths: $\frac{1}{4} \times \frac{2}{2} = \frac{2}{8}$ $\frac{2}{8} \times \frac{3}{3} = \frac{6}{24}$ or $\frac{1}{4} \times \frac{6}{6} = \frac{6}{24}$. The one number to multiply by (6) can be found by dividing the denominator (4) of the fraction, into the denominator (24) of the desired fraction.

In many problems improper fractions have to be reduced to mixed numbers. This may be accomplished as follows:

To reduce an improper fraction to a mixed number divide the denominator into the numerator. The quotient is the whole-number part of the mixed number and the remainder, placed over the denominator, is the fraction part of the mixed number. For example, $1\frac{1}{4}$ is reduced to the mixed number $2\frac{3}{4}$ thus: $11 \div 4 = 2$, the whole-number part of the mixed number, with 3 left over; the 3 placed over the denominator gives $\frac{3}{4}$, the fraction part of the mixed number. Hence: $1\frac{1}{4} = 2\frac{3}{4}$.

In many problems, especially in multiplying fractions, mixed numbers need to be changed to improper fractions which is accomplished as follows:

To reduce a mixed number to an improper fraction multiply the whole number by the denominator of the fraction, add to this result the numerator of the fraction and place the whole amount over the denominator of the fraction. Thus, to change $5\frac{3}{4}$ to an improper fraction, multiply 5 by 4 giving 20. Add the 3 to the 20, giving 23. Place the 23 over the 4, giving an improper fraction $\frac{23}{4}$. Hence: $5\frac{3}{4} = \frac{23}{4}$

Proper fractions: $\frac{1}{2}, \frac{2}{3}, \frac{3}{4}, \frac{4}{5}, \frac{5}{6}, \frac{6}{7}$, etc.
Improper fractions: $\frac{3}{2}, \frac{4}{3}, \frac{5}{4}, \frac{6}{5}, \frac{7}{6}$, etc.
Mixed numbers: $1\frac{1}{2}, 2\frac{2}{3}, 3\frac{3}{4}, 4\frac{4}{5}$, etc.

ADDITION

Example: Add $4\frac{1}{3}, \frac{3}{4}, \frac{2}{5}$ and $1\frac{1}{6}$.

$1\frac{1}{6} = 1\frac{5}{6}$ Hence the problem is to add $4\frac{1}{3}, \frac{3}{4}, \frac{2}{5}$ and $1\frac{5}{6}$.

L. C. D. $= 60$

$4\frac{1}{3} = 4\frac{20}{60}$
$\frac{3}{4} = \frac{45}{60}$
$\frac{2}{5} = \frac{24}{60}$
$1\frac{5}{6} = 1\frac{50}{60}$
$5\frac{139}{60} = 7\frac{19}{60}$

All improper fractions should be changed to mixed numbers before starting to add. If the L. C. D. can be determined at sight it does not need to be computed.[1] Each fraction is changed to an equivalent fraction having 60 for the denominator. The new numerators are then added and placed over the L. C. D. (60). This gives $\frac{139}{60}$. The whole numbers are added, making a total sum of $5\frac{139}{60}$ which reduces to $5 + 2\frac{19}{60}$ or $7\frac{19}{60}$.

Fractions can never be added or subtracted unless their denominators are alike. This places the fractions on the same basis. Hence, fractions with different denominators are all changed to new fractions having the same denominator, called the least common denominator (L.C.D.). It is the smallest denominator that can be used for all of the fractions.

[1] See explanation, p. 172.

When it is difficult to find the L. C. D. by inspection, it may be found mathematically, as illustrated for the denominators 3, 4, 5, and 6. The denominators are

$$3)\overline{3\text{--}4\text{--}5\text{--}6}$$
$$2)\overline{1\text{--}4\text{--}5\text{--}2}$$
$$1\text{--}2\text{--}5\text{--}1$$

written down in a row and then divided through by any number that will exactly divide two or more of them, such as 3 in the illustration. Any denominator not divided, as 4 and 5, is brought down unchanged. The second row of figures is treated in the same way as the first. The process is continued until no divisor can be found which will divide at least two of the remaining figures. Then all the divisors and the remaining figures in the last row are multiplied to give the L. C. D.   L.C.D. $3 \times 2 \times 2 \times 5 = 60$

Problems

216. Add $5\frac{1}{8}$, $\frac{2}{3}$, $\frac{1}{5}$, and $\frac{5}{4}$.

217. Find the sum of $2\frac{1}{2}$, $\frac{9}{4}$, $\frac{1}{5}$, and $\frac{3}{8}$.

218. Add $3\frac{1}{5}$, $2\frac{3}{4}$, $\frac{7}{8}$, and $\frac{4}{3}$.

219. How much is $10\frac{1}{2} + 21\frac{1}{4} + {}^{15}\!\!/_{16} + \frac{4}{3}$?

220. Add $19\frac{3}{4}$, $17\frac{1}{2}$, $\frac{9}{16}$, and $1\frac{1}{5}$.

221. Add $\frac{1}{4}$, $\frac{3}{8}$, $\frac{1}{2}$, and $\frac{5}{16}$.

222. Find the sum of $\frac{3}{16}$, $\frac{5}{16}$, $\frac{3}{8}$, $\frac{1}{2}$.

223. Add $\frac{5}{8}$, $\frac{5}{16}$, $\frac{3}{8}$, $\frac{3}{4}$, and $\frac{7}{8}$.

224. How much is $\frac{7}{8} + \frac{5}{16} + \frac{3}{4} + \frac{1}{2} + {}^{15}\!\!/_{16}$?

225. Add $\frac{5}{8}$, $\frac{1}{4}$, $\frac{7}{16}$, $\frac{1}{2}$, $\frac{7}{8}$, and ${}^{16}\!\!/_{15}$.

226. Add $2\frac{1}{4}$, $5\frac{3}{8}$, $7\frac{1}{2}$, and $10\frac{5}{16}$.

227. Add $5\frac{7}{16}$, $8\frac{5}{8}$, $11\frac{3}{8}$, $4\frac{1}{2}$, and $12\frac{1}{4}$.

228. How much is $15\frac{7}{8} + 20\frac{1}{2} + 14\frac{4}{16} + 12\frac{1}{8} + 3\frac{7}{16}$?

229. Find the sum of $2\frac{5}{4}$, $1\frac{7}{8}$, $2\frac{1}{2}$, $117\frac{7}{16}$.

230. Add $15\frac{1}{2}$, $10\frac{1}{4}$, $8\frac{3}{16}$, $24\frac{5}{8}$, and $17\frac{3}{4}$.

231. Add $12\frac{1}{4}$, $\frac{9}{5}$, $15\frac{7}{12}$, $\frac{7}{3}$, and $12\frac{1}{8}$.

232. Add 9, $29\frac{1}{4}$, $6\frac{3}{8}$, ${}^{15}\!\!/_{16}$, $\frac{9}{8}$, and $11\frac{3}{4}$.

233. Add $7\frac{1}{3}$, $\frac{5}{8}$, $2\frac{9}{4}$, $1\frac{7}{16}$, and $\frac{7}{8}$.

234. Find the sum of $21\frac{1}{4}$, $18\frac{5}{8}$, $\frac{1}{8}$, $1\frac{7}{16}$, and $7\frac{7}{12}$.

235. How much is $3\frac{1}{16} + \frac{3}{8} + 1\frac{1}{8} + 11\frac{1}{2} + 4\frac{3}{8} + 1\frac{1}{2}$?

The following problems are to be worked mentally; write only the answers:

236. Add $\frac{1}{8}$ and $\frac{1}{2}$.

237. Add $\frac{5}{8}$ and $\frac{1}{4}$.

238. Add $\frac{5}{16}$ and $\frac{1}{8}$.

239. Add $\frac{3}{8}$ and $\frac{1}{16}$.

240. Add $\frac{3}{4}$ and $\frac{1}{16}$.

241. Add $1\frac{5}{8}$ and $\frac{1}{4}$.

242. Add $2\frac{1}{8}$ and $\frac{3}{4}$.

243. Add $\frac{5}{8}$ and $4\frac{3}{16}$.

244. Add $\frac{5}{16}$ and $9\frac{3}{8}$.

245. Add $11\frac{1}{2}$ and $\frac{3}{16}$.

SUBTRACTION

Example: Subtract $2\frac{5}{8}$ from $7\frac{3}{16}$

L. C. D. $= 16$	All improper fractions should be changed to mixed numbers before subtracting. The L. C. D. can usually be determined at sight. $1\frac{0}{16}$ cannot be subtracted from $\frac{3}{16}$; hence, 1 is borrowed from the 7, giving $1\frac{6}{16}$ to add to

$7\frac{3}{16} = 7\ \frac{3}{16}$

$2\frac{5}{8} = 2^{1}\frac{0}{16}$

$\overline{4\ \frac{9}{16}}$

$\frac{3}{16}$, making $1\frac{9}{16}$. $1\frac{0}{16}$ can be subtracted from $1\frac{9}{16}$, leaving $\frac{9}{16}$; 2 is then subtracted from 6 (instead of 7), leaving an answer of $4\frac{9}{16}$. The $\frac{9}{16}$ would be reduced to lower terms if that were possible.

Problems

246. Subtract $1\frac{3}{8}$ from $4\frac{3}{16}$.
247. Subtract $5\frac{3}{4}$ from $8\frac{1}{2}$.
248. Find the difference between $4\frac{3}{16}$ and $9\frac{1}{8}$.
249. How much less is $7\frac{5}{8}$ than $15\frac{3}{16}$?
250. Subtract $11\frac{7}{8}$ from $24\frac{11}{16}$.
251. Subtract $\frac{5}{16}$ from $\frac{7}{12}$.
252. How much is $8\frac{3}{8}$ less $\frac{5}{12}$?
253. Subtract $\frac{9}{8}$ from $15\frac{2}{3}$.
254. Find the difference between $15\frac{7}{8}$ and $45\frac{3}{16}$.
255. Subtract $13\frac{9}{44}$ from 186.
256. How much less is $1\frac{9}{16}$ than 49?
257. Subtract $140\frac{15}{48}$ from 1728.
258. How much is $2\frac{9}{8}$ less $\frac{7}{16}$?
259. Find the difference between $2\frac{5}{16}$ and $2\frac{5}{12}$.
260. Subtract $28\frac{1}{2}$ from $33\frac{9}{8}$.

The following problems are to be solved mentally; write down only the answers:

261. Subtract $\frac{1}{4}$ from $\frac{7}{8}$.
262. Subtract $\frac{5}{16}$ from $1\frac{1}{2}$.
263. Subtract $\frac{3}{16}$ from 5.
264. Subtract $\frac{5}{8}$ from $\frac{5}{4}$.
265. Subtract $1\frac{7}{16}$ from $\frac{9}{8}$.
266. Subtract $\frac{3}{16}$ from $\frac{3}{4}$.
267. Subtract $1\frac{1}{2}$ from $5\frac{7}{8}$.
268. Subtract $1\frac{9}{8}$ from $5\frac{1}{2}$.
269. Subtract $5\frac{3}{4}$ from 7.
270. Subtract 3 from $\frac{9}{2}$.

Multiplication

Example: Multiply 11 by 2¼ by ⅔.

$$\frac{11}{1} \times \frac{\overset{3}{\cancel{9}}}{\underset{2}{\cancel{4}}} \times \frac{\overset{1}{\cancel{2}}}{\underset{1}{\cancel{3}}} = \frac{33}{2} = 16\tfrac{1}{2}$$

numbers $1 \times 2 \times 1 = 2.$

Change mixed numbers to improper fractions.
After cancellation, the numerator numbers left to be multiplied are $1 \times 3 \times 11 = 33$ and the denominator numbers $1 \times 2 \times 1 = 2$. This gives ³³⁄₂ which reduces to 16½.

Cancellation must always be performed from a numerator to a denominator, never from a numerator to a numerator.

Problems

271. Multiply 9 by ⅔ by 2½.
272. Multiply 15 by ¾ by 3⅕.
273. Find the product of ¹⁵⁄₁₆ and ²⁵⁄₁₄₄.
274. How much is $12 \times 7\tfrac{1}{2} \times \tfrac{3}{4}$?
275. Multiply 18 by 2¾ by ⅞.
276. Multiply ¹⁵⁄₁₆ by ⅗.
277. How much is $\tfrac{7}{8} \times 36$?
278. Multiply 15¾ by 2½.
279. Find the product of 75½ and 45¾.
280. Multiply 29½ by 30 by 10⅜.
281. Multiply 15½ by 17⅝.
282. Multiply 24⅜ by 14½.
283. How much is ¾ of 18⅞?
284. Find the product of 17⅝ and 24.
285. Multiply 18½ by 22⅝.

Problems for mental solution:

286. Multiply ½ by ¾.
287. Multiply 3⁄2 by ⅜.
288. Multiply 8½ by ¼.
289. Multiply 5⁄4 by 9⁄8.
290. Multiply ⅝ by 32.
291. Multiply 1½ by 5¼.
292. Multiply 9⁄8 by 32.
293. Multiply 3½ by 12.
294. Multiply 2½ by 3½.
295. Multiply 10 by 3½.

Another method of multiplying fractions can be used to advantage where one number is a whole number and the other a fraction or mixed number. This method may be used when convenient but the first method should be thoroughly mastered as a standard method for all situations.

Example: Multiply 12 by $2\frac{3}{4}$.

12 $2\frac{3}{4}$ 4)36 9 24 33	The 12 is first multiplied by $\frac{3}{4}$. Multiplying the 12 by the 3 and dividing by the 4, gives 9. Then 12 is multiplied by 2 giving 24. The 9 and 24 are then added to give the answer 33.

If this method were to be used for multiplying two mixed numbers such as $23\frac{1}{2}$ by $15\frac{1}{4}$, it would be necessary to multiply 15 by $23\frac{1}{2}$ and then add the result of $\frac{1}{4}$ by $23\frac{1}{2}$ to obtain the answer. Or, make four multiplications, thus, 15 by 23, 15 by $\frac{1}{2}$, $\frac{1}{4}$ by 23, $\frac{1}{4}$ by $\frac{1}{2}$ and add the four results to obtain the answer. In certain problems, this method can be used to advantage, though the possibility of error is probably greater.

Division

Example: Divide $4\frac{1}{2}$ by $\frac{7}{8}$.

$\frac{9}{2} \div \frac{7}{8} = \frac{9}{2} \times \frac{8}{7} = \frac{36}{7} = 5\frac{1}{7}$	$4\frac{1}{2}$ is changed to $\frac{9}{2}$ then $\frac{9}{2} \div \frac{7}{8} = \frac{9}{2} \times$ the $\frac{7}{8}$ inverted. By cancellation this gives $\frac{36}{7}$ which reduces to $5\frac{1}{7}$.

The number to be inverted is the divisor, which is also the number that follows the ÷ sign or the word "by." In order to show that the division process and not pure multiplication is being used, it is advisable to indicate always the division, thus, ($\frac{9}{2} \div \frac{7}{8} =$) before inverting and multiplying. This habit will prevent one from inverting in pure multiplication.

Problems

296. Divide $3\frac{1}{2}$ by $\frac{3}{4}$.
297. How much is $12\frac{1}{4}$ divided by $\frac{3}{8}$?
298. Find the quotient of $24\frac{5}{8}$ divided by $1\frac{7}{8}$.
299. Divide $36\frac{1}{2}$ by $4\frac{3}{8}$.
300. Divide $\frac{15}{16}$ by $\frac{5}{12}$.
301. How much is $48\frac{3}{4}$ divided by $\frac{5}{8}$?
302. Divide $25\frac{1}{2}$ by $\frac{17}{16}$.
303. Find the quotient of $20\frac{3}{4}$ divided by $4\frac{1}{2}$.
304. Divide $124\frac{7}{8}$ by 5.
305. Divide $18\frac{1}{2}$ by $\frac{7}{8}$.
306. Find the quotient of 24 divided by $\frac{7}{8}$.
307. Divide 154 by $5\frac{5}{8}$.
308. How much is $7\frac{15}{16}$ divided by $\frac{1}{8}$?
309. Divide $49\frac{1}{2}$ by 3.
310. Divide 172 by $2\frac{1}{2}$.

Problems for mental solution:

311. Divide ¾ by ⅔.
312. Divide 4 by ⅜.
313. Divide 2½ by ¼.
314. Divide ¹⁵⁄₁₆ by ³⁄₁₆.
315. Divide 7½ by ½.
316. Divide 8½ by ¼.
317. Divide 6 by ¾.
318. Divide 10½ by 2.
319. Divide 12 by ¼.
320. Divide 1½ by ⅛.

Reduction

Single Reduction—Higher to Lower and Lower to Higher Denominations.

See pages 156–157.

Problems

321. Reduce 2¾ ft. to inches.
322. Reduce 101″ to feet.
323. Change 17¾ ft. to inches.
324. Change 592″ to feet.
325. Reduce ⅞ cu. yd. to cu. ft.
326. Reduce 221 cu. ft. to cu. yds.
327. Change 15¾ doz. to number of pieces.
328. Change 1,700 pieces to dozens.
329. Change 39½ lin. ft. to number of pieces 2¼ ft. long.
330. Change 14 pieces 7⅛ ft. long to linear feet.

Double Reduction—Higher to Lower and Lower to Higher Denominations.

See pages 157–158.

331. Reduce ¾ yd. to inches.
332. Reduce 84 inches to yards.
333. Change ½ gross to number of piece
334. Change 408 pieces to gross.
335. Reduce ⅜ cu. yd. to cubic inches.
336. Reduce 46,656 cu. in. to cubic yards.
337. Change 10½ lin. ft. to number of pieces 6½″ long.
338. Change 48 pieces 11¼″ long to number of linear feet.
339. Change 15½ lin. ft. to number of pieces 9³⁄₁₆″ long.
340. Change 54 pieces 12½″ long to number of linear feet.

Compound Numbers (with fractional inches): $1'\ 1\frac{1}{2}''$, $2'\ 2\frac{1}{4}''$, $3'\ 3\frac{1}{8}''$ etc.

Addition

Example: Add $17'\ 8\frac{1}{2}''$, $15'\ 7\frac{3}{8}''$, $12'\ 6\frac{1}{4}''$, and $7'\ 8\frac{5}{8}''$.

		L.C.D. = 8
$17'$	$8\frac{1}{2}''$	$\frac{4}{8}$
$15'$	$7\frac{3}{8}''$	$\frac{3}{8}$
$12'$	$6\frac{1}{4}''$	$\frac{2}{8}$
$7'$	$8\frac{5}{8}''$	$\frac{5}{8}$
$53'$	$6\frac{3}{4}''$	$\frac{14}{8} = 1\frac{3}{4}$

Adding up the fractions of an inch gives $1\frac{3}{4}''$. Adding the $1\frac{3}{4}''$ into the column of inches gives a total of $30\frac{3}{4}''$. But $30\frac{3}{4}''$ equals $2'\ 6\frac{3}{4}''$. Hence the $6\frac{3}{4}''$ is written down under the column of inches and the $2'$ added into the column of feet, giving $53'$ or an answer of $53'\ 6\frac{3}{4}''$.

341. Add $2'\ 3\frac{1}{2}''$, $1'\ 4\frac{1}{2}''$, $3'\ 5\frac{3}{4}''$ and $3'\ 6\frac{1}{4}''$.
342. Add $7'\ 2\frac{1}{4}''$, $6'\ 1\frac{1}{2}''$, $5'\ 4\frac{3}{4}''$ and $9'\ 3\frac{1}{4}''$.
343. Add $1'\ 10\frac{1}{2}''$, $2'\ 8\frac{3}{8}''$, $3'\ 9\frac{1}{4}''$, $5'\ 6\frac{5}{8},''$ and $0'\ 6\frac{1}{8}''$.
344. Add $7'\ 9\frac{3}{4}''$, $0'\ 6\frac{7}{8}''$, $5'\ 11\frac{1}{4}''$, $9'\ 10\frac{5}{8}''$, and $3'\ 4\frac{1}{2}''$.
345. Add $3'\ 7\frac{1}{2}''$, $4'\ 9\frac{3}{8}''$, $6'\ 11\frac{5}{8}''$, $5'\ 4\frac{3}{4}''$, and $7'\ 3\frac{1}{2}''$.

Subtraction

Example: Subtract $11'\ 6\frac{1}{2}''$ from $18'\ 4\frac{3}{4}''$.

$18'$	$4\frac{3}{4}''$	$\frac{3}{4}$
$11'$	$6\frac{1}{2}''$	$\frac{2}{4}$
$6'$	$10\frac{1}{4}''$	$\frac{1}{4}$

Subtracting the fractions of an inch. $\frac{3}{4} - \frac{1}{2} = \frac{1}{4}$. Then, since $6''$ cannot be subtracted from $4''$, 1 is borrowed from $18'$ giving $12''$ to be added to $4''$; consequently, $6''$ is subtracted from $16''$, leaving $10''$, and $11'$ is taken away from $17'$, leaving $6'$, and giving an answer of $6'\ 10\frac{1}{4}''$.

346. Subtract $5'\ 6\frac{1}{2}''$ from $9'\ 10\frac{7}{8}''$.
347. Subtract $8'\ 5\frac{1}{4}''$ from $15'\ 7\frac{3}{8}''$.
348. Subtract $25'\ 10\frac{5}{8}''$ from $35'\ 11\frac{1}{2}''$.
349. Subtract $22'\ 9\frac{3}{4}''$ from $28'\ 5\frac{5}{8}''$.
350. Subtract $15'\ 3\frac{1}{2}''$ from $35'\ 3\frac{3}{8}''$.

Multiplication

Example: Multiply $7'\ 4\frac{1}{2}''$ by 7.

$$7'\ 4\frac{1}{2}''\quad \left(\frac{9}{2} \times \frac{7}{1} = \frac{63}{2} = 31\frac{1}{2}''\right)$$
$$\times\ 7$$
$$51'\ 7\frac{1}{2}''$$

Multiplying $7 \times 4\frac{1}{2} = 31\frac{1}{2}$. But $31\frac{1}{2}'' = 2'$ and $7\frac{1}{2}''$ The $7\frac{1}{2}''$ is written down and the $2'$ added into the product of $7 \times 7'$, giving $51'$ or an answer of $51'\ 7\frac{1}{2}''$.

351. Multiply 8' 5½" by 4.
352. Multiply 9' 4⅝" by 16.
353. Multiply 11' 7⅜" by 32.
354. Multiply 3' 2¾" by 21.
355. Multiply 2' 7⅞" by 19.

DIVISION

Example: Divide 15' 3½" by 2.

$$2)\overline{15'\ 3\frac{1}{2}''}\quad (1\frac{1}{2} \div \frac{2}{1} = \frac{3}{2} \times \frac{1}{2} = \frac{3}{4})$$
$$7'\ 7\frac{3}{4}''$$

Dividing 15' by 2 gives 7' and 1' left over. The 1' is changed to 12" and added into 3½", making 15½". Dividing 15½" by 2 gives 7" with 1½" left over. Then dividing 1½" by 2 gives ¾" and an answer of 7' 7¾".

356. Divide 6' 8½" by 3.
357. Divide 11' 7" by 5.
358. Divide 27' 7¾" by 2.
359. Divide 23' 0" by 4.
360. Divide 49' 9⅝" by 6.

REDUCTION

Example: Reduce to inches and multiply 3' 7½ " by 4' 3½".

$$
\begin{array}{ll}
3'\ 7\frac{1}{2}'' & 4'\ 3\frac{1}{2}'' \\
12'' = (1') & 12'' = (1') \\
\hline
36'' & 48'' \\
7\frac{1}{2}''\ \text{(added)} & 3\frac{1}{2}''\ \text{(added)} \\
\hline
43\frac{1}{2}'' & 51\frac{1}{2}''
\end{array}
$$

In order to multiply 3' 7½" × 4' 3½" reduce each compound number to inches first, and then multiply.

$$43\frac{1}{2}'' \times 51\frac{1}{2}'' = \frac{87}{2} \times \frac{103}{2} = \frac{8961}{4}$$

$$\frac{8,961}{4} = 2,240\frac{1}{4}\ \text{sq. in.}$$

361. Reduce to inches and multiply 1' 5½" by 2' 3½".
362. Change to inches and multiply 3' 6½" by 3' 4½".
363. Reduce to inches and multiply 5' 4⅜" by 2' 7½".
364. Change to inches and multiply 7' 2½" by 4' 3½".
365. Reduce to inches and multiply 8' 5½" by 5' 2½".

Example: Reduce to inches and divide 9′ 5¼″ by 1′ 3½″.

9′ 5¼″ 12″ = (1′) 108″ 5¼″ (added) 113¼″	1′ 3½″ 12″ = (1′) 12″ 3½″ (added) 15½″	In order to divide 9′ 5¼″ by 1′ 3½″ reduce each compound number to inches first, and then divide.

$$13\tfrac{1}{4}'' \div 15\tfrac{1}{2}'' = \frac{453}{4} \div \frac{31}{2}$$

But

$$\frac{453}{4} \div \frac{31}{2} = \frac{453}{\underset{2}{\not 4}} \times \frac{\not 2}{31} = \frac{453}{62}$$

and $\frac{453}{62} = 7\tfrac{19}{62}$

366. Reduce to inches and divide 3′ 2½″ by 0′ 6½″.
367. Change to inches and divide 4′ 5½″ by 1′ 2½″.
368. Change to inches and divide 5′ 7½″ by 2′ 2¼″.
369. Reduce to inches and divide 7′ 2¼″ by 1′ 5½″.
370. Reduce to inches and divide 11′ 9½″ by 2′ 4¼″.

Review

371. Subtract ⅞ from 5⁵⁄₁₆.
372. Add 8½ + 3¼ + ⅞ + 15⅛ + ³⁄₁₆.
373. Divide 42⅝ by 5³⁄₁₆.
374. Multiply 14¹⁄₁₆ by 3⅝.
375. Reduce ⅝ feet to inches.
376. Subtract 3¾ from 18⅝.
377. Convert 22½ lin. ft. to number of pieces 1½′ long.
378. Multiply 7⅜ by 42.
379. Divide 17¾ by ³⁄₁₆.
380. Change 9 pieces 18½″ long to linear feet.
381. Add 10 + ¼ + 5⅜ + 6¾ + ³⁄₁₆.
382. Subtract ¹⁵⁄₁₂ from ¹¹⁄₈.
383. Divide 17 by ⁵⁄₁₆.
384. Reduce 476″ to feet.
385. Find the cubic contents of a room 30½′ by 18½′ by 9′.
386. Find the area of a floor 29½′ × 19¾′.
387. Add 3′ 4½″, 1′ 7⅛″, 5′ 6¾″ and 7′ 11³⁄₁₆″.
388. Subtract 15′ 5½″ from 20′ 4⅜″.
389. Multiply 7′ 4⅜″ by 15.
390. Divide 15′ 4½″ by 2.
391. Change to inches and multiply 3′ 6½″ by 2′ 7½″.

392. Change to inches and divide 5′ 6½″ by 1′ 3¼″.
393. Find the area of a wall 15½′ by 8′.
394. Find the number of linear feet in 15 cripple studs 9¾″ long.
395. How much is ⅕ of 445 sq. ft. of siding?

V. PERCENTAGE[1]

The mathematical work in percentage problems is practically the same as that in ordinary decimal problems. The related information, the trade terms and the trade practice are so varied, that a careful study of the condensed facts about percentage is highly essential.

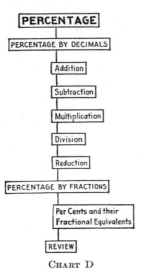

CHART D

In percentage problems the number by which the per cent is multiplied does not have the same trade name in each problem. In one problem it may be *cost times per cent*, in another *selling price times per cent*, in another *list price times per cent*, in another *investment times per cent*, etc. Hence, this quantity with its varying trade names has been given the general name of the **base** which is defined as follows: *The base is the quantity by which the rate is multiplied.*

The rate or per cent is a term which needs explanation. To illustrate, a contractor constructs a house for $3,600, sells it for $4,500, and thereby makes $900 profit. After building a number of houses of this type he finds that the $900 takes care of his overhead expense and the interest on the investment, and also leave him a fair amount of net profit. How much profit should be added for another type of house costing $8,000, the profit to be on the same basis as for the $3,600 house? He sees that $900 is ¼ of $3,600 and, therefore, multiplies $8,000 by ¼, which gives $2,000. In this way the interest, the overhead, and the net profit are taken care of in the same proportion as for the $3,600 house. The ¼ is a fraction which equals 25 per cent. This can also be written as a deci-

[1] See p. 101.

mal .25. These various ways of representing per cent have been given the name of **rate,** which is defined as follows: *The rate is the per cent (%) which* (changed to a fraction or a decimal) *is multiplied by the base.*

When multiplying the base times the rate the result is known by various trade names, such as *profit, loss, trade discount, cash discount, architect's fee, commission,* and *overhead.* These terms are given the general name of **percentage,** which is defined as follows: The *percentage is the product obtained by multiplying the base by the rate.*

When adding the percentage to the base (for example, profit added to cost) or subtracting the percentage from the base (loss subtracted from cost) the sum or difference is known by various names, as *selling price, contractor's bid, net cost, total amount, retail price,* and *wholesale price.* These sums or differences have not been given a general name when applied to percentage problems.

To determine, in each problem, which number is the base is very important. If it is incorrectly selected, the whole problem is worked in the wrong way. The tendency is to assume in each problem that the base is the cost, when often it is the selling price, the list price, or some other number. Certain phrases in each problem, containing "of" or "on" will aid in the selection; for example, "a discount of *25 per cent on the list price*," "a profit of *15 per cent on the cost*," "the discount is *10 per cent of the selling price*." In these phrases the "of" or "on" plainly indicates the base. In some problems it is merely implied, as a "*commission of 5 per cent*," and requires a knowledge of trade practice.

Because of the many variations in trade practice no definite rule for the selection of the base can be given. However, it may be stated as a percentage principle that the *base is always equal to 100 per cent.* It is also represented by the decimal 1.00 or a fraction, as $\frac{2}{2}$, $\frac{3}{3}$, and $\frac{4}{4}$.

It should be noted that all examples which are worked out are based on identically the same problem throughout. This method is used to emphasize the fact that for each percentage problem solved by multiplication, there is a reverse process solved by division.

For any given trade situation, the trade practice must first be known before the problem can be solved intelligently. Once this is known, the selection of the correct number to use as the base can be determined and then the problem worked according to the rules of percentage.

Percentage (by decimals): 1% (.01), 2% (.02), 3% (.03), 4% (.04), etc.

ADDITION

Example: Cost $3,600, profit $900; profit is 25 per cent of the cost. Find the selling price and the rate or per cent that represents it.

$3,600 cost	= 100%	Note that 100 per cent represents or
900 profit	= 25%	equals the cost ($3,600) and that
$4,500 selling price	= 125%	25% equals the profit ($900). As

$3,600 *cost* + $900 *profit* gives the selling price in dollars, so 100 per cent (cost) + 25 per cent (profit) gives the selling price in per cent, 125 per cent.

The following ten problems in addition and subtraction, although simple to figure, contain some of the most important principles of percentage. Hence, they should be written with thought and care just as in the example given. Notice that each amount of money is represented by a per cent.

Problems

396. Cost is $6,000; profit is $900, which is 15 per cent of the cost. Find the selling price and the per cent that represents it.

397. Estimated cost is $4,500, estimated profit is $540, which is 12 per cent of actual cost. Find per cent that represents the bid and also the amount of bid.

398. Cost is $32.40; discount is $3.60 which is 10 per cent of catalogue price. Find the catalogue price and the equivalent per cent.

399. Actual cost is $13.50; discount allowed was $4.50, which was 25 per cent of retail price. Find retail price and its equivalent per cent.

400. Cost is $3,465; profit is $277.20, which is 8 per cent of cost. Find selling price and its equivalent per cent.

Subtraction

Example: Cost is $3,200; loss is $160, which is 5 per cent of the cost. Find the selling price in per cent and the selling price in money.

$3,200 cost	=	100%	Note that 100 per cent represents the
160 loss	=	5%	cost ($3,200), and 5 per cent the loss
$3,040 selling price =		95%	($160). As the cost ($3,200) less

the loss ($160) gives the selling price in dollars, so 100 per cent (cost) less 5 per cent (loss) gives the selling price in per cent, 95 per cent.

Problems

401. Cost is $2,800; loss is $224, which is 8 per cent of cost. Find selling price and the per cent that represents it.

402. Catalogue price is $30; discount is $6, which is 20 per cent of the catalogue price. Find actual cost and the per cent that equals it.

403. List price is $29.50; discount is $3.54, which is 12 per cent of list price. Find cost and the per cent that equals it.

404. Selling price is $9,000, which is 120% of the cost. Cost is **$7,500.** Find profit and the per cent that equals it.

405. List price is $47.60; discount is $4.76, which is 10 per cent of list price. Find the cost and the per cent that equals it.

Multiplication

Example: Actual cost is $7,860; rate of profit is 15 per cent of the cost. Find the profit.

$7860 cost	= 100%	The cost times the rate gives
.15 rate	= 15%	the profit. A per cent is to
39300		be written representing each
7860 $(B \times R = P)$		number in the problem.
$1179.00 profit	= 15%	Since the terms "cost" and

"profit" do not apply in every problem, this process of multiplication is given the general rule of base × rate = percentage or $B \times R = P$.

Problems

406. Cost is $6,500; profit is $12\frac{1}{2}$ per cent of cost. Find the profit.

407. Selling price is $7,000; discount is $2\frac{1}{2}$ per cent of selling price for cash. Find discount.

408. Retail price is $53.50; discount is 15 per cent of retail price. Find the discount.

409. Bill is $169.58; cash discount is 2 per cent.   Find the discount.
410. Cost is $4,280; profit is 8 per cent of cost.   Find the profit.

Example: Cost is $7,860; rate of profit is 15 per cent.   Find the selling price.

$7860 cost	= 100%	The profit is computed the same as in the previous example on page 183. $B \times R = P$, and then the profit and cost are added to give the selling price.
.15 rate	= 15%	
39300		
7860 $(B \times R = P)$		
$1179.00 profit	= 15%	
7860.00 cost	= 100%	
$9039.00 selling price	= 115%	

411. Cost is $6,600; rate of profit is 12 per cent.   Find the selling price.

412. Daily wage is $6.40 per day; contractor's profit is 10 per cent of daily wage.   Find amount paid to contractor per day for labor.

413. Estimated cost is $2,300; profit is 12 per cent of cost.   Find amount of bid.

414. Labor for job is $750; profit is 15 per cent of cost.   Find amount charged for labor.

415. Estimated cost is $3,464; profit is 11 per cent of cost.   Find amount of bid.

Example: List price is $7,860; discount is 15 per cent of list price. Find cost to purchaser.

$7860 list price	= 100%	The same rule that was used in the previous example given on page 183 also applies here— $B \times R = P$. In that example, however, cost and profit were *added* to give the selling price; in this example, the discount is *subtracted* from the list price to give the cost.
.15 rate	= 15%	
39300		
7860 $(B \times R = P)$		
$1179.00 discount	= 15%	
$7860.00 list price	= 100%	
1179.00 discount	= 15%	
$6681.00 cost	= 85%	

416. List price is $5,670; discount is 12 per cent of this price.   Find cost.

417. Retail price is $45; discount is 25 per cent of retail price.   Find cost.

418. List price $75; discount is 8 per cent off list price. What is cost?

419. Retail price is $34.47; discount is 33⅓ per cent. Find cost.

420. Discount of 15 per cent is allowed on list price of $1,520. What is cost?

Example: Selling price is $7,860; a discount of 15 per cent is allowed on this price with 2 per cent off for cash. Find the net cost.

Part I	$7860 selling price	= 100%	This example is in two parts, each of which is based on the same rule of $B \times R = P$. It is important to note that although $6,681 is represented by 85 per cent at the end of the first part, it immediately becomes 100 per cent at the beginning of the second part, which is really a new problem.	
	.15 rate	= 15%		
	39300			
	7860 $(B \times R = P)$			
	$1179.00 discount	= 15%		
	$7860.00 catalogue price	= 100%		
	1179.00 discount	= 15%		
	$6681.00 cost	= 85%		
Part II	$(B \times R = P)$			
	$6681.00 cost	= 100%		
	.02 rate	= 2%		
	$133.6200 cash discount	= 2%		
	$6681.00 cost	= 100%		
	133.62 cash discount	= 2%		
	$6547.38 net cost	= 98%		

The ability to tell what per cent represents each number is needed when working this type of problem backward, from net cost to selling price (see page 189).

421. List price is $5,780; discount is 12 per cent of the list price; cash discount is 2 per cent. Find net cost.

422. Retail price is $58; discount is 20 per cent of retail price; cash discount is 3 per cent. Find net cost.

423. Retail price is $36; discount is 25 per cent of retail price; cash discount is 2 per cent. Find net cost.

424. List price is $73; discount is 10 per cent; cash discount is 2 per cent. Find net cost.

425. Bill is $948.50; discount is 15 per cent; cash discount is 2 per cent. Find net cost.

Division

Example: Profit is $1,179, which is 15 per cent of cost.   Find cost.

Cost   = 100%
Profit =   15%
$1179 =   15%

$$\frac{\$7860.}{\text{Rate }.15)\$1179.00} \quad \text{cost}$$

profit

105
———
129
120        $(P \div R = B)$
———
90
90
——

The phrase "15 *per cent of the cost* indicates that the cost was the 100 per cent number and the phrase "which is" indicates that $1,179 is the 15 per cent number or $1,179 = 15 per cent. For this type of problem, a rule may be stated: *Whenever* a number is found to be equal to a per cent, divide the number by the per cent (as a decimal) and the answer will be the 100 per cent number, or the base.   Percentage ÷ rate = base or $P \div R = B$. It is important to see that this division example is really working backward the example in multiplication on page 183. The multiplication was $7,860 × .15 = $1,179. The division is $1,179 ÷ .15 = $7,860.

Problems

426. Profit is $510, which is 12 per cent of cost.   Find cost.

427. Discount is $2.52, which is 7 per cent of retail price.   Find retail price.

428. Profit is $3.60, which is 15 per cent of wages paid.   Find wages paid.

429. Discount is $10.87½, which is equal to 25 per cent of retail price. Find retail price.

430. Discount is $2.52, which is 5 per cent of retail price.   What is retail price?

Example: Selling price is $9,039; profit is 15 per cent of cost. Find cost.

```
Cost        = 100%
Profit      =  15%
Selling price = 115%
∴ $9,039.00 = 115%

            $7860   cost
Rate 1.15)$9039.00  selling price
            805
            ───
            989
            920  (P ÷ R = B)
            ───
            690
            690
```

Note that the phrase *"15 per cent of the cost"* shows that the cost was the 100 per cent number. Hence, the selling price contains two amounts, cost and profit. If 15 per cent equals profit and 100 per cent equals cost, 115 per cent must equal the selling price or $9,039. The rule applies that when a number equals a per cent, divide the number by the per cent to get the 100 per cent number, (in this case the cost) $P ÷ R = B$.

This example is the same one as the multiplication problem on page 184, but worked backward, going from selling price to cost.

431. Selling price is $4,312; profit is 12 per cent of cost. Find cost.

432. Bid is $7,198; estimated profit is 18 per cent of estimated cost. Find estimated cost.

433. Contractor's charges for labor are $9.20 per day; estimated profit is 15 per cent of wage paid. Find wages per day.

434. Total charges for job are $198, which includes 10 per cent profit. What is actual cost of job?

435. Total charge for job is $179.20 which includes 12 per cent profit. What is actual cost of job?

Example: Cost is $6,681, which is a 15 per cent discount on the list price. Find list price.

List price   = 100%
Discount   = 15%
Cost   = 85%
∴ $6,681   = 85%

———————————
$7860   list price
Rate .85)$6681.00   cost
  595
  ———
  731
  680 $(P \div R = B)$
  ———
  510
  510
  ———

Note that the phrase *"15 per cent on the list price"* shows that the list price is the 100 per cent number. Since the house is sold at a discount of 15 per cent, the cost must be represented by 85 per cent, and consequently $6,681 equals 85 per cent. The rule applies that when a number equals a per cent, divide the number by the per cent to get the 100 per cent number (in this case the list price), $P \div R = B$.

Note that this example involves the same trade situations used in the example on page 184, but in this case, works from cost to list price.

436. Cost is $5,188.80 after taking 8 per cent off list price. Find list price.

437. Cost is $28.80 after discount of 20 per cent is allowed off retail price. Find retail price.

438. Two per cent was allowed for cash; amount of cash paid was $1,225. Find original amount of bill.

439. Cost is $15.86 after taking 35 per cent off catalogue price. Find catalogue price.

440. Amount paid is $154 after 12 per cent discount was allowed. Find original amount of bill.

Example: Net cost is $6,547.38; discount is 15 per cent of selling price; cash discount is 2 per cent. Find selling price.

Cash discounts are taken off the cost price. The result is then known as net cost.

Part I

Cost	=	100%
Cash discount	=	2%
Net cost	=	98%
∴ $6,547.38	=	98%

$6681 cost

Rate .98)$6547.38 net cost
   588
   ———
   667
   588
   ———
   793 $(P \div R = B)$
   784
   ———
    98
    98

PART II

Selling price	=	100%
Discount	=	15%
Cost	=	85%
∴ $6,681	=	85%

$7860 selling price

Rate .85)$6681.00 cost
   595
   ———
   731
   680 $(P \div R = B)$
   ———
   510
   510

The solution of this problem is more easily understood by referring to the example worked out on page 185, as this problem in division is the reverse of that one. Note the two facts that the net cost, $6,547.38, equals 98 per cent, and $6,681, the cost, equals 85 per cent.

This example is made up of two parts, each a problem in division, one using the 2 per cent cash discount and the other the 15 per cent discount.

Part I is based on the fact that $6,547.38 equals 98 per cent; hence, dividing the net cost by 98 per cent gives $6,681, the cost.

Part II is based on the fact that $6,681 equals 85 per cent; hence, dividing the cost by 85 per cent gives the selling price, $7,860. Both of the parts follow the rule that $P \div R = B$.

441. Net cost is $5,831; discount on selling price is 15 per cent; cash discount is 2 per cent. Find selling price.

442. Net cost is $26.46; discount is 25 per cent of retail price; cash discount is 2 per cent. Find retail price.

443. Net cost is $630.63; discount on retail price is 10 per cent; cash discount is 2 per cent. Find retail price.

444. Net cost is $17.64; discount is 25 per cent of retail price; cash discount is 2 per cent. Find retail price.

445. Net cost is $749.70; discount is 15 per cent of retail price; cash discount is 2 per cent. Find retail price.

For situations in which more than two discounts are given, such as, 25 per cent and 5 per cent off, with a cash discount of 2 per cent, the method is the same as used above. None of the discounts can be added, and consequently the problem must be worked as three separate divisions.

Example: What per cent is the profit $1,179 of the cost $7,860?

$$\begin{array}{r} .15 \\ \$7860\overline{)\$1179.00} \\ 7860 \\ \hline 39300 \\ (P \div B = R) \quad 39300 \\ \hline \end{array}$$

For this type of problem a rule may be stated that *whenever it is desired to find what per cent one number is of another, divide one number by the other,* **always** *using the number* (which is the base) *following the word "of" for the divisor.* Stated as a formula $P \div B = R$. In most cases, the base number used as the divisor is larger than the number to be divided, requiring the addition of ciphers in order to divide. .15 = 15 % profit.

446. The profit, $420, is what per cent of the cost, $2,800?

447. The discount, $4.38, is what per cent of the retail price, $36.50?

448. The profit, $6.75, is what per cent of the wages, $45?

449. The loss, $447, is what per cent of the cost, $8,940?

450. The selling price, $4,480, is what per cent of the cost, $4,000?

451. The total charge for a job, $198, is what per cent of the cost, $180?

452. The cost, $4,600, is what per cent of the list price, $5,000?

453. The cost, $33.60, is what per cent of the retail price, $42?

454. The net cost, $6,247.50, is what per cent of the cost, $6,375, and the cost, $6,375 is what per cent of the selling price, $7,500?

455. The net cost, $17.10, is what per cent of the cost $18, and the cost, $18, is what per cent of the retail price, $24?

REDUCTION

Example: Reduce 25 per cent to a decimal; also ½ per cent to a decimal.

$$25\% = \frac{25}{100} = .25$$

$$½\% = \frac{½}{100} = .00½$$

(This process is performed mentally; hence, no problems are given.)

Percentage (by fractions): $6\frac{1}{4}\%$ ($\frac{1}{16}$), $6\frac{2}{3}\%$ ($\frac{1}{15}$), $8\frac{1}{3}\%$ ($\frac{1}{12}$), $11\frac{1}{9}\%$ ($\frac{1}{9}$), etc.

Percentage by fractions cannot be used to advantage in all problems. For example, per cents such as 7 per cent, 23 per cent, 65 per cent, and 98 per cent, are more easily handled as decimals. Because of this fact, and since it is a short-cut method to be used only when convenient, problems of this kind are omitted. However, a table of per cents with fractional equivalents is given below. Problems involving percentages by fractions are worked in the same way as explained for percentage by decimals.

Percentage by decimals can be used in all cases and therefore should be thoroughly learned.

Per Cents and Their Fractional Equivalents

$6\frac{1}{4}\% = \frac{1}{16}$	$16\frac{2}{3}\% = \frac{1}{6}$	$50\% = \frac{1}{2}$	$80\% = \frac{4}{5}$
$6\frac{2}{3}\% = \frac{1}{15}$	$20\% = \frac{1}{5}$	$60\% = \frac{3}{5}$	$83\frac{1}{3}\% = \frac{5}{6}$
$8\frac{1}{3}\% = \frac{1}{12}$	$25\% = \frac{1}{4}$	$62\frac{1}{2}\% = \frac{5}{8}$	$87\frac{1}{2}\% = \frac{7}{8}$
$11\frac{1}{9}\% = \frac{1}{9}$	$33\frac{1}{3}\% = \frac{1}{3}$	$66\frac{2}{3}\% = \frac{2}{3}$	$90\% = \frac{9}{10}$
$12\frac{1}{2}\% = \frac{1}{8}$	$37\frac{1}{2}\% = \frac{3}{8}$	$70\% = \frac{7}{10}$	
$14\frac{2}{7}\% = \frac{1}{7}$	$40\% = \frac{2}{5}$	$75\% = \frac{3}{4}$	

Review

456. Retail price is $27.50; discount is 15 per cent of retail price. Find discount.

457. Cost for labor on job is $350; profit on labor is 15% of cost. Find amount charged for labor.

458. Retail price is $40; discount is 25 per cent on retail price. Find cost.

459. List price is $740; discount is 15 per cent on list price; cash discount is 2 per cent. Find net cost.

460. Discount is $91.20, which is 12 per cent of list price. Find list price.

461. Cost is $14.52; discount is 12 per cent on retail price. Find retail price.

462. Amount charged for labor is $412.02; profit on labor is 9 per cent of cost. Find cost for labor.

463. Net cost is $7.35; discount on retail price is 25 per cent; cash discount is 2 per cent. Find retail price.

464. Catalogue price is $66; discount is 18 per cent of catalogue price. Find cost.

465. List price is $346.50; cash discount is 2 per cent off list. How much was discount?

466. Bill is $750; cash discount is $15.   Find per cent of discount on bill.

467. Cost is $30.20; profit is $6.04.   Find per cent profit on cost.

468. List price is $409.50; discount is 12 per cent of list price; cash discount is 2 per cent.   Find net cost.

469. List price is $216; discounts are 10 and 2 per cent.   What was net cost?

470. Cost is $15.40; discount is 12 per cent of retail price.   Find retail price.

MENSURATION
SQUARE
Perimeter
Area
RECTANGLE
Perimeter
Area
CIRCLE
Circumference
Area
TRIANGLE
Hypotenuse
Area
CUBE
Wall Area
Volume
RECTANGULAR SOLID
Wall Area
Volume
REVIEW

Chart E

VI. MENSURATION[1]

Mensuration is divided into the three mathematical processes of finding lengths, areas, and volumes. Geometrical figures, such as a square, circle, triangle, and cube are used.

In working problems in mensuration it is an advantage to be able to condense a long rule into a brief statement. Such a statement is called a formula. The principal parts of the rule are represented by letters or signs, such as W for width, L for length, V for volume, and π for *pi*. (See key chart, page 109.)

A formula is always divided into two parts, which are separated by an equality sign ($=$). It is customary to use the letter on the left of the equality sign to represent the answer that is to be found. On the right of the equality sign will be the letters which indicate the method of working the problem. For example, the area of a rectangle is equal to width times length. Expressed as a formula this would read: $A = WL$.

NOTE: Two letters written together, as WL above, indicate that the numbers they represent are to be multiplied together. The times sign ($\times$) is omitted as it might be confused with the letter x which is used in formulas.

Plus and minus signs ($+$, $-$) are always written in the formula.   To illustrate: The perimeter of a triangle is equal to the base, plus the altitude, plus the hypotenuse. Expressed as a formula it would read, $P = a + b + h$.

[1] See p. 111.

Division may be indicated by the division sign (÷) but it is customary to state it in the same form as a fraction problem in arithmetic. For example: the area of a rectangle, divided by the width will give the length. In formula form this would be, $L = \dfrac{A}{W}$.

It should be emphasized that both parts of the formula must be equal or "balance" each other in the same sense that an article on the pan of a set of balances must be equaled by the weight in the other pan. The equality sign in a formula corresponds to the pivot in the scale, and the mathematical processes to be worked on the right of the equality sign must always be equal to the desired answer on the left.

A knowledge of this fact makes it possible to use formulas in an intelligent manner. To illustrate: A rectangle is 30″ wide and 8′ 0″ long. What is its area? Condensed to a formula $A = WL$. If A is to be in square inches, then the length 8′ 0″ must be changed to 96″ or $A = 30″ \times 96″$; if the answer is desired in square feet the width, 30″, must be changed to feet; or $A = 2\frac{1}{2}′ \times 8′ 0″$.

In working the following problems it is very important that the plan of working each problem, as outlined in the examples given, be followed step by step. This will develop the habit of working a problem systematically which is very valuable particularly when more difficult problems have to be solved.

THE SQUARE

Perimeter: $P = 4S$

Example: The side of a square is 9′. Find the perimeter.

$P = 4S$	P = perimeter, or the distance around the square.
$S = 9′$	S = length of one side.
$P = 4 \times 9′$	The perimeter equals four times the length of one side.
$P = 36′$	If S is in inches, then the perimeter will be in inches.

Problems

Find the perimeter of the following squares:

471. Side 18″.
472. Side 34″.
473. Side 25′.
474. Side 32′.
475. Side 42′.

476. Side 53'.
477. Side 2' 5''.
478. Side 4' 7''.
479. Side 14' 6''.
480. Side 22' 9''.

Area: $A = S^2$ or $S \times S$

Example: Find the area of a square, one side of which measures 7 ft.

$A = S^2$	A = area. S = length of one side.
$S = 7'$	Area equals the square of one side or $S \times S$.
$A = 7' \times 7'$	If the length of the side is expressed in feet, the
$A = 49'$	area will be in square feet.

Find the area of the following squares:

481. Side 11'.
482. Side 14'.
483. Side 28''.
484. Side 42''.
485. Side 2' 9''.
486. Side 5' 3''.
487. Side 25' 6''.
488. Side 38' 3''.
489. Side 3' 6''.
490. Side 6' 9''.

The Rectangle

Perimeter: $P = (W + L)2$

Example: Find the perimeter of a rectangle with a length of 9' and a width of 5'.

$P = (W + L)2$	P = perimeter or the distance around.
$W = 5'$	W = width of one end.
$L = 9'$	L = length of one side.
$P = (5 + 9)2$	The perimeter equals two times the sum of,
$P = 14 \times 2$	one end plus one side. Both dimensions must
$P = 28'$	be expressed in terms of the same denomination
	which will be the denomination of the perimeter.
	The times sign is omitted in the formula between

the parenthesis and the figure 2.

The use of parentheses, in a formula, needs some explanation. It shows that the operations indicated inside the parentheses must be performed before working the rest of the formula.

Problems

Find the perimeter of the following rectangles:

491. Width 11′, length 14′.
492. Width 12′, length 16′.
493. Width 15″, length 22″.
494. Width 18″, length 32″.
495. Width 2′ 1″, length 4′ 3″.
496. Width 3′ 7″, length 4′ 9″.
497. Width 5′, length 15′ 11″.
498. Width 8′, length 14′ 5″.
499. Width 25′ 6″, length 45′ 6″.
500. Width 18′ 9″, length 38′ 6″.

Area: $A = WL$
Example: Find the area of a rectangle 8′ long and 6′ wide

$A = WL$	A = area. W = width. L = length.
$W = 6'$	The area equals the width times the length.
$L = 8'$	Both dimensions must be in the same denomina-
$A = 6 \times 8$	tion and the area will be in square units of the
$A = 48$ sq. ft.	same denomination.

Find the area of the following rectangles:

501. Width 5′, length 7′.
502. Width 9′, length 11′.
503. Width 9″, length 17″.
504. Width 19″, length 37″.
505. Width 3′ 1″, length 5′ 7″.
506. Width 4′ 10″, length 8′ 2″.
507. Width 23′ 6″, length 38′ 6″.
508. Width 16′ 3″, length 20′ 3″.
509. Width 12′ 9″, length 22′ 0″.
510. Width 15′ 0″, length 36′ 6″.

THE CIRCLE

Circumference: $c = \pi d$ $\qquad d = 2r$

Example: Find the circumference of a circle with a radius of 4′.

$C = \pi d$

$r = 4'$

$d = 8'$

$c = (3.1416)8$

$c = 25.1328'$

But $.1328' \times 12'' = 1.5936''$

and $.5936 \times \dfrac{16}{16} = \dfrac{9.4976}{16}$

$c = 25'\ 1\%_{6}''$

C = circumference, or the distance around.

d = diameter, or twice the radius.

The circumference equals 3.1416 times the diameter. The circumference will have the same denomination that the diameter has. 25.1328′ can be reduced to feet and inches by multiplying the decimal part (.1328′) by 12″, giving 1.5936″. The decimal part of an inch, .5936″, can be reduced to 16ths of an inch by multiplying .5936 by 16 giving 9.4976 which makes 9 whole sixteenths and .4976 of a sixteenth. This decimal part of a sixteenth is dropped.

Problems

Find the circumference of the following circles:

511. Diameter 16″.
512. Diameter 32″.
513. Diameter 13′ 0″.
514. Diameter 18′ 0″.
515. Radius 4″.
516. Radius 15′ 0″.
517. Diameter 16′ 6″.
518. Diameter 22′ 4″.
519. Radius 4′ 9″.
520. Radius 6′ 3″.

Any one of the following formulas may be used to obtain the circumference.

Using the radius	Using the diameter	
$c = 2\pi r$	$c = \pi d$	Using $\pi = \dfrac{22}{7}$ is not as accurate as using π equal to 3.1416.
$c = \dfrac{2(22)r}{7}$	$c = \dfrac{22d}{7}$	
$c = 2(3.1416)r$	$c = 3.1416d$	The radius of a circle is always one-half of the diameter.

Area: $A = \pi r^2$ $r = d/2$

Example: Find the area of a circle with a 12′ diameter.

$A = \pi r^2$ $d = 12'$ $r = 6'$ $A = \pi(6)^2$ $A = (3.1416) \times 6 \times 6$ $A = 113.0976$ sq. ft. But .0976 sq. ft. $\times$ 144 sq. in. $= 14.0544$ sq. in., or 14 sq. in. $A = 113$ sq. ft. 14 sq. in.	$A = $ area. $r = $ radius. Area equals the product of 3.1416 times the radius squared. The area will be units of the same denomination that the radius is. The answer can be left as 113.0976 sq. ft., or the decimal part .0976 can be reduced to square inches by multiplying by 144 sq. in. This gives 14.0544 sq. in. which is considered as 14 sq. in.

Find the area of the following circles:

521. Diameter 8′ 0″.
522. Diameter 20″.
523. Radius 6′ 0″.
524. Radius 9′ 0″.
525. Diameter 14′ 0″.
526. Diameter 3′ 0″
527. Radius 11″.
528. Radius 18″.
529. Radius 4′ 6″.
530. Radius 6′ 8″.

Any one of the following formulas may be used to obtain the **area.**

Using the radius	Using the diameter	
$A = \pi r^2$	$A = \dfrac{\pi d^2}{4}$	Using π equal to $\dfrac{22}{7}$ is not as accurate as using π equal to 3.1416. The radius of a circle is always equal to one-half of the diameter.
$A = \dfrac{22r^2}{7}$	$A = \dfrac{11d^2}{14}$	
$A = 3.1416r^2$	$A = .7854d^2$	

The Triangle

Hypotenuse : $h = \sqrt{a^2 + b^2}$

Example: Find the hypotenuse of a triangle whose altitude is 15′ and base 36′.

$h = \sqrt{a^2 + b^2}$
$a = 15'$
$b = 36'$
$h = \sqrt{15^2 + 36^2}$
$h = \sqrt{225 + 1296}$
$h = \sqrt{1521}$

$$\begin{array}{r} /3 \quad 9 \\ \overline{15} \ \ \overline{21} \\ 9 \\ \overline{621} \\ 69/ \ \ 621 \\ \end{array}$$

$h = 39'$

h = hypotenuse. a = altitude. b = base. The hypotenuse of a triangle equals the square root of the sum of the altitude squared plus the base squared. The altitude and base must be of the same denomination, which will be the denomination of the hypotenuse. The square root of 1,521 is found as follows: Point off 1,521 into groups of two figures each, beginning at the right. Indicate each group by drawing a line above the two figures. Find the largest perfect square that can be subtracted from the left-hand period.

The largest square is 9. Since it is the square of 3, 3 becomes the first number in the answer. Subtract 9 from 15 and bring down the second group, giving 621.

Double the first number in the answer, which gives 6 as the trial divisor. This trial divisor is divided into 62, giving 9. Place the 9 after the 6, making 69. Also place the 9 in the answer.

Multiply 69 by 9, giving 621, which subtracts with no remainder.

Therefore the square root of 1521 is **39.**

Problems

Find the hypotenuse of the following triangles. (Use either the square root method or the steel square method as outlined below.)

531. Altitude 6′, base 8′.
532. Altitude 9″, base 12″.
533. Altitude 12′, base 16′.
534. Altitude 10″, base 24″.
535. Altitude 15′, base 20′.
536. Altitude 5″, base 12″.
537. Altitude 18′, base 24′.
538. Altitude 21″, base 28″.
539. Altitude 20′, base 48′.
540. Altitude 24″, base 32″.

The second method for finding the hypotenuse of a triangle is by the use of the carpenter's steel square (see Fig. 94). This process is much more adaptable to the problems a carpenter meets and is fully explained on page 115 in Chap. VI.

541. Altitude 8″, base 17″.
542. Altitude 7″, base 14″.
543. Altitude 13″, base 15½″.
544. Altitude 5¼″, base 9⅝″.
545. Altitude 3½″, base 11″.
546. Altitude 6′ 0″, base 9′ 0″.

Work this problem as usual but "read" the answer in terms of feet instead of inches. The problem is greatly simplified if a square that is stamped in 12th's is used (see Fig. 96).

547. Altitude 5′ 8″, base 10′ 2″.
548. Altitude 7′ 4″, base 15′ 3″.
549. Altitude 11′ 6″, base 9′ 7″.
550. Altitude 9′ 5″, base 7′ 11″.
551. Altitude 10′ 7″, base 5′ 1″.
552. Altitude 8′ 3″, base 11′ 10″.
553. Altitude 6′ 9″, base 8′ 2″.
554. Altitude 16′ 8″, base 30′ 4″.

For problems that are too large to be measured on the square, divide each number by 2, measure as usual, and then multiply the answer by 2. Any reduction will do, provided that the hypotenuse as measured is increased as much as the original figures were decreased.

555. Altitude 20′ 6″, base 28′ 8″.
556. Altitude 14′ 10″, base 26′ 2″.
557. Altitude 18′ 4″, base 32′ 6″.
558. Altitude 22′ 2″, base 34′ 10″.
559. Altitude 7′ 5″, base 15′ 3″.
560. Altitude 9′ 7″, base 11′ 11″.

Area: $A = \frac{1}{2}ab$

Example: Find the area of a triangle whose base is 7′ and whose altitude is 12′.

$A = \frac{1}{2}ab$ $a = 7'$ $b = 12'$ $A = \frac{1}{2} \times \frac{7}{1} \times \frac{\overset{6}{\cancel{12}}}{1}$ $A = 42$ sq. ft.	A = area. a = altitude. b = base. The area of a triangle equals one-half the product of the base, times the altitude. (The area of a triangle equals one-half the area of a rectangle.) The altitude and base must be of the same denomination, and the area will be in square units of the same denomination.

Find the area of the following triangles:
561. Altitude 9′, base 16′.
562. Altitude 7″, base 12″.
563. Altitude 7′, base 11′.
564. Altitude 16″, base 22″.
565. Altitude 2′ 5″, base 3′ 1″.
566. Altitude 3′ 10″, base 5′ 5″.
567. Altitude 10′ 6″, base 17′ 4″.
568. Altitude 5′ 3″, base 6′ 8″.
569. Altitude 3′ 6″, base 14′ 9″.
570. Altitude 2′ 8″, base 18′ 6″.

CUBE

Wall Area: $WA = 4S^2$

Example: Find the wall area of a cube, each side being 8′.

A, B, C, D, equals walls of cube.

$WA = 4S^2$ $S = 8'$ $WA = 4(8)^2$ $WA = 4 \times 8 \times 8$ $WA = 256$ sq. ft.	WA = wall area or the total area of the four vertical sides. S = length of one side. The wall area of a cube equals four times the area of one vertical side. The wall area will be in square units of the same denomination as the length of each side.

Problems

Find the wall area of the following cubes:

571. $S = 7'$.
572. $S = 15''$.
573. $S = 5'$.
574. $S = 12''$.
575. $S = 8' 7''$.
576. $S = 3' 5''$.
577. $S = 6' 10''$.
578. $S = 15' 6''$.
579. $S = 10' 6''$.
580. $S = 24' 4''$.

Volume: $V = S^3$

Example: Find the volume of a cube, each side of which is 8′.

$V = S^3$ $S = 8'$ $V = (8)^3$ $V = 8 \times 8 \times 8$ $V = 512$ cu. ft.	V = volume. S = length of one side. The volume of a cube equals the length of one side cubed, for example $(8)^3 = 8 \times 8 \times 8$. The volume will be in cubic units of the same denomination as the length of one side.

Find the volume of the following cubes:

581. $S = 9'$.
582. $S = 14''$.
583. $S = 5'$.
584. $S = 8''$.
585. $S = 8' 11''$.
586. $S = 4' 7''$.
587. $S - 2' 10''$.
588. $S = 15' 8''$.
589. $S = 12' 6''$.
590. $S = 16' 9''$.

RECTANGULAR SOLID

Wall Area: $WA = 2(W + L)H$

Example: Find the wall area of a rectangular solid 11' long, 6' wide and 8' deep.

A, B, C, D equals wall area.

$WA = 2(L + W)H$ $L = 11'$ $W = 6'$ $D = 8'$ $WA = 2(11 + 6)8$ $WA = 2(17)8$ $WA = 272$ sq. ft.	WA = wall area. W = width. L = length. H = height. The wall area of rectangle equals two times the sum of the length plus the width, and this product times the height. The wall area will be in square units of the same denomination as the dimensions. All three dimensions must be in terms of the same denomination when substituted in the formula.

Problems

Find the wall area of the following rectangles:

591. $W = 8', L = 9', H = 7'$.
592. $W = 11'', L = 15'', H = 10''$.
593. $W = 6', L = 6', H = 8'$.
594. $W = 7'', L = 11'', H = 5''$.
595. $W = 5' 2'', L = 9' 5'', H = 7' 7''$.
596. $W = 6' 7'', L = 15' 2'', D = 5' 7''$.
597. $W = 8' 3'', L = 22' 7'', D = 6' 10''$.
598. $W = 18' 4'', L = 25' 6'', H = 9' 3''$.
599. $W = 20' 6'', L = 32' 4'', D = 9' 3''$.
600. $W = 12' 3'', L = 46' 3'', D = 7' 6''$.

Volume: $V = LWH$

Example: Find the volume of a rectangular solid 9' long, 7' wide and 8' deep.

$V = LWH$ $L = 9'$ $W = 7'$ $D = 8'$ $V = 9 \times 7 \times 8$ $V = 504$ cu. ft.	V = volume. L = length. W = width. H = height. The volume of a rectangular solid is the product of the length, times the width, times the height. The volume will be in cubic units of the same denomination as the dimensions used. All three dimensions must be in terms of the same denomination when substituted in the formula.

Find the volume of the following rectangular solids:

601. $W = 8', L = 10', D = 7'$.
602. $W = 10'', L = 16'', D = 8''$.
603. $W = 14'', L = 34'', D = 16''$.
604. $W = 16', L = 44', D = 8'$.
605. $W = 6'\ 2'', L = 8'\ 5'', D = 7'\ 5''$.
606. $W = 9'\ 2'', L = 28'\ 6'', D = 6'\ 7''$.
607. $W = 19'\ 7'', L = 84'\ 2'', D = 12'\ 1''$.
608. $W = 15'\ 6'', L = 18'\ 6'', D = 9'\ 0''$.
609. $W = 32'\ 6'', L = 80'\ 6'', D = 12'\ 3''$.
610. $W = 28'\ 3'', L = 36'\ 4'', D = 8'\ 6''$.

REVIEW

611. What is the perimeter of a square that is 9' 0'' in size?
612. A rectangle is 4' 0'' wide and 8' 0'' long.   What is the perimeter?
613. What is the volume of a rectangular solid 4' 0'' × 6' 6'' × 3' 8''?
614. What is the area of a circle that is 5' 0'' in diameter?
615. If the side of a square is 52'', what is the perimeter?
616. What is the volume of a 9'' cube?
617. What is the area of a rectangle that is 6' 0'' wide and 34' 0'' long?
618. What is the wall area of a rectangular solid 3' 4'' × 11' 0'' × 9' 0''?
619. What is the area of a square that is 10' 6'' × 10' 6'' in size?
620. A 11'' cube has how much wall area?
621. A square 13' × 13' contains how many square feet of area?
622. What are the contents of a 4' 6'' cube?
623. What is the area of a circle 6' 0'' in diameter?
624. A rectangle 3' 8'' × 7' 6'' contains how many square feet?
625. What is the circumference of a circle that has a 9'' diameter?
626. Using the steel square, find the hypotenuse of a triangle that has a base of 4' 8'' and an altitude of 5' 2''.
627. What is the perimeter of a rectangle 22' 8'' × 34' 8''?
628. A triangle has a base measurement of 4' 0'' and an altitude of 7' 6''.   What is its area?
629. What is the hypotenuse of a triangle with a 3' 10'' base and a 6' 7'' altitude?   Use the steel square in solving.

630. A circle has a radius of 7' 6". What is the circumference?

631. What is the wall area of a rectangular solid 2' 6" × 3' 0" × 8' 4"?

632. What is the area of a triangle that has a base of 5' 8" and an altitude of 7' 0"?

633. What is the volume of a rectangular solid 3' 0" × 6' 8" × 2' 4"?

634. What is the square root of 2,209?

635. What is the wall area of a 6' 6" cube?

VII. LUMBER AND BOARD MEASURE[1]

A detailed description of lumber, its uses, and how it is figured is given in Chap. VII; hence, the information given here will be brief.

Original Sizes of Lumber.— Lumber is always figured on the basis of its original size, as cut in the sawmill. Owing to shrinkage, a rough piece of lumber will usually measure a little "under" the rough size. These sizes are from 1" in thickness and up; 2" in width and "up," and on the even-foot length, beginning with an 8' length.

Thickness of Lumber.—Lumber less than 1" thick is always counted as 1" stock, as a 1" piece of stock is usually planed down to the desired thickness. Above 1", it can be purchased in 1¼", 1½", 2", 3", 4", 6", etc., thick.

LUMBER AND BOARD MEASURE
BOARD MEASURE
Piece Rule
Running Foot Rule
School Practice
LUMBER COSTS
Price per M. to Price per bd. ft.
Price per bd. ft. to Price per M.
Bd. ft. to Total Cost
Lumber Sizes to Total Cost
REVIEW

CHART F

Width of Lumber.—Standard widths of lumber are 2", 3", 4", 5" (5" in 1" finish stock only) 6", 8", 10", 12", etc. A piece of lumber wider than any one of these widths is figured the next standard width above; as a 6½" board is counted as 8", 4⅛" as 6", 9⅝" as 10", etc. Hardwoods are also purchased in odd widths.

Lengths of Lumber.—Lengths of lumber are generally on the even-foot basis, as 8', 10', 12', 14', 16', etc., up to 24'. Above 24', lengths can be secured on special orders. Also, 3', 5', 7', 9', and 11' can be cut from twice their length.

[1] See p. 129.

Narrow stock is generally ordered by the running or linear foot, although paid for by the board foot.

Unit of Measurement.—The unit or basis of measurement for lumber is the board foot, which is a piece of lumber $1''$ thick, $12''$ wide and $12''$ long, *or its equivalent value* (see Fig. 104).

Basic Rule.—The basic rule for finding the number of board feet in a piece of lumber is: *Number of pieces times thickness in inches times width in feet times length in feet.* Expressed as a formula, this becomes: bd. ft. = pc. $\times T'' \times W' \times L'$. The width measurement, however, is commonly stated in terms of inches and not feet. Also, in schoolwork, the length is often computed in inches and not feet. Again, lumber may be purchased by the piece and then sometimes by the running or linear foot. This accounts for the other three formulas given in Chart VI, namely, piece rule, running-foot rule, and school practice. The relationship of these rules to the basic rule is shown by the following chart and explanation:

Basic rule..............	pc.	T''	W'	L'	=	bd. ft.	
Piece rule..............	pc.	T''	$\dfrac{W''}{12}$	L'	=	bd. ft.	or $\dfrac{\text{Pc. } T''W''L'}{12}$ = bd. ft.
Running-foot rule.......		T''	$\dfrac{W''}{12}$	L'	=	bd. ft.	or $\dfrac{T''W''L'}{12}$ = bd. ft.
School-practice rule	pc.	T''	$\dfrac{W''}{12}$	$\dfrac{L''}{12}$	=	bd. ft.	or $\dfrac{\text{Pc. } T''W''L''}{144}$ = bd. ft.

In the running-foot rule the term piece (pc.) is omitted because it would always be equal to one. If it were used in the formula the answer would not be changed.

In all of the formulas, except the basic rule, the width (W) is expressed in inches. But the width in inches is divided by 12, which makes $W''/12$. This gives an answer in feet or parts of a foot. In other words, $W''/12 =$ feet $= W'$, as given in the basic rule. For example, $6''/12 = \frac{1}{2}'$.

In the school-practice formula the length (L) is expressed in inches. But the L in inches is divided by 12 which makes the $L''/12 =$ feet $= L'$, as given in the basic rule. For example, $18''/12 = \frac{3}{2}'$.

In this way, each of the special rules takes the dimensions as given and reduces them to the denominations given in the basic rule.

All problems that are to be solved by any one of the special rules can be solved directly by the use of the basic rule as illustrated below:

Piece-rule problem: (RULE: pc. $\times T'' \times \dfrac{W''}{12} \times L' =$ bd. ft.)

How many board feet are there in six pieces $2'' \times 8'' \times 10'$?
Substituting directly into the basic rule: pc. $= 6$; $T''' = 2$; $W' = \frac{8}{12}$; $L' = 10$

Hence: $\dfrac{6}{1} \times \dfrac{2}{1} \times \dfrac{8}{12} \times \dfrac{10}{1} =$ bd. ft.

Running-foot problem: (RULE: $T'' \times W''/12 \times L' \times$ bd. ft.)

How many board feet are there in 150 lin. feet of $2'' \times 4''$?
Substituting directly into the basic rule: pc. $= 1$, $T''' = 2$, $W' = \frac{4}{12}$, $L' = 150$.

Hence: $\dfrac{1}{1} \times \dfrac{2}{1} \times \dfrac{4}{12} \times \dfrac{150}{1} =$ bd. ft.

School-practice problem: (RULE: pc. $\times T'' \times W''/12 \times L''/12 =$ bd. ft.)

How many board feet are there in four pieces $1'' \times 6'' \times 30''$?
Substituting directly into the basic rule: pc. $= 4$, $T''' = 1$, $W' = \frac{6}{12}$, $L' = {}^{30}\!\!/_{12}$.

Hence: $\dfrac{4}{1} \times \dfrac{1}{1} \times \dfrac{6}{12} \times \dfrac{30}{12} =$ bd. ft.

The above explanations should make it clear that the three special rules, as given, are derived from the basic rule.

The following problems will be classified and explained according to the three rules given. All fractional answers of $\frac{1}{2}$ or over are to be counted as the next whole number above, as lumber is always sold on that basis.

PIECE RULE

Board Measure.

Example: Find the number of board feet in six pieces $2'' \times 10''$ $16' 0''$?

$\dfrac{\text{pc. } T''W''L'}{12} =$ bd. ft. Substituting: $\dfrac{\cancel{6} \times \cancel{2} \times 10 \times 16}{\underset{\cancel{6}}{\cancel{12}}} = 160$ bd. ft.	pc. $= 6$ $T'' = 2''$ $W'' = 10''$ $l' = 16'$	Substituting these values for each letter in the formula and cancelling gives 160 bd. ft.

In any of these rules the method of using one line beneath all of the letters indicates the fact that the 12 below the line can be cancelled into any of the numbers above the line. So far as the final answer is concerned, it does not matter whether the 12 is divided into W'', reducing the width to feet, or divided into one or more of the numbers above the line.

Problems

Find the number of board feet in the following problems:[1]

636. 5 pcs. $1'' \times 6'' \times 18'$.
637. 24 pcs. $1'' \times 8'' \times 14'$.
638. 6 pcs. $2'' \times 3'' \times 12'$.
639. 14 pcs. $1'' \times 4'' \times 18'$.
640. 34 pcs. $2'' \times 4'' \times 16'$.
641. 54 pcs. $1'' \times 3'' \times 20'$.
642. 28 pcs. $2'' \times 6'' \times 10'$.
643. 32 pcs. $1'' \times 10'' \times 16'$
644. 22 pcs. $2'' \times 12'' \times 22'$
645. 62 pcs. $1'' \times 10'' \times 18'$.
646. 10 pcs. $1\frac{1}{2}'' \times 8'' \times 14'$.

When thickness is in terms of a mixed number, as $1\frac{1}{2}''$ or $1\frac{1}{4}''$, convert to an improper fraction and then proceed as usual, placing the denominators 2 or 4 below the line.

647. 26 pcs. $1\frac{1}{4}'' \times 4'' \times 18.'$
648. 38 pcs. $1\frac{1}{2}'' \times 10'' \times 20'$
649. 75 pcs. $1\frac{1}{4}'' \times 8'' \times 16'$.
650. 126 pcs. $1\frac{1}{4}'' \times 6'' \times 14'$.
651. 44 pcs. $\frac{3}{4}'' \times 6\frac{1}{2}'' \times 12'$.

Lumber less than $1''$ thick is counted as the full inch, as $1''$ lumber is required to make $\frac{3}{4}''$ stock. Above $1''$ thick, standard thicknesses are $1\frac{1}{4}''$, $1\frac{1}{2}''$, $2''$, $3''$, $4''$, $6''$, etc; hence, board measure problems are figured on this basis. For odd widths, count the next standard width above the exact width required. Standard widths are $2''$, $3''$, $4''$, $5''$, $6''$, $8''$, $10''$, $12''$.

652. 18 pcs. $\frac{1}{2}'' \times 4'' \times 16'$.
653. 62 pcs. $\frac{3}{4}'' \times 9\frac{1}{4}'' \times 14'$.
654. 84 pcs. $\frac{5}{8}'' \times 10'' \times 16'$.
655. 77 pcs. $\frac{3}{4}'' \times 3\frac{1}{2}'' \times 18'$.
656. 64 pcs. $1\frac{3}{4}'' \times 5\frac{1}{2}'' \times 20'$.
657. 30 pcs. $\frac{1}{2}'' \times 4\frac{1}{2}'' \times 12'$.
658. 58 pcs. $1''$ net $\times 7\frac{3}{8}'' \times 16'$.

The term "net" indicates the stock must be milled to that exact dimension but next size stock must be figured.

659. 22 pcs. $\frac{3}{4}'' \times 6\frac{3}{4}'' \times 10'$.
660. 18 pcs. $\frac{5}{8}'' \times 4\frac{1}{8}'' \times 8'$.
661. 134 pcs. $\frac{3}{4}'' \times 3\frac{1}{2}'' \times 12'$.
662. 42 pcs. $1\frac{3}{4}'' \times 4\frac{3}{4}'' \times 20'$.
663. 6 pcs. $1\frac{1}{4}''$ net $\times 4'' \times 18'$.
664. 88 pcs. $1\frac{1}{2}''$ net $\times 8''$ net $\times 16'$.
665. 38 pcs. $\frac{3}{4}'' \times 5''$ net $\times 18'$.

Running Foot Rule

Example: Find the number of board feet in 150 lin. ft. of $2'' \times 4''$ stock.

[1] See footnote, p. 128.

$\dfrac{T''W''L'}{12} = \text{bd. ft.}$ $\dfrac{2 \times 4 \times \cancel{150}^{50}}{\cancel{12}_{3}} = 100 \text{ bd. ft.}$	$T'' = 2''$. $W'' = 4''$. $L' = 150'$. Substituting these values for each letter in the formula and cancelling gives 100 bd. ft.

Find the number of board feet of lumber in the following problems:[1]

666. 240 lin. ft. $2'' \times 6''$.
667. 134 lin. ft. $1'' \times 3''$.
668. 76 lin. ft. $1'' \times 2''$.
669. 26 lin. ft. $1'' \times 4''$.
670. 360 lin. ft. $1'' \times 3''$.
671. 188 lin. ft. $1\frac{1}{4}'' \times 3''$.

See note, problem 646.

672. 155 lin. ft. $1\frac{1}{2}'' \times 4''$.
673. 82 lin. ft. $1\frac{1}{4}'' \times 2''$.
674. 60 lin. ft. $1\frac{1}{2}'' \times 3''$.
675. 46 lin. ft. $1\frac{1}{4}'' \times 3''$.
676. 96 lin. ft. $\frac{3}{4}'' \times 2\frac{1}{2}''$.

See note, problem 651.

677. 450 lin. ft. $\frac{1}{2}'' \times 1\frac{1}{2}''$.
678. 648 lin. ft. $\frac{3}{4}'' \times 2\frac{3}{8}''$.
679. 156 lin. ft. $\frac{3}{4}'' \times 3''$ net.

See note, problem 658.

680. 432 lin. ft. $\frac{1}{2}'' \times 2''$ net.

SCHOOL-PRACTICE RULE

Example: Find the number of board feet in three pieces $2'' \times 8'' \times 48''$.

$\dfrac{\text{pc. } T''W''L''}{144} = \text{bd. ft.}$ $\dfrac{3 \times 2 \times 8 \times \cancel{48}}{\cancel{144}_{3}} = 16 \text{ bd. ft.}$	pc. = 3. $T'' = 2''$. $W'' = 8''$. $L'' = 48''$. Substituting these values for each letter in the formula and cancelling gives 16 bd. ft.

In the following problems find the number of board feet of lumber:[1]

681. 4 pcs. $1'' \times 6'' \times 42''$.
682. 8 pcs. $1'' \times 3'' \times 36''$.
683. 8 pcs. $2'' \times 3'' \times 48''$.
[1] See footnote p. 128.

684. 3 pcs. $1'' \times 4'' \times 18''$.
685. 7 pcs. $1'' \times 6'' \times 30''$.
686. 12 pcs. $1\frac{1}{4}'' \times 4'' \times 36''$.

See note under problem 646

687. 5 pcs. $1\frac{1}{4}'' \times 3'' \times 24''$.
688. 8 pcs. $1\frac{1}{2}'' \times 5'' \times 42''$.
689. 3 pcs. $1\frac{1}{4}'' \times 3'' \times 20''$.
690. 9 pcs. $1\frac{1}{2}'' \times 6'' \times 54''$.
691. 10 pcs. $\frac{1}{2}'' \times 4\frac{1}{2}'' \times 48''$.

See note under problem 651.

692. 14 pcs. $\frac{5}{8}'' \times 3\frac{1}{2}'' \times 36''$.
693. 12 pcs. $\frac{3}{4}'' \times 2\frac{1}{2}'' \times 42''$.
694. 6 pcs. $\frac{5}{8}'' \times 4''$ net $\times 54''$.
695. 5 pcs. $1''$ net $\times 3''$ net $\times 36''$.

Lumber Costs.

The basis for figuring the cost of lumber is in terms of a thousand board feet, usually written MB.F. or simply M, as $32.50 per M. Since the price varies as to the kind of lumber, its grade, its size, etc., it is necessary to figure various parts of a lumber bill separately. As the price is often given on the basis of a thousand feet, it is often necessary to find the cost of a single foot. This is quickly found by the following rule:

To change the price per MB.F. to the price of one board foot, move the decimal point three places to the left as $49.00 per M reduces to $0.049 per board foot.

$$\text{Stated as a formula:} \frac{\text{price per M}}{1,000} = \text{price per bd. ft.}$$

The opposite of this is also true: To change the cost per board foot to the cost per M, move the decimal point three places to the right, as $0.036 per board foot, changes to $36.00 per M.
Stated as a formula: price per board foot times 1,000 = price per M.

To find the cost of a given amount of lumber, multiply the total number of board feet by its cost per M and move the decimal point *five* places (two places for cents and three places for MB.F.).

$$\text{Stated as a formula:} \frac{\text{bd. ft. times price per M}}{1,000} = \text{cost.}$$

Price per M to Price per Board Foot

Example: Change $28.50 per M to price per board foot.

$\dfrac{\text{price per M}}{1,000}$ = price per board foot.	Dividing 1,000 into $28.50 can be performed mentally by moving the decimal point three places to the left.
$\dfrac{\$28.50}{1,000}$ = $0.028 per board foot.	

Problems

In the following problems, find the cost per board foot by moving the decimal point:

696. Change $48.50 per M to price per board foot.
697. Change $32.50 per M to price per board foot.
698. Change $44.00 per M to price per board foot.
699. Change $87.50 per M to price per board foot.
700. Change $63.25 per M to price per board foot.

PRICE PER BOARD FOOT TO PRICE PER M

Example: Change $0.0365 per board foot to price per M.

price per bd. ft. × 1,000 = price per M $0.0365 × 1,000 = $36.50	Multiplying 1,000 by $0.0365 can be performed mentally by moving the decimal point three places to the right.

Problems

Work the following five problems, performing the multiplication by moving the decimal point:

701. Change $0.048 per board foot to price per M.
702. Change $0.072 per board foot to price per M.
703. Change $0.064 per board foot to price per M.
704. Change $0.05 per board foot to price per M.
705. Change $0.041 per board foot to price per M.

BOARD FEET TO TOTAL COST

Example: Find the cost of 540 bd. ft. of lumber at $45.50 per M.

$\dfrac{\text{bd. ft.} \times \text{price per M}}{1,000}$ = cost $\dfrac{540 \times \$45.50}{1,000}$ = $24.57	This problem can also be worked by multiplying 540 × $45.50 and pointing off five places (two places for cents and three places for M).

Problems

What is the cost of lumber in the following problems?

706. 385 bd. ft. at $44 per M.
707. 850 bd. ft. at $52.50 per M.
708. 1,240 bd. ft. at $35.70 per M.
709. 2,720 bd. ft. at $62.25 per M.
710. 4,570 bd. ft. at $57.50 per M.

LUMBER SIZES TO TOTAL COST

Example: Find the cost of 5 pieces of 2 × 4 × 12 at $24.50 per M.

Find the number of board feet (using one of the formulas). Multiply the number of board feet by the cost per M.

711. What is the cost of 10 pcs. 2″ × 8″ × 16′ @ $32.50 per M?
712. 24 pcs. 1″ × 10″ × 18′ costs how much at $47 per M?
713. At $54 per M, what is the cost of 188 pcs. 1″ × 8″ × 14′?
714. What is the cost of 30 pcs. 2″ × 10″ × 22′ at $31.50 per M?
715. 74 pcs. 1″ × 4″ × 18′ are worth how much at $42 per M?
716. What is the cost of 138 lin. ft. 2″ × 4″ at $33 per M?
717. 240 lin. ft. of 1″ × 2″ at $72 per M are worth how much?
718. 680 lin. ft. 1″ × 3″ are worth how much at $56 per M?
719. What is the cost of 1,240 lin. ft. of ½″ × 4″ at $47 per M?
720. 760 lin. ft. of 2″ × 2″ at $39 per M are worth how much?

REVIEW

721. How many board feet are there in 16 pcs. 2″ × 8″ × 22′?
722. 34 pcs. of ¾″ × 3⅝″ × 18′ contain how many board feet of lumber?
723. What is the "footage" of 16 pcs. 1¼″ × 10″ × 12′?
724. How many board feet are there in 36 pcs. ½″ × 2⅜″ × 16′?
725. What is the cost per M at $0.038 per foot?
726. 156 lin. ft. of ⅝″ × 3″ net contain how many board feet?
727. 12 pcs. ¾″ × 3½″ × 54″ contain how many board feet?
728. What is the cost of 458 bd. ft. of lumber at $64 per M?
729. At $35 per M, what is the cost of 68 pcs. 2″ × 12″ × 24′?
730. How much are 138 pcs. of 2″ × 6″ × 18′ worth at $44.25?
731. At $0.034 per foot, what is the cost per M?
732. At $52.50 per M, what is the cost of 890 lin. ft. of ½″ × 2″?
733. How many board feet are there in 78 pcs. of 1¼″ × 8″ × 14′?
734. 286 lin. ft. of 1″ × 4″ contain how many board feet of lumber?
735. What is the cost per bd. ft. at $56.50 per M?
736. What is the cost of 22 pcs. ⅝″ × 10½″ × 48″ at $118 per M?
737. At $180 per M, what is the cost of 18 pcs. ¾″ × 5″ net × 8′ 0″?
738. At $37 per M, what is the cost per foot?

739. 144 lin. ft. of $1\frac{1}{2}'' \times 8''$ contain how many board feet of lumber?

740. What is the cost of 88 pcs. $\frac{5}{8}'' \times 10''$ net $\times 10'$?   Cost $64 per M.

741. How many board feet are there in 56 pcs. $\frac{5}{8}'' \times 10\frac{1}{2}'' \times 14'$?

742. What is the cost of 48 pcs. $\frac{1}{2}'' \times 5\frac{1}{2}'' \times 54''$ at $98 per M?

743. $88 per M is how much per foot?

744. What is the cost of 250 pcs. $1\frac{1}{2}''$ $\times 6'' \times 10'$ at $45 per M?

745. At $63 per M, what is the cost of 500 lin. ft. $1'' \times 3''$?

VIII. CORRELATED REVIEW

ADDITION

Whole Numbers.

746. Add 876, 263, 482, 763.

747. Add 17' 5'', 9' 6'', 35' 10''.

Decimals.

748. Add 38.29, 79.834, 50.7, 830.5.

Fractions.

749. Add $5\frac{1}{3}$, $1\frac{3}{4}$, $\frac{3}{5}$, $1\frac{5}{6}$.

750. Add 16' $7\frac{1}{2}''$, 12' $5\frac{1}{8}''$, 11' $7\frac{1}{4}''$, 5' $3\frac{7}{8}''$.

Percentage.

751. Add: cost $3,000; profit $1,000, which is $33\frac{1}{3}$ per cent.   Find selling price and per cent that equals it.

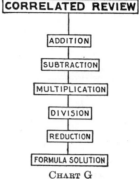

CORRELATED REVIEW

ADDITION

SUBTRACTION

MULTIPLICATION

DIVISION

REDUCTION

FORMULA SOLUTION

CHART G

SUBTRACTION

Whole Numbers.

752. Subtract 83465 from 92564.

753. Subtract 15' 7'' from 22' 6''.

Decimals.

754. Subtract 84.396 from 103.07.

Fractions.

755. Subtract $3\frac{7}{8}$ from $9\frac{11}{16}$.

756. Subtract 9' $4\frac{1}{2}''$ from 15' $3\frac{7}{8}''$.

Percentage.

757. Subtract: cost $4,000; loss $500, which is $12\frac{1}{2}$ per cent.   Find selling price and per cent that equals it.

MULTIPLICATION

Whole Numbers.

758. Multiply 9834 by 736.

759. Multiply 19′ 3″ by 4.

Decimals.

760. Multiply 34.3 by .27.

Fractions.

761. Multiply 15 × 3⅛ × 4⅗ × ⅔.
762. Multiply 9′ 5¼″ by 4.

Percentage.

763. Multiply: actual cost $8,600; profit 12 per cent of actual cost. Find profit.
764. Multiply: cost $9,530; profit 15 per cent of cost. Find selling price.
765. Multiply: list price is $8,320; discount is 25 per cent of list price. Find cost.
766. Multiply: selling price is $534; discount is 30 per cent, with 2 per cent off for cash. Find net cost.

Division

Whole Numbers.

767. Divide 3468 by 6.
768. Divide 53898 by 78.
769. Divide 28′ 6″ by 9.

Decimals.

770. Divide 44.38 by 7.
771. Divide 20.736 by 14.4.

Fractions.

772. Divide 18½ by ⅞.
773. Divide 11′ 7½″ by 4.

Percentage.

774. Divide: profit is $45, which is 15 per cent of wages paid. Find wages paid
775. Divide: selling price is $630.56; profit is 12 per cent of cost. Find cost.
776. Divide: cost is $30.38, after discount of 2 per cent is allowed off retail price. Find retail price.
777. Divide: net cost is $301.84; discount is 12 per cent of retail price; cash discount is 2 per cent. Find retail price.

REDUCTION

Whole Numbers.

778. Reduce 11 ft. to inches.
779. Reduce 207 in. to feet.
780. Reduce 4 gross to number of pieces.
781. Reduce 432 pcs. to number of gross.
782. Reduce 11' 5'' to inches.
783. Reduce 175'' to feet and inches.
784. Reduce 4 yd., 2 ft., 5 in. to inches.
785. Reduce 484 in. to yards, feet, and inches.
786. Reduce to inches and multiply 3' 7'' by 5' 9''.
787. Reduce to inches and divide 6' 3'' by 1' 3''.

Decimals.

788. Reduce 3.52 M bd. ft. to bd. ft.
789. Reduce 3,750 bd. ft. to M bd. ft.
790. Reduce $0.375 per board foot to price M bd. ft.
791. Reduce $84.50 per M bd. ft. to price per board foot.
792. Reduce $0.49 per piece to the price per dozen.
793. Reduce $42 per dozen to the price per piece.

Fractions.

794. Reduce $3\frac{1}{4}$ ft. to inches.
795. Reduce 99 in. to feet.
796. Reduce 43 pcs. $9\frac{1}{2}$ ft. long to linear feet.
797. Reduce $10\frac{1}{2}$ lin. ft. to number of pieces $6\frac{1}{2}$ ft. long.
798. Reduce to inches and multiply 8' $5\frac{1}{2}$'' by 4' $3\frac{1}{2}$''.
799. Reduce to inches and divide 7' $2\frac{1}{4}$'' by 1' $5\frac{1}{2}$''.
800. Reduce 15 per cent to a decimal.
801. Reduce $\frac{7}{8}$ per cent to a decimal.

FORMULA SOLUTION

Mensuration.

802. Find the perimeter of a square, side = 34''.
803. Find the area of a square, side = 14''.
804. Find the perimeter of a rectangle, length = 15', width = 12'
805. Find the area of a rectangle, length = 16', width = 15'
806. Find the circumference of a circle, diameter = 17'.
807. Find the area of a circle, radius = 8'.
808. Find the hypotenuse of a triangle, altitude = 9', base = 16'.
809. Find the area of a triangle, altitude = 8', base = 11'.
810. Find the wall area of a cube, side = 15'.
811. Find the volume of a cube, side = 12'.

812. Find the wall area of a rectangular solid: width = 17″, length = 23,′ height = 5′

813. Find the volume of a rectangular solid: width = 14′, length = 19′, height = 3′.

814. Find the number of board feet in 5 pcs. 2″ × 3″ × 16′.

815. Find the number of board feet in 230 lin. ft. of 1″ × 3″.

816. Find the number of board feet in 5 pcs. 1″ × 6″ × 40″.

817. At $45.30 per M, find the price per board foot.

818. At $0.055 per board foot, find the price per M bd. ft.

819. Find the cost of 752 bd. ft. at $45 per M.

820. Find the cost of 9 pcs. 2 × 4 × 14 at $24.50 per M.

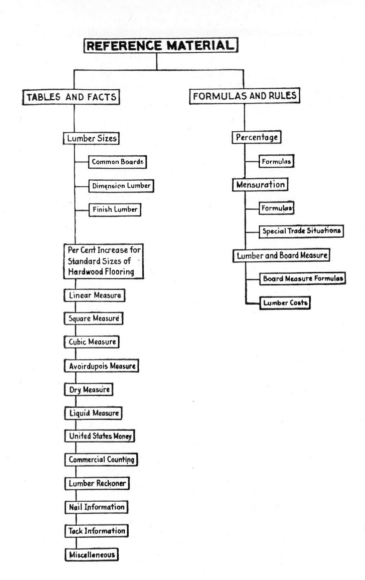

REFERENCE MATERIAL

TABLES AND FACTS

Lumber Sizes
- Common Boards
- Dimension Lumber
- Finish Lumber

Per Cent Increase for Standard Sizes of Hardwood Flooring

Linear Measure

Square Measure

Cubic Measure

Avoirdupois Measure

Dry Measure

Liquid Measure

United States Money

Commercial Counting

Lumber Reckoner

Nail Information

Tack Information

Miscellaneous

FORMULAS AND RULES

Percentage
- Formulas

Mensuration
- Formulas
- Special Trade Situations

Lumber and Board Measure
- Board Measure Formulas
- Lumber Costs

CHAPTER IX

TABLES AND FORMULAS

As reference material the following pages include a number of the standard measuring tables that are in common usage. The lumber and hardwood-flooring tables are particularly applicable to the field of carpentry.

1. Lumber Sizes[1]

American standard thickness and widths of dressed softwood lumber. Finished sizes of lumber are the same regardless of whether S1S, S2S, S1S1E, S1S2E or S4S.

COMMON BOARDS

Rough sizes	Standard dressed sizes
$1'' \times 3''$	$2\frac{5}{32}'' \times 2\frac{5}{8}''$
$1'' \times 4''$	$2\frac{5}{32}'' \times 3\frac{5}{8}''$
$1'' \times 6''$	$2\frac{5}{32}'' \times 5\frac{5}{8}''$
$1'' \times 8''$	$2\frac{5}{32}'' \times 7\frac{1}{2}''$
$1'' \times 10''$	$2\frac{5}{32}'' \times 9\frac{1}{2}''$
$1'' \times 12''$	$2\frac{5}{32}'' \times 11\frac{1}{2}''$
$1\frac{1}{4}'' \times 3''$	$1\frac{1}{16}'' \times 2\frac{5}{8}''$
$1\frac{1}{4}'' \times 4''$	$1\frac{1}{16}'' \times 3\frac{5}{8}''$
$1\frac{1}{4}'' \times 6''$	$1\frac{1}{16}'' \times 5\frac{5}{8}''$
$1\frac{1}{4}'' \times 8''$	$1\frac{1}{16}'' \times 7\frac{1}{2}''$
$1\frac{1}{4}'' \times 10''$	$1\frac{1}{16}'' \times 9\frac{1}{2}''$
$1\frac{1}{4}'' \times 12''$	$1\frac{1}{16}'' \times 11\frac{1}{2}''$
$1\frac{1}{2}'' \times 3''$	$1\frac{5}{16}'' \times 2\frac{5}{8}''$
$1\frac{1}{2}'' \times 4''$	$1\frac{5}{16}'' \times 3\frac{5}{8}''$
$1\frac{1}{2}'' \times 6''$	$1\frac{5}{16}'' \times 5\frac{5}{8}''$
$1\frac{1}{2}'' \times 8''$	$1\frac{5}{16}'' \times 7\frac{1}{2}''$
$1\frac{1}{2}'' \times 10''$	$1\frac{5}{16}'' \times 9\frac{1}{2}''$
$1\frac{1}{2}'' \times 12''$	$1\frac{5}{16}'' \times 11\frac{1}{2}''$

DIMENSION LUMBER

$2'' \times 2''$	$1\frac{5}{8}'' \times 1\frac{5}{8}''$
$2'' \times 3''$	$1\frac{5}{8}'' \times 2\frac{5}{8}''$
$2'' \times 4''$	$1\frac{5}{8}'' \times 3\frac{5}{8}''$

[1] Table, courtesy National Lumber Manufacturers Association.

1. LUMBER SIZES.—(*Continued*)

DIMENSION LUMBER

Rough sizes	Standard dressed sizes
$2'' \times 6''$	$1\frac{5}{8}'' \times 5\frac{5}{8}''$
$2'' \times 8''$	$1\frac{5}{8}'' \times 7\frac{1}{2}''$
$2'' \times 10''$	$1\frac{5}{8}'' \times 9\frac{1}{2}''$
$2'' \times 12''$	$1\frac{5}{8}'' \times 11\frac{1}{2}''$
$3'' \times 4''$	$2\frac{5}{8}'' \times 3\frac{5}{8}''$
$3'' \times 6''$	$2\frac{5}{8}'' \times 5\frac{5}{8}''$
$3'' \times 8''$	$2\frac{5}{8}'' \times 7\frac{1}{2}''$
$3'' \times 10''$	$2\frac{5}{8}'' \times 9\frac{1}{2}''$
$3'' \times 12''$	$2\frac{5}{8}'' \times 11\frac{1}{2}''$
$4'' \times 4''$	$3\frac{5}{8}'' \times 3\frac{5}{8}''$
$4'' \times 6''$	$3\frac{5}{8}'' \times 5\frac{5}{8}''$
$4'' \times 8''$	$3\frac{5}{8}'' \times 7\frac{1}{2}''$
$4'' \times 10''$	$3\frac{5}{8}'' \times 9\frac{1}{2}''$
$4'' \times 12''$	$3\frac{5}{8}'' \times 11\frac{1}{2}''$

FINISH LUMBER

$1'' \times 3''$	$2\frac{5}{32}'' \times 2\frac{5}{8}''$
$1'' \times 4''$	$2\frac{5}{32}'' \times 3\frac{1}{2}''$
$1'' \times 5''$	$2\frac{5}{32}'' \times 4\frac{1}{2}''$
$1'' \times 6''$	$2\frac{5}{32}'' \times 5\frac{1}{2}''$
$1'' \times 8''$	$2\frac{5}{32}'' \times 7\frac{1}{4}''$
$1'' \times 10''$	$2\frac{5}{32}'' \times 9\frac{1}{4}''$
$1'' \times 12''$	$2\frac{5}{32}'' \times 11\frac{1}{4}''$
$1\frac{1}{4}'' \times 3''$	$1\frac{1}{16}'' \times 2\frac{5}{8}''$
$1\frac{1}{4}'' \times 4''$	$1\frac{1}{16}'' \times 3\frac{1}{2}''$
$1\frac{1}{4}'' \times 6''$	$1\frac{1}{16}'' \times 5\frac{1}{2}''$
$1\frac{1}{4}'' \times 8''$	$1\frac{1}{16}'' \times 7\frac{1}{4}''$
$1\frac{1}{4}'' \times 10''$	$1\frac{1}{16}'' \times 9\frac{1}{4}''$
$1\frac{1}{4}'' \times 12''$	$1\frac{1}{16}'' \times 11\frac{1}{4}''$
$1\frac{1}{2}'' \times 3''$	$1\frac{5}{16}'' \times 2\frac{5}{8}''$
$1\frac{1}{2}'' \times 4''$	$1\frac{5}{16}'' \times 3\frac{1}{2}''$
$1\frac{1}{2}'' \times 6''$	$1\frac{5}{16}'' \times 5\frac{1}{2}''$
$1\frac{1}{2}'' \times 8''$	$1\frac{5}{16}'' \times 7\frac{1}{4}''$
$1\frac{1}{2}'' \times 10''$	$1\frac{5}{16}'' \times 9\frac{1}{4}''$
$1\frac{1}{2}'' \times 12''$	$1\frac{5}{16}'' \times 11\frac{1}{4}'$
$2'' \times 3''$	$1\frac{5}{8}'' \times 2\frac{5}{8}''$
$2'' \times 4''$	$1\frac{5}{8}'' \times 3\frac{1}{2}''$
$2'' \times 6''$	$1\frac{5}{8}'' \times 5\frac{1}{2}''$
$2'' \times 8''$	$1\frac{5}{8}'' \times 7\frac{1}{4}''$
$2'' \times 10''$	$1\frac{5}{8}'' \times 9\frac{1}{4}''$
$2'' \times 12''$	$1\frac{5}{8}'' \times 11\frac{1}{4}'$
$3'' \times 3''$	$2\frac{5}{8}'' \times 2\frac{5}{8}''$
$3'' \times 4''$	$2\frac{5}{8}'' \times 3\frac{1}{2}''$

1. Lumber Sizes.—(*Continued*)

FINISH LUMBER

Rough sizes	Standard dressed sizes
3″ × 6″	2⅝″ × 5½″
3″ × 8″	2⅝″ × 7¼″
3″ × 10″	2⅝″ × 9¼″
3″ × 12″	2⅝″ × 11¼″

S1S means surfaced one side.
S2S means surfaced two sides.
S1S1E means surfaced one side and one edge.
S1S2E means surfaced one side and two edges.
S4S means surfaced four sides.

2. Percentage Increase for Standard Sizes of Hardwood Flooring

⅜″ × 1½″, face width..................add 36 per cent
⅜″ × 2″, face width....................add 28 per cent
½″ × 1½″, face width..................add 36 per cent
½″ × 2″, face width....................add 28 per cent
13/16″ × 1½″, face width..............add 52½ per cent
13/16″ × 2¼″, face width..............add 36 per cent

3. Linear Measure

12 inches	= 1 foot
3 feet	= 1 yard
5½ yards, or 16½ feet	= 1 rod
320 rods, or 5,280 feet	= 1 mile

4. Square Measure

144 square inches	= 1 square foot
9 square feet	= 1 square yard
30¼ square yards	= 1 square rod
160 square rods	= 1 acre
640 acres	= 1 square mile

5. Cubic Measure

1,728 cubic inches	= 1 cubic foot
27 cubic feet	= 1 cubic yard
128 cubic feet	= 1 cord
24¾ cubic feet	= 1 perch

6. Avoirdupois Weight

16 ounces	= 1 pound
100 pounds	= 1 hundredweight
2,000 pounds	= 1 ton

7. Dry Measure

2 pints   = 1 quart
8 quarts = 1 peck
4 pecks = 1 bushel

8. Liquid Measure

4 gills   = 1 pint
2 pints   = 1 quart
4 quarts = 1 gallon
1 gallon = 231 cubic inches

9. United States Money

10 mills   = 1 cent
10 cents   = 1 dime
10 dimes   = 1 dollar
10 dollars = 1 eagle

10. Commercial Counting

12 things = 1 dozen
12 dozen = 1 gross
12 gross = 1 great gross

11. Lumber Reckoner[1]

Table shows number of board feet in one piece

Sizes, in.	Length, ft.											
	10	12	14	16	18	20	22	24	26	28	30	32
1 × 2	1⅔	2	2⅓	2⅔	3	3⅓						
1 × 3	2½	3	3½	4	4½	5						
1 × 4	3⅓	4	4⅔	5⅓	6	6⅔						
1 × 6	5	6	7	8	9	10						
1 × 8	6⅔	8	9⅓	10⅔	12	13⅓						
1 × 10	8⅓	10	11⅔	13⅓	15	16⅔						
1 × 12	10	12	14	16	18	20						
1 × 14	11⅔	14	16⅓	18⅔	22⅔	23⅓						
1 × 16	13⅓	16	18⅔	21⅓	24	26⅔						
1¼ × 4	4⅙	5	5⅚	6⅔								
1¼ × 6	6¼	7½	8¾	10								
1¼ × 8	8⅓	10	11⅔	13⅓								
1¼ × 10	10 5/12	12½	14 7/12	16⅔								
1¼ × 12	12½	15	17½	20								
1½ × 4	5	6	7	8								
1½ × 6	7½	9	10½	12								
1½ × 8	10	12	14	16								
1½ × 10	12½	15	17½	20								
1½ × 12	15	18	21	24								
2 × 4	6⅔	8	9⅓	10⅔	12	13⅓	14⅔	16	17⅓	18⅔	20	21⅓
2 × 6	10	12	14	16	18	20	22	24	26	28	30	32
2 × 8	13⅓	16	18⅔	21⅓	24	26⅔	29⅓	32	34⅔	37⅓	40	42⅔
2 × 10	16⅔	20	23⅓	26⅔	30	33⅓	36⅔	40	43⅓	46⅔	50	53⅓
2 × 12	20	24	28	32	36	40	44	48	52	56	60	64
2 × 14	23⅓	28	32⅔	37⅓	42	46⅔	51⅓	56	60⅔	65⅓	70	74⅔
2 × 16	26⅔	32	37⅓	42⅔	48	53⅓	58⅔	64	69⅓	74⅔	80	85⅓
2½ × 12	25	30	35	40	45	50	55	60	65	70	75	80
2½ × 14	29⅙	35	40⅚	46⅔	52½	58⅓	64⅙	70	75⅚	81⅔	87½	93⅓
2½ × 16	33⅓	40	46⅔	53⅓	60	66⅔	73⅓	80	86⅔	93⅓	100	106⅔
3 × 6	15	18	21	24	27	30	33	36	39	42	45	48
3 × 8	20	24	28	32	36	40	44	48	52	56	60	64
3 × 10	25	30	35	40	45	50	55	60	65	70	75	80
3 × 12	30	36	42	48	54	60	66	72	78	84	90	96
3 × 14	35	42	49	56	63	70	77	84	91	98	105	112
3 × 16	40	48	56	64	72	80	88	96	104	112	120	128
4 × 4	13⅓	16	18⅔	21⅓	24	26⅔	29⅓	32	34⅔	37⅓	40	42⅔
4 × 6	20	24	28	32	36	40	44	48	52	56	60	64
4 × 8	26⅔	32	37⅓	42⅔	48	53⅓	58⅔	64	69⅓	74⅔	80	85⅓
4 × 10	33⅓	40	46⅔	53⅓	60	66⅔	73⅓	80	86⅔	93⅓	100	106⅔
4 × 12	40	48	56	64	72	80	88	96	104	112	120	128
4 × 14	46⅔	56	65⅓	74⅔	84	93⅓	102⅔	112	121⅓	130⅔	140	149⅓
6 × 6	30	36	42	48	54	60	66	72	78	84	90	96
6 × 8	40	48	56	64	72	80	88	96	104	112	120	128
6 × 10	50	60	70	80	90	100	110	120	130	140	150	160
6 × 12	60	72	84	96	108	120	132	144	156	168	180	196
6 × 14	70	84	98	112	126	140	154	168	182	196	210	224
6 × 16	80	96	112	128	144	160	176	192	208	224	240	256
8 × 8	53⅓	64	74⅔	85⅓	96	106⅔	117⅓	128	138⅔	149⅓	160	170⅔
8 × 10	66⅔	80	93⅓	106⅔	120	133⅓	146⅔	160	173⅓	186⅔	200	213⅓
8 × 12	80	96	112	128	144	160	176	192	208	224	240	256
8 × 14	93⅓	112	130⅔	149⅓	168	186⅔	205⅓	224	242⅔	261⅓	280	298⅔
10 × 10	83⅓	100	116⅔	133⅓	150	166⅔	183⅓	200	216⅔	233⅓	250	266⅔
10 × 12	100	120	140	160	180	200	220	240	260	280	300	320
10 × 14	116⅔	140	163⅓	186⅔	210	233⅓	256⅔	280	303⅓	326⅔	350	373⅓
10 × 16	133⅓	160	186⅔	213⅓	240	266⅔	293⅓	320	346⅔	373⅓	400	426⅔
12 × 12	120	144	168	192	216	240	264	288	312	336	360	384
12 × 14	140	168	196	224	252	280	308	336	364	392	420	448
12 × 16	160	192	224	256	288	320	352	384	416	448	480	512
14 × 14	163⅓	196	228⅔	261⅓	294	326⅔	359⅓	392	424⅔	457⅓	490	522⅔
14 × 16	186⅔	224	261⅓	298⅔	336	373⅓	410⅔	448	485⅓	522⅔	560	597⅓

[1] **For sizes not listed, use size twice as large, and divide answer by 2.**

12. Nail Information

Table of sizes

Standard steel wire nails				Steel wire spikes		Common iron nails		
Sizes	Length, in.	Common	Finishing					
		No. per lb.	No. per lb.	Length, in.	No. per lb.	Size	Length, in.	No. per lb.
2d.....	1	1,060	1,558	3	41	2d	1	800
3d.....	1¼	640	913	3½	30	3d	1¼	400
4d.....	1½	380	761	4	23	4d	1½	300
5d.....	1¾	275	500	4½	17	5d	1¾	200
6d.....	2	210	350	5	13	6d	2	150
7d.....	2¼	160	315	5½	11	7d	2¼	120
8d.....	2½	115	214	6	10	8d	2½	85
9d.....	2¾	93	195	6½	7½	9d	2¾	75
10d.....	3	77	137	7	7	10d	3	60
12d.....	3¼	60	127	8	5	12d	3¼	50
16d.....	3½	48	90	9	4 ½	16d	3½	40
20d.....	4	31	62	....	....	20d	4	20
30d.....	4½	22	....	....	....	30d	4½	16
40d.....	5	17	....	....	....	40d	5	14
50d.....	5½	13	....	....	....	50d	5½	11
60d.....	6	11	....	....	....	60d	6	8

13. Tacks

Title, oz.	Length, in.	No. per lb.	Title, oz.	Length, in.	No. per lb.	Title oz.	Length, in.	No. per lb.
1	⅛	16,000	4	7/16	4,000	14	13/16	1,143
1½	3/16	10,666	6	9/16	2,666	16	⅞	1,000
2	¼	8,000	8	⅝	2,000	18	15/16	888
2½	5/16	6,400	10	11/16	1,600	20	1	800
3	⅜	5,333	12	¾	1,333	22	1 1/16	727
						24	1 ⅛	666

14. Miscellaneous

Square: 100 sq. ft. = 1 square
Roofing Material: 108 sq. ft. = 1 roll (36″ wide); 1 roll covers 1 square
Building Paper: 500 sq. ft. = 1 roll (36″ wide)
Mesh Wire: 50 sq. yd. = 1 roll (36″ wide)
Shingles: 4″ exposure, 900 shingles cover 1 square
4½″ exposure, 800 shingles cover 1 square
5″ exposure, 720 shingles cover 1 square
4 bundles = 1,000 shingles

Lath: 1 bundle = 100 lath
Shakes: 1 bundle = 25 shakes
Cement: 1 sack = 94 lb.
Sand: 1 cu. yd. = 1.3 tons (approximately)
Rock: 1 cu. yd. = 1.3 tons (approximately)
Nails: 1 keg = 100 lb.
Screws: 1 box = 144 screws (except in very large sizes)
Sash cord: 1 hank = 100 lin. ft. (two connected)

FORMULAS AND RULES

There are a number of basic rules that can be expressed in formula or rule form. Ability to work problems according to these formulas or rules will simplify the mathematical work of a carpenter and save considerable time.

PERCENTAGE

$$B \times R = P$$
$$P \div B = R$$
$$P \div R = B$$

B = base (always the 100 per cent number)
R = rate or per cent (%)
P = percentage

MENSURATION

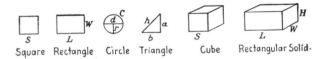

Square   Rectangle   Circle   Triangle   Cube   Rectangular Solid.

FIG. 115.—Mensuration figures.

Formulas.

Square
$$P = 4S$$
$$A = S^2$$

Rectangle
$$P = 2(W + L)$$
$$A = WL$$

Circle
$$C = \pi d \text{ or } 2\pi r$$
$$A = \tfrac{1}{4}\pi d^2 \text{ or } \pi r^2$$

Triangle
$$h = \sqrt{a^2 + b^2}$$
or use steel square
$$A = \tfrac{1}{2}ab$$

Cube
$$Aw. = PH \text{ or } 4S^2$$
$$V = S^3$$

Rectangular solid
$$Aw. = PH \text{ or } 2(L + W)H$$
$$V = LWD$$

P = perimeter
S = side
A = area
W = width
L = length
C = circumference
d = diameter
r = radius (½ the diameter)
π = 3¼, or 3.142 or 3.1416
h = hypotenuse
a = altitude
b = base
$Aw.$ = of wall area
D = depth
H = height
V = volume

Special Trade Situations.

Generally speaking, the simplest process, when figuring the perimeter or area of a square or rectangle is to estimate it on the basis of the smallest square or rectangle that will entireiy surround it. Figure 116 indicates the formulas for different situations.

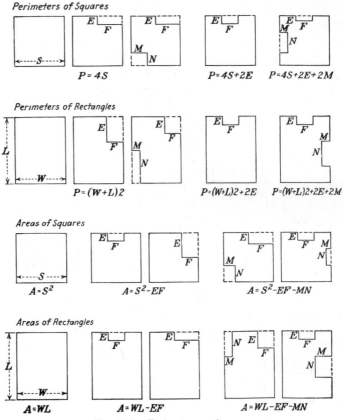

Fig. 116.—Perimeters and areas.

Board Measure.

Standard practice..............
$$\begin{cases} \text{Piece rule } \dfrac{\text{pc.}T''W''L'}{12} = \text{bd. ft.} \\[2ex] \text{Running foot rule } \dfrac{T''W''L'}{12} = \text{bd. ft.} \end{cases}$$

School practice...............
$$\begin{cases} \text{Inch rule } \dfrac{\text{pc.}T''W''L''}{144} = \text{bd. ft.} \end{cases}$$

pc. = number of pieces
T = thickness
W = width
L = length
bd. ft. = board feet
$''$ = inches
$'$ = feet

Thickness less than $1''$ is counted as $1''$.

Thicknesses over $1''$ are counted as $1\frac{1}{4}''$, $2''$, $3''$, etc.

Fractional parts of a board foot are counted as whole board feet.

Finish sizes are computed according to the original rough sizes (see Table 1).

Widths in uneven inches (excepting the hardwoods) are counted the next even inch width as $1 \times 6\frac{1}{2} = 1 \times 8$. In a few cases lumber can be secured in odd inch widths as $3''$ and $5''$.

Odd lengths are to be figured as the next even foot length, excepting that in some cases short lengths are procurable from $4''$ to $10'$.

Woodshop students usually figure the actual length used.

Lumber Costs.

Board feet to
dollars and cents

$$\begin{cases} \dfrac{\text{bd. ft. } \$}{1,000} = \text{cost} \\[2ex] \dfrac{\text{pc.}T''W''L' \quad \$}{12 \quad 1,000} = \text{cost} \end{cases}$$

Lumber bill
to
board feet
to
dollars and cents

$$\begin{cases} \dfrac{T''W''L' \quad \$}{12 \quad 1,000} = \text{cost} \\[2ex] \dfrac{\text{pc.}T''W''L'' \quad \$}{144 \quad 1,000} = \text{cost} \end{cases}$$

$\$$ = $\$$ per 1,000 W = width
M = thousand L = length
pc. = piece $''$ = inches
T = thickness $'$ = feet

INDEX

ANSWERS TO PROBLEMS

Chapter I

No Problems

Chapter II

Mathematical Check-up

1. 71,983	**8.** 2 sq. ft.	**15.** 200″
2. 851	**9.** 513 cu. ft.	**16.** 6′ 3″
3. 2,896,781	**10.** 348 pcs.	**17.** 5
4. 11	**11.** 67′ 3″	**18.** 3,570 sq. in.
5. 31′	**12.** 3′ 11″	**19.** 763 cu. ft.
6. 108″	**13.** 75′ 4″	**20.** 5 cu. yd. 24
7. 55 sq. yd.	**14.** 3′ 10″	cu. ft.

Text Problems

1. 962 bd. ft.	**8.** 381 loads	**15.** $5,906
2. 1,558 bd. ft.	**9.** 276 loads	**16.** 158′ 0″; 108′ 0″
3. 1,654 bd. ft.	**10.** 316 loads	**17.** 444′ 0″; 132′ 0″
4. 3,985 bd. ft.	**11.** $229	**18.** 284′ 0″; 288′ 0″
5. 6,556 bd. ft.	**12.** $839	**19.** 338′ 0″; 226′ 0″
6. 300 loads	**13.** $3,743	**20.** 548′ 0″; 272′ 0″
7. 395 loads	**14.** $4,633	

21. Walk......... 45 lin. ft.
Driveway.....110 lin. ft.
Garage........ 56 lin. ft.
 Total.......211 lin. ft.
22. Walk.........115 lin. ft.
Driveway.....369 lin. ft.
Garage........ 72 lin. ft.
 Total.......556 lin. ft.
23. 432 lin. ft.
24. 924 lin. ft.

25. Walks.. 116 lin. ft. 2 × 4
Drive-
way... 308 lin. ft. 2 × 4
Garage. 88 lin. ft. 2 × 4
 Total.. 512 lin. ft. 2 × 4
House..1,344 lin. ft. 1 × 6
26. 417 lin. ft.
27. $6,315.00
28. 27′ from alley.
29. Jones bid, $19.00 lower

30. 1,164 bd. ft.	**37.** 11′ 0″	**44.** 2,391 sq. ft.
31. 14 sacks	**38.** 7′ 0″	**45.** 15,912 sq. ft.
32. 17′	**39.** 11′ 0″	**46.** 1,872 sq. ft
33. $119,161.00	**40.** 12′ 0″	**47.** 3,040 sq. ft.
34. 109′	**41.** 1,536 sq. ft.	**48.** 2,860 sq. ft.
35. $63,099.00	**42.** 7,616 sq. ft.	**49.** 3,864 sq. ft.
36. 12′ 0″	**43.** 2,736 sq. ft.	**50.** 3,312 sq. ft.

51. 384 cu. ft.; 1,144 cu. ft.;
1,344 cu. ft.; 2,565 cu. ft.
52. 360 cu. ft.; 2,016 cu. ft.;
1,989 cu. ft.; 2,880 cu. ft.
53. 630 cu. ft.; 2,970 cu. ft.;
3,135 cu. ft.; 3,388 cu. ft.

54. 405 cu. ft.; 1,600 cu. ft.;
3,366 cu. ft.; 5,472 cu. ft.
55. 192 cu. ft.; 1,152 cu. ft.;
2,304 cu. ft.; 5,720 cu. ft.

56. 1,862 bd. ft.	**68.** 30 joists	**80.** 94 lin. ft.
57. 3,352 bd. ft.	**69.** 50 joists	**81.** 68 sq. yd.
58. 3,222 bd. ft.	**70.** 237 joists	**82.** 112 sq. yd.
59. 13,142 bd. ft.	**71.** 4 girders	**83.** 156 sq. yd.
60. 3,358 bd. ft.	**72.** 7 girders	**84.** 2,079 sq. yd.
61. 36 sacks	**73.** 10 piers	**85.** 98⅔ sq. yd.
62. 196 sacks	**74.** 55 piers	**86.** 4,004 cu. yd.
63. 76 sacks	**75.** 11 girders	**87.** 302 cu. yd.
64. 1,620 sacks	**76.** 16 lin. ft.	**88.** 822⅔ cu. yd.
65. 420 sacks	**77.** 142 lin. ft.	**89.** 200 loads
66. 47 joists	**78.** 76 lin. ft.	**90.** 3,338⅔ cu. yd.
67. 35 joists	**79.** 300 lin. ft.	

91. 15′ 1″	**101.** 10′ 3″	**115.** 10′ 1″	**127.** 3′ 6⅔″
92. 18′ 3″	**102.** 13′ 2″	**116.** 3′ 2″	2′ 11⅓″
93. 23′ 2″	**103.** 28′ 4″	**117.** 1′ 7″	3′ 10″
94. 28′ 5″	**104.** 30′ 9″	**118.** 16′ pc.	3′ 2⅔″
95. 21′ 5″	**105.** 26′ 10″	**119.** 20′ 10″	**128.** 3′ 10⅔″
96. 121′ 10″	**106.** 14′ 3″	**120.** 63 lin. ft.	3′ 0⅔″
261′ 6″	**107.** 1′ 1″	**121.** 15′ 6″	4′ 5⅓″
97. 115′ 2″	**108.** 6″ left	**122.** 11″	4′ 3″
140′ 2″	**109.** 16′ piece;	**123.** 3′ 3″	**129.** 4′ 7½″
98. 130′ 2″	6″ waste	**124.** 83′ 2″	3′ 11¼″
147′ 10″	**110.** 11′ 8″	**125.** 5′ 4″	4′ 0″
99. 243′ 2″	**111.** 12′ 10″	**126.** 4′ 2″	4′ 3¾″
158′ 8″	**112.** 7′ 8″	5′ 0″	**130.** 4′ 4⅙″
100. 181′ 2″	**113.** 16′ 9″	4′ 11″	2′ 6′
250′ 6″	**114.** 16′ 3″	5′ 6″	4′ 6⅗″
			3′ 9⅗″

131. 5′ 2″	133. 3′ 1″	135. 2′ 9⅓″	139. 9″
4′ 3″	4′ 2″	2′ 2⅔″	140. 16 pcs.
4′ 8″	3′ 10″	2′ 8½″	141. 7″
3′ 10″	3′ 3″	3′ 1⅚″	142. 8′ 4″
132. 4′ 1″	134. 4′ 2″	136. 9 pcs.	143. 7″
3′ 2″	3′ 11″	137. 16″	144. 14′ 8″
3′ 8″	3′ 5⅕″	138. 14 pcs.	145. 8″
3′ 6⅓″	3′ 10″		

Chapter III

MATHEMATICAL CHECK-UP

1. 8,799.2942
2. 81.1006
3. 73.9735476
4. 1.2
5. $0.025 per bd. ft.
6. 65.207 M bd. ft.
7. 737.1 cu. ft.
8. 14.518 + cu. yd.

9. $15.4425
10. $162.56
11. $1,266.81
12. $5,023.70
13. $14,135.22
14. 480.9012
15. $0.0697 per bd. ft.

16. $125.00 per M bd. ft.
17. $0.79 each
18. $5.64 per doz.
19. $14.50 per 50
20. $0.515 each

TEXT PROBLEMS

146. $221.36
147. $143.39
148. $301.62
149. $323.74
150. $361.07
151. $6.98
152. $158 75

153. $65.49
154. $369.70
155. $29.22
156. $226.91
157. $11,165.63
158. $156.18
159. $2,409.51

160. $230.19
161. $370.95
162. $6,040.11
163. $1,394.00
164. $142.70
165. $2,700.52
166. $475.72

167. $88.06
168. $1,302.70
169. $382.44
170. $403.52

171. $23,235.06
172. $11,243.10
173. $64,673.07
174. $101,938.97

175. $33,851.94
176. $446.79
177. $33.75
178. $559.37

179. $6,500.35
180. $3,167.33

181. The account agrees. Reconcilement total $621.37
182. The account agrees. Reconcilement total $654.34
183. Last stub balance $485.91; reconcilement total $771.65

184. Last stub balance $237.58; reconcilement total $293.50
185. Last stub balance $357.00; reconcilement total $401.55

186. $26.25	**191.** $36.72	**196.** $12.88	**201.** $7.44
187. $1,665.60	**192.** $93.50	**197.** $138.03	**202.** $16.94
188. $2,814.80	**193.** $4,950.40	**198.** $3,817.75	**203.** $18.74
189. $19.25	**194.** $186.00	**199.** $647.42½	**204.** $19.97
190. $104.85	**195.** $4,586.26	**200.** $336.60	**205.** $68.11

206. $0.03 per lin. ft.
207. $0.0155 per lin. ft.
208. $0.45
209. $0.60
210. $0.125 (nearly) per sq. ft.
211. $3.40 per sq. ft.
212. $3.25 per sq. ft.
213. $2.85 per sq. ft.
214. $2.673+ per sq. ft.
215. $3.30 per sq. ft.
216. $1.32 per cu. yd.
217. $0.87 per cu. yd.
218. $0.92 per cu. yd.
219. $1.259 (nearly) per cu. yd.

220. $0.785 (nearly) per cu. yd.
221. $0.065 per ft.
222. $35.00 per M.
223. Shelving $0.033 per bd. ft.
Inside trim $0.11 per bd. ft.
Gum $0.349 per bd. ft.
224. $0.0328 (nearly) per bd. ft.
225. $72.00 per M.
226. $6.46 each
227. $0.93+ per hr.
228. $1.50 per hr.
229. $0.935+ per hr. carpenters
$0.90 per hr. painters

230. $0.908+ per hr.
231. $92.00
232. $206.00
233. $274.88
234. $322.63

235. $197.25
236. $24.15
237. $5.80 (4 full hanks)
238. $64.53+

239. $9.90 (5 full hanks)
240. $3.75 (5 full hanks)

241. $5.60	**249.** $6.34	**257.** $108.00 MB.F.	**263.** $38.33
242. $16.80	**250.** $8.16		**264.** $99.60
243. $36.30	**251.** $3.47	**258.** $215.49	**265.** $20.67
244. $100.80	**252.** $3.26	**259.** $30.00 MB.F.	**266.** $1,248.00
245. $25.60	**253.** $15.90		**267.** $292.00
246. $1.80	**254.** $13.60	**260.** $43.42	
247. $5.40	**255.** $2.41	**261.** $8.55	
248. $36.58	**256.** $13.61	**262.** $51.68	

268. 6-day week:
Carpenters av. daily wage
$6.99
Bricklayers av. daily wage
$6.83

5½-day week:
Carpenters av. daily wage
$7.63
Bricklayers av. daily wage
$7.46

269. $4,924.80
270. $1,092.50

271. 20.8 tons
272. $14.58

273. $49.06
274. $985.16

275. $116.29

Chapter IV

MATHEMATICAL CHECK-UP

1. $1^{15}\!\!/_{16}$
2. $\frac{3}{16}$
3. $\frac{1}{12}$
4. $3\frac{1}{3}$
5. $\frac{6}{16}$
6. $\frac{3}{4}$
7. $9''$

8. $\frac{5}{6}'$
9. $16\frac{7}{8}$ cu. ft.
10. $\frac{2}{3}$ cu. yd.
11. $5\frac{1}{2}$
12. $\frac{3}{8}$
13. $1^{55}\!\!/_{64}$

14. $^{19}\!\!/_{20}$
15. $1\frac{1}{17}$
16. $\frac{7}{12}$
17. $8\frac{1}{16}$
18. $8\frac{7}{16}$
19. $1'\,3''$
20. $\frac{5}{4}$ or $1\frac{1}{4}$

21. $13^{11}\!\!/_{16}$
22. $13\frac{1}{32}$
23. $512^{7}\!\!/_{32}$ ✓
24. $3\frac{7}{16}$
25. $43\frac{1}{2}''$
26. $1\frac{3}{4}'$
27. 45 pcs.

28. $17^{1}\frac{1}{12}$ doz.
29. 45 cu. ft.
30. $8\frac{1}{3}$ cu. yd.
31. $16'\,6\frac{9}{16}''$
32. $4'\,11\frac{7}{16}''$

33. $124'\,9''$
34. $4'\,7\frac{5}{8}''$
35. $2,550\frac{3}{4}$ sq. in.
36. $735^{145}\!\!/_{288}$ cu. ft.
37. $165^{341}\!\!/_{576}$ sq. ft.

38. 8 pcs.
39. $17'\,7\frac{1}{2}''$
40. $9^{11}\!\!/_{24}'$

TEXT PROBLEMS

276. $5\frac{1}{8}''$
277. $18\frac{3}{4}''$
278. $8\frac{7}{8}''$

279. $22\frac{5}{8}''$
280. $14\frac{3}{8}$
281. $6^{5}\!\!/_{16}''$

282. $12^{5}\!\!/_{16}''$
283. $9\frac{1}{8}''$
284. $29^{11}\!\!/_{16}''$

285. $14\frac{1}{16}''$
286. $9'\,4\frac{1}{4}''$
287. $9'\,3^{3}\!\!/_{16}''$

288. $19'\,6\frac{5}{8}''$ (allow for 2 sub floors)
289. $7'\,5\frac{1}{2}''$ (allow for 2 sub-floors)
290. $10'\,10^{9}\!\!/_{16}''$
291. $6\frac{1}{8}''$, order $6\frac{1}{2}''$
292. $5\frac{3}{4}''$, order $6''$
293. $8''$, order $8''$
294. (A) $7\frac{1}{4}''$ use $7\frac{1}{2}''$ (includes $\frac{1}{2}''$ nut)
    (B) $5\frac{3}{4}''$ use $6''$ (includes $\frac{1}{2}''$ nut)

295. $12''$ (includes $\frac{1}{2}''$ for nut)
296. $12'\,2\frac{7}{8}''$, order $14'$
297. $17'\,4\frac{1}{4}''$, order $18'$
298. $12'\,11\frac{7}{16}''$, order $14'$
299. $6'\,9\frac{1}{2}$, order $8'$
    $9'\,9\frac{3}{4}$, order $10'$
    $7'\,7\frac{1}{4}$, order $8'$
    $8'\,11\frac{1}{2}$, order $10'$
300. $15'\,4^{7}\!\!/_{16}''$, order $16'$

301. $8^{7}\!\!/_{16}''$
302. $1^{13}\!\!/_{16}''$
303. $1^{7}\!\!/_{16}''$
304. $4^{15}\!\!/_{16}''$

305. $4'\,9\frac{3}{8}''$
306. $12''$
307. $14^{7}\!\!/_{16}''$
308. $1'\,9\frac{1}{4}''$

309. $3'\,7^{5}\!\!/_{16}''$
310. $7^{15}\!\!/_{16}''$
311. $5\frac{5}{8}''$
312. $32\frac{3}{8}''$

313. $28\frac{3}{4}''$
314. $10\frac{1}{2}''$

315. $22\frac{1}{8}'' \times 64\frac{1}{2}''$
316. $6\frac{5}{8}''$
317. $4\frac{1}{4}''$
318. $1\frac{1}{16}''$
319. $\frac{1}{4}''$
320. $8\frac{1}{24}''$, figured 8″ net

321. $12'\ 11\frac{1}{4}''$
322. $9'\ 7''$
323. $23'\ 6\frac{5}{8}''$
324. $3'\ 8\frac{3}{8}''$
325. $24'\ 5^{13}\!\!/_{16}''$
326. 2,016 bd. ft. (or sq. ft.)

327. 1,532 bd. ft.
328. 1,150 bd. ft.

329. 6.73 M bd. ft. or 6,734 bd. ft.
330. 1,675 bd. ft.
331. 875 bd. ft.
332. 2,198 bd. ft.
333. 3,713 bd. ft. of 4″; 4,851 bd. ft. of 6″
334. $649.52
335. 4,965 bd. ft.
336. 3,456 sq. ft.

337. 2,083 sq. ft.
338. $205.50
339. 15,888 bd. ft.
340. 3,529 bd. ft.
341. $19'\ 2''$, order 20′
342. $12'\ 10''$, select 14′
343. $17'\ 4''$, order 18′
344. $13'\ 1\frac{1}{2}''$, purchase 14′
345. 57.3, or 58 lin. ft. required

346. $26.83
347. $14.53
348. $58.33

349. $31.04
350. $8.30
351. $7.43

352. $102.12
353. $10.20
354. $2.92

355. $7.59
356. $47.25
357. $175.00

358. $290.70
359. $28.40 more
360. $0.45 for 2 sides
361. 26 bolts
362. 120 bolts
363. 47 bolts for $7'\ 3''$ o.c.
364. 448 bolts

365. 40 spaces, 39 bolts required
366. 18+, buy 19 boards
367. 182+, buy 183 boards
368. 32+, buy 33 boards
369. 60+, buy 61 boards
370. 21+, buy 22 boards

371. 9 risers
372. 14 risers

373. 26 risers

374. 19 risers

375. 32 risers

Chapter V

MATHEMATICAL CHECK-UP

1. $137\frac{1}{2}\%$
2. $76\frac{1}{3}\%$
3. $92.16
4. 20 %

5. $60.00
6. $12\frac{1}{2}\%$; 40 %
7. $0.325 each
8. 25 %

9. $20.40
10. $4.90

TEXT PROBLEMS

376. $4,602.29
377. Smiths $64.46 lower
378. $203,986.96
379. $47,995.44
380. $86,897.88

381. $18,118.13
382. $8,052.56
383. Tub......$29.58
Lavatory $19.03
Sink......$ 7.04
384. $14,242.69

385. $308.55 gain

386. $31.10
387. $192.54
388. $21.48
389. $100.04

390. $16.08
391. $631.14
392. $318.56
393. $106.41

394. $513.32
395. $63.91
396. $3,387.08
397. $3,383.54

398. $163.90
399. $119.63
400. $149.01

401. 1,132 sq. ft.
402. $525.09
403. $252.64
404. 1 building....$ 66.52
9 buildings...$598.68
405. $2,018.59
406. 18%
407. 15%

408. 12%
409. 27.3%
410. 15.3%
411. $7,250
412. $191,924.77
413. $27,922.89
414. $15,592.23
415. 1,188.45 sq. ft.

Chapter VI

MATHEMATICAL CHECK-UP

1. 116'
2. 144 sq. ft.
3. 68'
4. 105 sq. ft.
5. 50.2656'
6. 254.46+ sq. ft.
7. 113.09+ sq. ft.
8. 15'
9. 54 sq. ft.
10. 256 sq. ft. (4 side walls)

11. 343 cu. ft.
12. 522 sq. ft.
13. 2,310 cu. ft.
14. 20'
15. 45' 0''
16. 49' 0''
17. 47.124'
18. 240.25 sq. ft.
19. 132⅝ sq. ft.
20. 962.115 sq. ft.
21. 60.06 sq. ft.

22. 1,681 sq. ft. (4 side walls)
23. 790 sq. ft. (4 side walls)
24. 3,723.875 cu. ft.
25. 1,811.25 cu. ft.

TEXT PROBLEMS

416. 48' lin. ft.
417. 1,320 lin. ft.
418. 104 lin. ft.

419. 348 lin. ft.
420. 3,912 lin. ft.
421. (a) 39' 6''

422. (b) 34' 0''
423. (c) 26' 6''
424. (d) 48' 4''

425. (e) 45′ 6″
426. (a) 40′ 8″
427. (b) 53′ 0″
428. (c) 68′ 4″
429. (d) 81′ 4″
430. (e) 91′ 0″
431. 160 lin. ft.
432. 142 lin. ft.

433. 411′ 4″
434. 310 lin. ft.
435. 2,816 lin. ft.
436. 41′ 0″
437. 41′ 6″
438. 43′ 0″
439. 48′ 0″
440. 68′ 0″

441. 82′ 0″
442. 95′ 0″
443. 76′ 0″
444. 74′ 0″
445. 162′ 0″
446. 464.9568 lin. ft.
447. 25.2328 lin. ft.

Answers on steel square for problems 451–485 will vary slightly according to accuracy of reading.

448. 69.1152 (figured 70 lin. ft.)
449. 6.2832 (figured 8 lin. ft.)
450. 12.5664 (figured 14 lin. ft.)

451. 10′ 9¾″
452. 13′ 0½″
453. 14′ 5½″
454. 7′ 8″
455. 7′ 5¾″

456. 15′ 10″
457. 31′ 8″
458. 23′ 1″
459. 17′ ½″
460. 11′ 9½″

461. 7′ 6″
462. 8′ 3″
463. 13′ 8½″
464. 19′ 0″
465. 21′ 7½″

466. 17′ 10½″
467. 28′ 3½″
468. 19′ 3″
469. 12′ 3½″
470. 21′ 11″

471. (15′ 8″) + (1′ 6″), order 18′
472. (8′ 5″) + (1′ 3″), order 10′
473. (8′ 11½″) + (0′ 8″), order 10′
474. (25′ 6″) + (1′ 4″), order 28′
475. (16′ 3″) + (2′ 8″), order 20′
476. 12′ 3½″, order 14′
477. 20′ 6½″, order 22′
478. 18′ 0″, order 18′
479. 17′ 0″, order 18′
480. 9′ 8″, order 10′
481. 6′ 6″, order 14′ for two
482. 9′ 1½″, order 10′
483. 4′ 7″, order 10′ for two
484. 20′, order 20′
485. 17′, order 18′
486. (a) $82\frac{17}{72} = 83$ sq. ft.
487. (b) $50\frac{1}{4} = 51$ sq. ft.
488. (c) $33\frac{1}{2} = 34$ sq. ft.
489. (d) $115\frac{19}{36} = 116$ sq. ft.
490. (e) $103\frac{1}{4} = 104$ sq. ft.
491. 648 sq. ft.
492. 1,316 sq. ft.
493. 3,640 sq. ft.

494. 6,863½, called 6,864 sq. ft.
495. 17,328 sq. ft.
496. (a) $903\frac{1}{36} = 91$ sq. ft.
497. (b) $149\frac{2}{48}\frac{9}{} = 150$ sq. ft.
498. (c) $265\frac{49}{144} = 266$ sq. ft.
499. (d) $355\frac{7}{8} = 356$ sq. ft.
500. (e) $459\frac{19}{48} = 460$ sq. ft.
501. (a) $67\frac{1}{2} = 68$ sq. ft.
502. (b) $72\frac{7}{16} = 73$ sq. ft.
503. (c) $78\frac{1}{2} = 79$ sq. ft.
504. (d) 95 sq. ft.
505. (e) 154 sq. ft.
506. (a) 255 sq. ft.
507. (b) 398 sq. ft.
508. 304 sq. ft.
509. 260 sq. ft.
510. 1,332 sq. ft.
511. 54 sq. ft.
512. 150 sq. ft.
513. 224 sq. ft.
514. 288 sq. ft.
515. 86¼, called 87 sq. ft.
516. 114 sq. ft.
517. $49\frac{1}{2} = 50$ sq. ft.
518. $94\frac{1}{2} = 95$ sq. ft.

519. $452\frac{1}{3} = 453$ sq. ft.
520. $234\frac{1}{9} = 235$ sq. ft.
521. $201.0624 = 201$ sq. ft.
522. $804.2496 = 804$ sq. ft.
523. $452.3904 = 452$ sq. ft.
524. $1,520.5344 = 1,521$ sq. ft.
525. $132.7326 = 133$ sq. ft.
526. 896 cu. ft.
527. 9,576 cu. ft.
528. 108 cu. ft.
529. 2,496 cu. yd.
530. 480 cu. ft. (using perimeter)
$474\frac{2}{3} = 475$ actual cu. ft.
531. (a) $337\frac{1}{2} = \ulcorner 338$ cu. ft. or
$121\frac{4}{27}$ cu. yd.
532. (b) $470\frac{27}{32} = 471$ cu. ft. or

$17\frac{4}{9}$ cu. yd.
533. (c) $353\frac{1}{4} = 353$ cu. ft. or
$13\frac{2}{27}$ cu. yd.
534. (d) 855 cu. ft. or $31\frac{2}{3}$ cu. yd.
535. 1,078 cu. ft. or $39\frac{25}{27}$ cu. yd.
536. $1,657\frac{1}{2} = 1,658$ cu. ft. or
$61\frac{11}{27}$ cu. yd.
537. $3,316\frac{2}{3} = 3,317$ cu. ft. or
$122\frac{23}{27}$ cu. yd.
538. 3,648 cu. ft. or $135\frac{1}{9}$ cu. yd.
539. $1,473\frac{1}{3} = 1,473$ cu. ft. or
$54\frac{5}{9}$ cu. yd.
540. 9,990 cu. ft. or 370 cu. yd.

Chapter VII

MATHEMATICAL CHECK-UP

1. 140 bd. ft.
2. 352 bd. ft.
3. 140 bd. ft.
4. 120 bd. ft.
5. 140 bd. ft.
6. 75 bd. ft.
7. 10 bd. ft.
8. 20 bd. ft.

9. 125 bd. ft.
10. 75 bd. ft.
11. 18 bd. ft.
12. $5\frac{5}{16} = 6$ bd. ft.
13. $18\frac{3}{4} = 19$ bd. ft.
14. $112\frac{3}{4} = 113$ bd. ft.
15. 24 bd. ft.

16. $17.41
17. $27.12
18. $10.62
19. $10.33
20. $3.75

TEXT PROBLEMS

541. 160 bd. ft.
542. 523 bd. ft.
543. 528 bd. ft.
544. 635 bd. ft.
545. 1,579 bd. ft.
546. 864 bd. ft.
547. 3,600 bd. ft.

548. 932 bd. ft.
549. 2,752 bd. ft.
550. 12,076 bd. ft.
551. 1,665 bd. ft.
552. 1,171 bd. ft.
553. 4,381 bd. ft.
554. 3,475 bd. ft.

555. 683 bd. ft.
556. 203 bd. ft.
557. 225 bd. ft.
558. 756 bd. ft.
559. 325 bd. ft.
560. 1,287 bd. ft.

561. 165 bd. ft.
562. 140 bd. ft.
563. 236 bd. ft.
564. 131 bd. ft.

565. 292 bd. ft.
566. 69 bd. ft.
567. 24 bd. ft.
568. 126 bd. ft.

569. 84 bd. ft.
570. 30 bd. ft.
571. 128 bd. ft.
572. 98 bd. ft.

573. 393 bd. ft.
574. 371 bd. ft.
575. 407 bd. ft.
576. 63 bd. ft.

577. 103 bd. ft.	**582.** $20.76	**587.** $8.61	**592.** $142.80
578. 21 bd. ft.	**583.** $119.20	**588.** $6.55	**593.** $1,738.88
579. 41 bd. ft.	**584.** $74.55	**589.** $46.20	**594.** $48.34
580. 84 bd. ft.	**585.** $33.55	**590.** $98.60	**595.** $145.99
581. $18.61	**586.** $210.67	**591.** $90.03	

Chapter VIII

II. Whole Numbers

1. 10, 7, 11, 2, 10, 8, 14, 8, 11, 9, 15, 8

2. 10, 9, 12, 9, 16, 10, 7, 18, 13, 4, 10, 9

3. 16, 5, 13, 6, 15, 6, 12, 9, 12 8, 12, 7

4. 10, 17, 13, 3, 14, 11, 4, 11, 5, 14, 6, 7

5. 1,215	**13.** 500,059	**19.** 3,183,284	**27.** 7,391,400
6. 34,939	**14.** 19, 6, 26,	**20.** 229,768	**28.** 16,061,750
7. 31,155	16, 8	**21.** 7,948,875	**29.** 54,818,400
8. 539	**15.** 15, 9, 9, 8,	**22.** 5,341,708	**30.** 21,772,520
9. 42,449	18	**23.** 3,540,912	**31.** 85,877,400
10. 30,815,491	**16.** 373,044	**24.** 8,814,876	**32.** 5,710,332
11. 34,791	**17.** 197,199	**25.** 2,750,782	**33.** 2,469,500
12. 899,398	**18.** 141,499	**26.** 331,100	**34.** 2,663,580

35. 643,653,810	**44.** 1,046	**53.** 3 sq. ft.
36. 36	**45.** 115	**54.** 23 cu. yd.
37. 53⅕	**46.** 300″	**55.** 21⅚ doz.
38. 881⅝	**47.** 468 sq. ft.	**56.** 720 pcs.
39. 109,333⅓	**48.** 720 sq. in.	**57.** 72″
40. 109,028⁴⁄₇	**49.** 348 pcs.	**58.** 56 pts.
41. 53⅝	**50.** 41,472 cu. in.	**59.** 288″
42. 1,084¹⁶⁄₂₇	**51.** 12 ft.	**60.** 93,312 cu. in
43. 395	**52.** 388⅓ sq. yd.	

61. 7 gross	**69.** 79′ 7″	**77.** 62′ 6″	**85.** 12′ 2″
62. 4 yd.	**70.** 160′ 3″	**78.** 55′ 9″	**86.** 183″
63. 12 gal.	**71.** 4′ 4″	**79.** 306′ 0″	**87.** 335″
64. 8 yd.	**72.** 5′ 10″	**80.** 570′ 8″	**88.** 472 sq. ft.
65. 1 cu. yd.	**73.** 2′ 9″	**81.** 2′ 3″	**89.** 503 sq. in.
66. 19′ 11″	**74.** 5′ 4″	**82.** 2′ 6″	**90.** 225 pcs.
67. 58′ 9″	**75.** 6′ 1″	**83.** 3′ 2″	**91.** 5′ 7″
68. 20′ 1″	**76.** 9′ 6″	**84.** 7′ 6″	

92. 499 sq. yd. 5 sq. ft.
93. 2 cu. yd. 9 cu. ft.
94. 30 doz. 4 pcs.
95. 3 sq. ft. 96 sq. in.
96. 321″
97. 499 pcs.
98. 63 pts.

99. 203″
100. 50,115 cu. in.
101. 10 yds. 0 ft. 11 in.
102. 2 gr. 1 doz. 5 pcs.
103. 7 gal. 1 qt. 1 pt.
104. 4 yds. 2 ft. 2 in.
105. 2 cu. yd. 1 cu. ft. 5 cu. in.

106. 2,759 sq. in.
107. 11,100 sq. in.
108. 16,544 sq. in.
109. 33,824 sq. in.
110. 88,935 sq. in.
111. 5
112. 5
113. 2
114. 5
115. 5
116. 242 ft.
117. 996,668

118. 82 ft.
119. 183 pcs.
120. 47 ft.
121. 6 doz. 6 pcs.
122. 81′ 10″
123. 93′ 1″
124. 67 pcs.
125. 103′ 6″
126. 7,119 sq. in.
127. 1′ 3″
128. 60
129. 2′ 11″

130. 18 yd.
131. 9 doz. 3 pcs.
132. 83′ 9″
133. 51 ft.
134. 8 gr. 0 doz. 0 pcs.
135. 8,640 cu. in.
136. 186 in.
137. 28
138. $436\frac{4}{11}$
139. 176 sq. yd.
140. 6′ 8″

III. Decimals

141. 552.496
142. 186.385
143. $10,393.75
144. 6.4063
145. 20.82 cu. yd.
146. 1.027
147. 0.071
148. $1.985
149. $98.875
150. 80.888.801

151. 146.4285
152. 11.8625
153. 0.0086188
154. 883.09375
155. 156,505.73701
156. 1,489.4
157. 0.0216
158. 1,056
159. 26,804.2857
160. 8,818.22⅔

161. 44
162. 0.144
163. 440
164. 0.1225
165. 14.25
166. 12,500 bd. ft.
167. 250 bd. ft.
168. 6,750 bd. ft.
169. 25,500 bd. ft.
170. 569,000 bd. ft.

171. $48.00 per M bd. ft.
172. $72.50 per M bd. ft.
173. $37.50 per M bd. ft.
174. $29.50 per M bd. ft.
175. $36.40 per M bd. ft.
176. $4.92 per doz.
177. $4.75 per 50

178. $8.10 per doz.
179. $1.12½ per 50
180. $31.50 per doz.
181. 5.55 M bd. ft.
182. 17.295 M bd. ft.
183. 8.075 M bd. ft.
184. 0.620 M bd. ft.

185. 985.7 M bd. ft.
186. $0.0625 per bd. ft.
187. $0.084 per bd. ft.

188. $0.246 per bd. ft.
189. $0.11 per bd. ft.
190. $0.364 per bd. ft.

191. $0.29 each
192. $0.035 each
193. $4.50 each
194. $3.50 each
195. $0.23\frac{1}{2}$ each
196. 9,960.797
197. 19.1325
198. 0.54775
199. 90.88

200. 9,250 bd. ft.
201. 191.444
202. 0.0675 per bd. ft.
203. 8.976 M bd. ft.
204. $0.07576
205. $0.81 each
206. $47.50 per M bd. ft.
207. $57.333

208. $4.08 per doz.
209. $688.45
210. $0.0478 each
211. $0.12 per bd. ft.
212. $2,030.47
213. $1.579 each
214. $3,913.14
215. $0.1914 each

IV. FRACTIONS

216. $7\frac{29}{120}$
217. $5\frac{13}{40}$
218. $8\frac{19}{120}$
219. $34\frac{1}{48}$
220. $36\frac{1}{80}$
221. $1\frac{7}{16}$
222. $1\frac{3}{8}$
223. $2\frac{15}{16}$
224. $3\frac{3}{8}$
225. $3\frac{181}{240}$
226. $25\frac{7}{16}$
227. $42\frac{3}{16}$
228. $66\frac{3}{16}$
229. $19\frac{1}{16}$
230. $76\frac{5}{16}$
231. $44\frac{11}{120}$
232. $58\frac{7}{16}$
233. $17\frac{7}{48}$
234. $48\frac{31}{48}$
235. $21\frac{15}{16}$
236. $\frac{5}{8}$
237. $\frac{7}{8}$
238. $\frac{7}{16}$
239. $\frac{7}{16}$
240. $\frac{13}{16}$
241. $1\frac{7}{8}$
242. $2\frac{7}{8}$
243. $4\frac{13}{16}$

244. $9\frac{11}{16}$
245. $11\frac{11}{16}$
246. $2\frac{13}{16}$
247. $2\frac{3}{4}$
248. $4\frac{15}{16}$
249. $7\frac{9}{16}$
250. $12\frac{13}{16}$
251. $1\frac{3}{48}$
252. $7\frac{23}{24}$
253. $14\frac{13}{24}$
254. $29\frac{5}{16}$
255. $185\frac{5}{144}$
256. $47\frac{13}{16}$
257. $1,587\frac{11}{16}$
258. $3\frac{13}{16}$
259. $\frac{25}{48}$
260. $5\frac{5}{8}$
261. $\frac{5}{8}$
262. $1\frac{3}{16}$
263. $4\frac{13}{16}$
264. $\frac{5}{8}$
265. $\frac{1}{16}$
266. $\frac{9}{16}$
267. $4\frac{3}{8}$
268. $3\frac{3}{8}$
269. $1\frac{1}{4}$
270. $1\frac{1}{2}$
271. 15

272. 36
273. $\frac{125}{768}$
274. $67\frac{1}{2}$
275. $43\frac{5}{16}$
276. $\frac{9}{16}$
277. $31\frac{1}{2}$
278. $39\frac{3}{8}$
279. $3,454\frac{1}{8}$
280. $9,181\frac{7}{8}$
281. $273\frac{3}{16}$
282. $253\frac{7}{16}$
283. $14\frac{5}{32}$
284. 423
285. $418\frac{9}{16}$
286. $\frac{3}{8}$
287. $\frac{9}{16}$
288. $2\frac{1}{8}$
289. $1\frac{13}{32}$
290. 20
291. $7\frac{7}{8}$
292. 36
293. 42
294. $8\frac{3}{4}$
295. 35
296. $4\frac{2}{3}$
297. $32\frac{2}{3}$
298. $13\frac{2}{5}$
299. $8\frac{12}{35}$

300. $2\frac{1}{4}$
301. 78
302. 24
303. $4\frac{11}{18}$
304. $24\frac{39}{40}$
305. $21\frac{1}{4}$
306. $27\frac{3}{4}$
307. $27\frac{17}{45}$
308. $63\frac{1}{2}$
309. $16\frac{1}{2}$
310. $68\frac{4}{5}$
311. $1\frac{1}{8}$
312. $10\frac{2}{3}$
313. 10
314. 5
315. 15
316. 34
317. 8
318. $5\frac{1}{4}$
319. 48
320. 12
321. 33″
322. $8\frac{5}{12}$ ft.
323. 213″
324. $49\frac{1}{3}′$

325. $23\frac{5}{8}$ cu. ft.
326. $8\frac{5}{27}$ cu. yd.
327. 189 pcs.
328. $141\frac{2}{3}$ doz.
329. $17\frac{5}{9}$ pcs.
330. $99\frac{3}{4}$ lin. ft.
331. 27″
332. $2\frac{1}{3}$ yd.
333. 72 pcs.
334. $2\frac{5}{6}$ gr.
335. 17,496 cu. in.
336. 1 cu. yd.
337. $19\frac{5}{13}$ pcs.
338. 45 lin. ft.
339. $20\frac{12}{49}$ pcs.
340. $56\frac{1}{4}$ lin. ft.

341. 10′ 8″
342. 27′ $11\frac{3}{4}$″
343. 14′ $4\frac{7}{8}$″
344. 27′ 7″
345. 28′ $0\frac{3}{4}$″
346. 4′ $4\frac{3}{8}$″
347. 7′ $2\frac{1}{8}$″
348. 10′ $0\frac{7}{8}$″
349. 5′ $7\frac{7}{8}$″
350. 9′ $11\frac{7}{8}$″
351. 33′ 10″
352. 150′ 2″
353. 371′ 8″
354. 67′ $9\frac{3}{4}$″
355. 50′ $5\frac{5}{8}$″
356. 2′ $2\frac{5}{6}$″
357. 2′ $3\frac{4}{5}$″
358. 13′ $9\frac{7}{8}$″
359. 5′ 9″
360. 8′ $3\frac{29}{48}$″

361. $481\frac{1}{4}$ sq. in.
362. $1{,}721\frac{1}{4}$ sq. in.
363. $2{,}027\frac{13}{16}$ sq. in.
364. $4{,}454\frac{3}{4}$ sq. in.
365. $6{,}343\frac{3}{4}$ sq. in.
366. $5\frac{12}{13}$
367. $3\frac{20}{29}$
368. $2\frac{4}{7}$
369. $4\frac{13}{14}$
370. $5\frac{1}{113}$
371. $4\frac{7}{16}$
372. $27\frac{15}{16}$
373. $8\frac{18}{83}$
374. $50\frac{125}{128}$
375. $7\frac{1}{2}$″
376. $14\frac{7}{8}$
377. 15 pcs.
378. $309\frac{3}{4}$
379. $94\frac{2}{3}$
380. $13\frac{7}{8}$ lin. ft.
381. $22\frac{9}{16}$
382. $\frac{1}{8}$
383. $54\frac{2}{5}$
384. $39\frac{2}{3}$ ft.
385. $5{,}078\frac{1}{4}$ cu. ft.
386. $582\frac{5}{8}$ sq. ft.
387. 18′ $5\frac{9}{16}$″
388. 4′ $10\frac{7}{8}$″
389. 110′ $5\frac{5}{8}$″
390. 7′ $8\frac{1}{4}$″
391. $1{,}338\frac{3}{4}$ sq. in.
392. $4\frac{22}{61}$
393. 124 sq. ft.
394. 12′ $2\frac{1}{4}$″
395. 89 sq. ft.

V. Percentage

396. \$6,900 selling price = 115%
397. \$5,040 bid = 112%
398. \$36.00 catalogue price = 100%
399. \$1,800 retail price = 100%
400. \$3,742.20 selling price = 108%
401. \$2,576.00 selling price = 92%
402. \$24.00 actual cost = 80%
403. \$25.96 cost = 88%
404. \$1,500 profit = 20%
405. \$42.84 cost = 90%

406. \$812.50
407. \$175.00
408. \$8.03
409. \$3.39
410. \$342.40
411. \$7,392.00
412. \$7.04
413. \$2,576.00
414. \$862.50
415. \$3,845.04
416. \$4,989.60
417. \$33.75
418. \$69.00
419. \$22.99
420. \$1,292.00
421. \$4,984.67
422. \$45.01
423. \$26.46
424. \$64.39
425. \$790.10
426. \$4,250.00
427. \$36.00
428. \$24.00
429. \$43.50
430. \$50.40
431. \$3,850.00
432. \$6,100.00
433. \$8.00

434. $180.00	**439.** $24.40	**444.** $24.00	**449.** 5%
435. $160.00	**440.** $175.00	**445.** $900.00	**450.** 112%
436. $5,640.00	**441.** $7,000.00	**446.** 15%	**451.** 110%
437. $36.00	**442.** $36.00	**447.** 12%	**452.** 92%
438. $1,250.00	**443.** $715.00	**448.** 15%	**453.** 80%

454. 98% of cost;
　　85% of selling price

455. 95% of cost;
　　75% of retail price

456. $4.12½	**460.** $760.00	**464.** $54.12	**468.** $353.15
457. $402.50	**461.** $16.50	**465.** $6.93	**469.** $190.51
458. $30.00	**462.** $378.00	**466.** 2%	**470.** $17.50
459. $616.42	**463.** $10.00	**467.** 20%	

VI. Mensuration

471. 72″	**473.** 100′	**475.** 168′
472. 136″	**474.** 128′	**476.** 212′

477. 116″ = 9′ 8″	**482.** 196 sq. ft.	**487.** 650¼ sq. ft.
478. 220″ = 18′ 4″	**483.** 784 sq. in.	**488.** 1,463 1⁄16 sq. ft.
479. 58′ 0″	**484.** 1,764 sq. in.	**489.** 12¼ sq. ft.
480. 91′ 0″	**485.** 1,089 sq. in.	**490.** 45 9⁄16 sq. ft.
481. 121 sq. ft.	**486.** 3,969 sq. in.	

491. 50′	**495.** 12′ 8″	**499.** 142′	**503.** 153 sq. in.
492. 56′	**496.** 16′ 8″	**500.** 114′ 6″	**504.** 703 sq. in.
493. 74″	**497.** 41′ 10″	**501.** 35 sq. ft.	
494. 100″	**498.** 44′ 10″	**502.** 99 sq. ft.	

505. 2,479 sq. in.	**514.** 56′ 6 9⁄16″	**523.** 113.0976 sq. ft.
506. 5,684 sq. in.	**515.** 25⅛″	**524.** 254.4696 sq. ft.
507. 904¾ sq. ft.	**516.** 94′ 2 15⁄16″	**525.** 153.9384 sq. ft.
508. 329 1⁄16 sq. ft.	**517.** 51′ 10 1⁄32″	**526.** 7.0686 sq. ft.
509. 280½ sq. ft.	**518.** 70′ 1 15⁄16″	**527.** 380.1336 sq. in.
510. 547½ sq. ft.	**519.** 29′ 10⅛″	**528.** 1,017.8784 sq. in.
511. 50.2656″	**520.** 39′ 3 3⁄16″	**529.** 63.6174 sq. ft.
512. 100.5312″	**521.** 50.2656 sq. in.	**530.** 139.626 sq. ft.
513. 40′ 10 1⁄16″	**522.** 314.16 sq. in.	

531. 10′	**534.** 26″	**537.** 30′	**540.** 40″
532. 15″	**535.** 25′	**538.** 35″	**541.** 18 13⁄16″
533. 20′	**536.** 13″	**539.** 52′	**542.** 15⅝″

543. 20¼"	**548.** 16' 11"	**553.** 10' 7½"	**558.** 41' 4"
544. 11"	**549.** 15' 0"	**554.** 34' 8"	**559.** 16' 11½"
545. 11⁹⁄₁₆"	**550.** 12' 4"	**555.** 35' 4"	**560.** 15' 3½"
546. 10' 10"	**551.** 11' 9"	**556.** 30' 2"	**561.** 72 sq. ft.
547. 11' 8"	**552.** 14' 5"	**557.** 37' 4"	**562.** 42 sq. in.

563. 38½ sq. ft.	**588.** 3,845⁸⁄₂₇ cu. ft.	**613.** 95⅓ cu. ft.
564. 177 sq. in.	**589.** 1,953⅛ cu. ft.	**614.** 19.635 sq. ft.
565. 536½ sq. in.	**590.** 4,699²⁷⁄₆₄ cu. ft.	**615.** 208"
566. 1,495 sq. in.	**591.** 238 sq. ft.	**616.** 729 cu. in.
567. 91 sq. ft.	**592.** 520 sq. in.	**617.** 204 sq. ft.
568. 17½ sq. ft.	**593.** 192 sq. ft.	**618.** 258 sq. ft.
569. 25¹³⁄₁₆ sq. ft.	**594.** 180 sq. in.	**619.** 110¼ sq. ft.
570. 24⅔ sq. ft.	**595.** 31,850 sq. in.	**620.** 484 sq. in.
571. 196 sq. ft.	**596.** 34,974 sq. in.	**621.** 169 sq. ft.
572. 900 sq. in.	**597.** 60,680 sq. in.	**622.** 91⅛ cu. ft.
573. 100 sq. ft.	**598.** 810¹¹⁄₁₂ sq. ft.	**623.** 28.2744 sq. ft.
574. 4 sq. ft.	**599.** 977⁵⁄₁₂ sq. ft.	**624.** 27½ sq. ft.
575. 42,436 sq. in.	**600.** 877½ sq. ft.	**625.** 28.2744 in.
576. 6,724 sq. in.	**601.** 560 cu. ft.	**626.** 6' 11½"
577. 26,896 sq. in.	**602.** 1,280 cu. in.	**627.** 114' 8"
578. 921 sq. ft.	**603.** 7,616 cu. in.	**628.** 15 sq. ft.
579. 441 sq. ft.	**604.** 5,632 cu. ft.	**629.** 7' 7½"
580. 2,368⁴⁄₉ sq. ft.	**605.** 665,186 cu. in.	**630.** 47.124'
581. 729 cu. ft.	**606.** 2,971,980 cu. in.	**631.** 91⅔ sq. ft
582. 2,744 cu. in.	**607.** 34,415,750 cu. in.	**632.** 19⅚ sq. ft.
583. 125 cu. ft.	**608.** 2,580¾ cu. ft.	**633.** 46⅔ cu. ft.
584. 512 cu. in.	**609.** 32,049¹⁄₁₆ cu. ft.	**634.** 47
585. 1,225,043 cu. in.	**610.** 8,724¹³⁄₂₄ cu. ft.	**635.** 169 cu. ft.
586. 166,375 cu. in.	**611.** 36'	
587. 39,304 cu. in.	**612.** 24'	

VII. Lumber and Board Measure

636. 45 bd. ft.	**646.** 140 bd. ft.	**656.** 1,280 bd. ft.
637. 224 bd. ft.	**647.** 195 bd. ft.	**657.** 150 bd. ft.
638. 36 bd. ft.	**648.** 950 bd. ft.	**658.** 773 bd. ft.
639. 84 bd. ft.	**649.** 1,000 bd. ft.	**659.** 147 bd. ft.
640. 363 bd. ft.	**650.** 1,103 bd. ft.	**660.** 60 bd. ft.
641. 270 bd. ft.	**651.** 352 bd. ft.	**661.** 536 bd. ft.
642. 280 bd. ft.	**652.** 96 bd. ft.	**662.** 840 bd. ft.
643. 427 bd. ft.	**653.** 723 bd. ft.	**663.** 54 bd. ft.
644. 968 bd. ft.	**654.** 1,120 bd. ft.	**664.** 2,347 bd. ft.
645. 930 bd. ft.	**655.** 462 bd. ft.	

665. 342 bd. ft. **673.** 17 bd. ft. **681.** 7 bd. ft. **689.** 2 bd. ft.
666. 240 bd. ft. **674.** 23 bd. ft. **682.** 6 bd. ft. **690.** 30 bd. ft.
667. 34 bd. ft. **675.** 14 bd. ft. **683.** 16 bd. ft. **691.** 17 bd. ft.
668. 13 bd. ft. **676.** 24 bd. ft. **684.** 2 bd. ft. **692.** 14 bd. ft.
669. 9 bd. ft. **677.** 75 bd. ft. **685.** 9 bd. ft. **693.** 11 bd. ft.
670. 90 bd. ft. **678.** 162 bd. ft. **686.** 15 bd. ft. **694.** 11 bd. ft.
671. 59 bd. ft. **679.** 52 bd. ft. **687.** 3 bd. ft. **695.** 6 bd. ft.
672. 78 bd. ft. **680.** 108 bd. ft. **688.** 21 bd. ft.

696. \$0.0485 per bd. ft. **701.** \$48.00 per M bd. ft.
697. \$0.0325 per bd. ft. **702.** \$72.00 per M bd. ft.
698. \$0.044 per bd. ft. **703.** \$64.00 per M bd. ft.
699. \$0.0875 per bd. ft. **704.** \$50.00 per M bd. ft.
700. \$0.06325 per bd. ft. **705.** \$41.00 per M bd. ft.

706. \$16.94 **711.** \$6.94 **716.** \$3.04 **721.** 469 bd. ft.
707. \$44.63 **712.** \$16.92 **717.** \$2.88 **722.** 204 bd. ft.
708. \$44.27 **713.** \$94.72 **718.** \$9.52 **723.** 200 bd. ft.
709. \$169.32 **714.** \$34.65 **719.** \$19.41 **724.** 144 bd. ft.
710. \$262.78 **715.** \$18.65 **720.** \$9.87

725. \$38.00 per M **736.** \$10.38
726. 52 bd. ft. **737.** \$12.96
727. 18 bd. ft. **738.** \$0.037 per bd. ft.
728. \$29.31 **739.** 144 bd. ft. (omit the 14')
729. \$114.24 **740.** \$56.32 @ \$64.00 per M
730. \$109.92 **741.** 784 bd. ft.
731. \$34.00 per M bd. ft. **742.** \$10.58
732. \$7.77 **743.** \$0.088 per bd. ft.
733. 910 bd. ft. **744.** \$84.37
734. 95 bd. ft. **745.** \$7.88
735. \$0.0565 per bd. ft.

VIII. Correlated Review

746. 2,384 **753.** 6' 11''
747. 62' 9'' **754.** 18,674
748. 999.324 **755.** $5\frac{13}{16}$
749. $101\frac{1}{60}$ **756.** 5' $11\frac{3}{8}$''
750. 45' $11\frac{3}{4}$'' **757.** \$3,500 selling price = $87\frac{1}{2}\%$
751. \$4,000 selling price = $133\frac{1}{3}\%$
752. 9,099 **758.** 7,237,824
  759. 77' 0''

760. 9.261

761. 143¾

762. 37' 9"

763. $1,032.00

764. $10,959.50

765. $6,240

766. $366.324

767. 578

768. 691

769. 3' 2"

770. 6.34

771. 1.44

772. 21½

773. 2' 10⅞"

774. $300 wages paid = 100%

775. $563 cost = 100%

776. $31 retail price = 100%

777. $350.00 retail price = 100%

778. 132"

779. 17' 3"

780. 576 pcs.

781. 3 gr.

782. 137"

783. 14' 7"

784. 173"

785. 13 yds. 1 ft. 4 in.

786. 2,967 sq. in.

787. 5

788. 3,520 bd. ft.

789. 3.75 M bd. ft.

790. $375.00 per M bd. ft.

791. $0.0845 per bd. ft.

792. $5.88 per doz.

793. $3.50 per pc.

794. 39"

795. 8' 3"

796. 408½ lin. ft.

797. 1⁹⁄₁₃ pcs.

798. 5,227¼ sq. in.

799. 4¹³⁄₁₄

800. 0.15

801. 0.00875

802. 136 in.

803. 196 sq. in.

804. 54 in.

805. 240 sq. ft.

806. 53.4072 ft.

807. 201.0624 sq. ft.

808. 18' 4"

809. 44 sq. ft.

810. 900 sq. ft.

811. 1,728 cu. ft.

812. 240⅙ sq. ft.

813. 798 cu. ft.

814. 40 bd. ft.

815. 58 bd. ft.

816. 8 bd. ft.

817. $0.0453 per bd. ft.

818. $55.00 per M bd. ft.

819. $33.84

820. $2.06